Concrete Masonry
Construction
Inspector's
Handbook

4th EDITION

Reinforced Concrete Masonry Construction

Inspector's Handbook

4th EDITION

John Chrysler, P.E.
Executive Director
Masonry Institute of America

Based on previous editions developed by:
James E. Amrhein, S.E. and Michael W. Merrigan, P.E.

Published by

Masonry Institute of America
386 Beech Avenue, Unit #4
Torrance, CA 90501-6202
www.masonryinstitute.org

in cooperation with

International Code Council
5203 Leesburg Pike, Suite 600
Falls Church, Virginia 22041-3401
www.intlcode.org

4th Edition

ISBN 0-940116-37-5
Library of Congress Cataloging-in-Publication Data
Printed in the United States of America

In this publication the Masonry Standards Joint Committee's
(MSJC) *Building Code Requirements for Masonry Structures*
(ACI 530/ASCE 5/TMS 402) is hereafter referred to as the MSJC

Code, and the MSJC's *Specification for Masonry Structures* (ACI 530.1/ASCE 6/TMS 602) is hereafter referred to as the MSJC Specification.

This book was prepared in keeping with current information and practice for the present state of the art of masonry design and construction.

MIA 206   12-02 2M

TABLE OF CONTENTS

SECTION 12. CONSTRUCTION IN SEVERE WEATHER CONDITIONS ---------- 339

Acknowledgments

The Masonry Institute of America appreciates the past review and suggestions received by the California Construction Inspectors Association and its Board of Registered Construction Inspectors. Donald A. Wakefield's input in previous editions of this book were again incorporated into this edition.

Special appreciation is extended to those that reviewed the current edition for editorial and technical content. They are:

Gregg Borchelt	Brick Industry Association
James Feagin	City of Los Angeles
William Fitzjohn	Construction Inspection Training and Reasearch
Roger Utesch	McGalliard Masonry
William Wood	Youngstown State University

The Masonry Institute of America and the author is pleased to acknowledge the extensive work of Thomas Escobar, Design Director for MIA, for the drawings, page makeup and layout of this publication. His dedication and continual concern to make this publication the very best is appreciated. The author also acknowledges Dan Zechmeister of the Masonry Institute of Michigan for his active role in the masonry inspection process.

The Masonry Institute of America appreciates the use of the 4th edition of the CMACN "Reinforced Concrete Masonry Inspector's Manual" which served as a source document.

Masonry Institute of America
Torrance, California

John Chrysler, P.E.
Executive Director

Masonry Institute of America

The Masonry Institute of America, founded in 1957 under the name of Masonry Research, is a promotional, technical research organization established to improve and extend the use of masonry. The Masonry Institute of America is supported by the mason contractors through a labor agreement contract between the unions and contractors.

The Masonry Institute of America is active in California promoting new ideas and masonry work, improving building codes, conducting research projects, presenting design, construction and inspection seminars and writing technical and non-technical papers, all for the purpose of improving the masonry industry.

The Masonry Institute of America does not engage in the practice of architectural or engineering design or construction nor does it sell masonry materials.

International Code Council®

Since the early 1900s, the United States has been served by three sets of building codes developed by three separate model code groups: Building Officials and Code Administrators International, Inc. (BOCA), International Conference of Building Officials (ICBO), and Southern Building Code Congress International, Inc. (SBCCI). These codes were extremely effective and responsive to regional needs. But, in 1994, recognizing the urgent need for a single set of codes that would serve national needs, the three groups united to form the International Code Council® (ICC®) with the express purpose of creating and developing one master set of comprehensive, coordinated, construction codes.

Substantial advantages are inherent to this single set of codes. Code enforcement officials, architects, engineers, designers, and contractors throughout the United States can now work with a consistent set of requirements. States and localities that currently write their own codes or amend the early model codes may choose to adopt the International Codes without technical amendments, which encourages consistent code enforcement and higher quality construction. Enhanced membership services are an additional benefit. All issues and concerns of a regulatory nature now have a single forum for discussion, consideration, and resolution. Whether the concern is disaster mitigation, energy conservation, accessibility, innovative technology, or fire protection, the ICC offers a means of focusing national and international attention on these concerns.

The ICC makes available an impressive inventory of International Codes™, including:
- *International Building Code®*
- *International Energy Conservation Code®*
- *International Fire Code®*

- *International Fuel Gas Code®*
- *International Mechanical Code®*
- *International Plumbing Code®*
- *International Private Sewage Disposal Code®*
- *International Property MaintenanceCode®*
- *International Residential Code® for One-and Two-Family Dwellings*
- *International Zoning Code®*
- *ICC Performance Code for Buildings and Facilities™*
- *International Existing Building Code™*
- *International Urban-Wildland Interface Code™*

These codes provide a comprehensive package for adoption and use in the 21st Century.

The ICC also offers unmatched technical, educational, and informational products and services in support of the International Codes, with more than 300 highly qualified staff members at 16 offices throughout the United States and in Latin America. Products and services readily available to code users include:

- Code application assistance
- Educational programs
- Certification programs
- Technical handbooks and workbooks
- Plan reviews
- Automated products
- Monthly magazines and newsletters
- Publication of proposed code changes
- Training and informational videos

Masonry Standards Joint Committee

The Masonry Standards Joint Committee (MSJC) is an organization comprised of volunteers who through background, use, and education have established experience in the manufacturing of masonry units and materials and the design and construction of masonry structures.

Working under its three sponsoring organizations, the American Concrete Institute (ACI), the American Society of Civil Engineers (ASCE), and The Masonry Society (TMS), the Committee is charged with developing and maintaining consensus standards suitable for adoption into model building codes.

In the pursuit of its goals, Committee activities include:

1. Evaluate and ballot proposed changes to existing standards of the Committee.

2. Develop and ballot new standards for masonry.

3. Resolve negative votes from ballot items.

4. Provide interpretation of existing standards of the Committee.

5. Identify areas of needed research.

6. Sponsor educational seminars and symposia.

7. Monitor international standards

We gratefully acknowledge MSJC and the three sponsoring organizations for permission to reproduce certain sections of the MSJC Code for the educational and application benefit of those who use this book.

The Masonry Society

The Masonry Society, founded in 1977, is an international gathering of people interested in masonry. It is a professional, technical, and educational association dedicated to the advancement of knowledge on masonry. TMS members are design engineers, architects, builders, researchers, educators, building officials, material suppliers, manufacturers, and others who want to contribute to and benefit from the global pool of knowledge on masonry.

American Concrete Institute

ACI is a technical and educational society founded in 1904 with 30,000 members and 93 chapters in 30 countries.

As ACI approaches a century of progress through knowledge, it has retained the same basic mission: develop, share, and disseminate the knowledge and information needed to utilize concrete to its fullest potential.

American Society of Civil Engineers

The American Society of Civil Engineers (ASCE) was founded in 1852 and currently represents 125,000 members of the civil engineering profession worldwide. ASCE's vision is to position engineers as industry leaders building a better quality of life.

To provide essential value to our members, their careers, our partners and the public by developing leadership, advancing technology, advocating lifelong learning, and promoting the profession.

SECTION 1

Introduction

1.1   GENERAL

This manual has been developed to provide the inspector with information and to serve as a general guide for **reinforced hollow concrete masonry construction.**

Reinforced hollow concrete masonry construction uses concrete blocks (also called masonry units, or CMU for short) with steel reinforcement embedded in grout or mortar so that the separate materials act together to form a single effective structural system.

This publication has been prepared to assist masonry construction inspectors with the information needed to do a thorough professional job.

In order to understand a material and system, it is necessary to know its terminology. The first section of this book includes terms and definitions used in reinforced concrete masonry construction; Section 15 contains a more detailed glossary.

Since a construction project cannot begin until the proper materials are selected, materials are discussed first.

The Materials Section is followed by Quality Control, Sampling and Testing, describing the sampling and testing of masonry necessary to assure that the materials used are in keeping with the prescribed standards and specifications.

Inspection of the actual construction follows, and this specifically deals with code concerns and inspection requirements of reinforced concrete masonry.

The handbook's last sections are on typical concrete masonry shapes, names and functions, glossary of terms and general information that relate to concrete masonry.

In addition to the 1997 Uniform Building Code, this edition incorporates *Building Code Requirements for Masonry Structures* (ACI 530-99/ASCE 5-99/TMS 402-99) and *Specification for Masonry Structures* (ACI 530.1-99/ASCE 6-99/TMS 602-99), also known as the *Masonry Standards Joint Committee Code* referred to as the *MSJC Code* and *MSJC Specification*; and the *2000 International Building Code (IBC)*. It also contains metric (SI) references in parenthesis after the English dimension or quantity.

1.2   THE INSPECTOR

A vital part of any construction project is good inspection. The inspector's job is, therefore, quite important. Knowledge and good judgment are essential in obtaining the results required by the approved plans and specifications. The materials furnished on the project represent the manufacturers' efforts to supply products meeting applicable industry standards and project specifications. It is the inspector's responsibility to verify that these products are properly used to construct the project as designated.

1.3   RESPONSIBILITIES AND DUTIES

Prior to starting masonry construction, the inspector must verify that necessary material testing has been performed as required. Some tests may have to be conducted well in advance of job site delivery such as high strength block testing and advance prism testing. All materials must meet the specified requirements.

The inspector should keep a daily log from the first day on the project. The status of the project from the beginning should be noted.

The daily log should record weather, temperature and project conditions. The inspector should record all materials, test specimens and construction progress and note what work was accomplished and where it was done. This includes laying of masonry units and grout pours that are completed.

It is also suggested that the inspector note how many masons and laborers are on the project each day and the delivery of materials. Any special conditions, problems or adverse events that may take place should be noted.

If there are project conferences, a list of who attended, what was accomplished and the decisions made should also be noted.

Complete and thorough project records are very important and the inspector is invaluable in maintaining the records.

1.4   EQUIPMENT AND MATERIALS FOR THE INSPECTOR

As with all competent and skilled professionals and craft workers, construction inspectors must have tools and materials to properly carry out their inspection duties and responsibilities. The following is a minimum suggested list that an inspector should have:

1.   A current set of plans and specifications, including all change orders.
2.   Applicable building codes and standards to which the project was designed and the requirements of the jurisdiction it is under.
3.   A list of architects, engineers, contractors and sub-contractors; names, addresses, telephone numbers and responsible persons.
4.   A notebook or log to keep daily notes as described above.
5.   Necessary forms for filing reports with required agencies
6.   Pens, pencils and erasers.
7.   Folding rule or retractable tape and long steel tape.
8.   String to check straightness and plumbness.
9.   Keel-yellow, blue and black.
10.   Permanent felt tip markers for labeling specimens.
11.   Hand level and plumb bob.
12.   Small trowel and smooth rod for making and rodding mortar and grout samples.
13.   Sample molds obtained from testing laboratory.
14.   Absorbent paper towels and masking tape to take grout specimens.
15.   Watch.

There can be more items needed, depending on the project and scope of duties required of the inspector.

1.5   TERMINOLOGY

Masonry, like all materials, systems and specialties, has its own vocabulary. Knowing and understanding the terms is a basic requirement.

IBC Section 2102 provides selected terms relative to masonry materials, design and construction with which masonry inspectors should be familiar. Also included are other definitions listed in *MSJC Code and MSJC Specification* as noted. Additional information is contained in the Glossary, Chapter 15.

IBC Section 2102, except as noted

2102 DEFINITIONS

2102.1 General. The following words and terms shall, for the purposes of this chapter and as used elsewhere in this code, have the meaning shown herein.

ADOBE CONSTRUCTION. Construction in which the exterior bearing and nonbearing walls and partitions are of unfired clay masonry units, and floors, roofs and interior framing are wholly or partly of wood or other approved materials.

Adobe, stabilized. Unfired clay masonry units to which admixtures, such as emulsified asphalt, are added during the manufacturing process to limit the units' water absorption so as to increase their durability.

Adobe, unstabilized. Unfired clay masonry units which do not meet the definition of adobe, stabilized.

ACCEPTABLE/ACCEPTED. Acceptable to or accepted by the Architect/Engineer (*MSJC Specification*).

ANCHOR. Metal rod, wire, or strap that secures masonry to its structural support.

ARCHITECT/ENGINEER. The architect, engineer, architectural firm, engineering firm, or architectural and engineering firm issuing drawings and specifications, or administering the work under contract specifications and project drawings, or both (*MSJC Code*).

ARCHITECTURAL TERRA COTTA. Plain or ornamental hard-burned modified clay units, larger in size than brick, with glazed or unglazed ceramic finish.

AREA:

> **Bedded.** The area of the surface of a masonry unit which is in contact with mortar in the plane of the joint.

> **Gross cross-sectional.** The area delineated by the out-to-out specified dimensions of masonry in the plane under consideration.

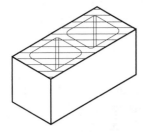 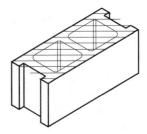

Figure 1.1 Gross cross-sectional area.

> **Net cross-sectional.** The area of masonry units, grout and mortar crossed by the plane under consideration based on out-to-out specified dimensions.

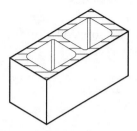 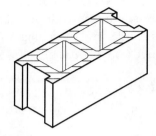

Figure 1.2 Net cross-sectional area.

BACKING. The wall or surface to which the veneer is secured. The backing shall be concrete, masonry, steel framing, or wood framing (*MSJC Code*).

BED JOINT. The horizontal layer of mortar on which a masonry unit is laid.

BOND BEAM. A horizontal grouted element within masonry in which reinforcement is embedded.

BOND REINFORCING. The adhesion between steel reinforcement and mortar grout.

BRICK

> **Calcium silicate (sand lime brick).** A building unit made of sand and lime.

> **Clay or shale.** A masonry unit made of clay or shale, usually formed into a rectangular prism while in the plastic state and burned or fired in a kiln.

> **Concrete.** A masonry unit having the approximate shape of a rectangular prism and composed of inert aggregate particles embedded in a hardened cementitious matrix.

BUILDING OFFICIAL. The officer or other designated authority charged with the administration and enforcement of this Code, or the building official's duly authorized representative (*MSJC Code*).

BUTTRESS. A projecting part of a masonry wall built integrally therewith to provide lateral stability.

CAST STONE. A building stone manufactured from Portland cement concrete precast and used as a trim, veneer or facing on or in building or structures.

CELL. A void space having a gross cross-sectional area greater than $1\frac{1}{2}$ square inches. (967 mm^2).

CHIMNEY. A primarily vertical enclosure containing one or more passageways for conveying flue gases to the outside atmosphere.

CHIMNEY TYPES

> **High-heat appliance type.** An approved chimney for removing the products of combustion from fuel-burning, high-heat appliances producing combustion gases in excess of 2,000°F (1093°C) measured at the appliances flue outlet (see IBC Section 2113.11.3).

> **Low-heat appliance type.** An approved chimney for removing the products of combustion from fuel-burning, low-heat appliances producing combustion gases not in excess of 1,000°F (538°C) under normal operating conditions, but capable of producing combustion gases of 1,400°F (760°C) during intermittent forces firing for periods up to 1 hour. Temperatures shall be measured at the appliance flue outlet.

Masonry type. A field-constructed chimney of solid masonry units or stones.

Medium-heat appliance type. An approved chimney for removing the products of combustion from fuel-burning, medium heat appliances producing combustion gases not exceeding 2,000°F (1093°C) measured at the appliance flue outlet (see IBC Section 2113.11.2).

CLEANOUT. An opening to the bottom of a grout space of sufficient size and spacing to allow the removal of debris.

Figure 1.3 Cleanouts.

COLLAR JOINT. Vertical longitudinal joint between wythes of masonry or between masonry and back-up construction which is permitted to be filled with mortar or grout.

COLUMN, MASONRY. An isolated vertical member whose horizontal dimension measured at right angles to its thickness does not exceed three times its thickness and whose height is at least three times its thickness.

COMPOSITE ACTION. Transfer of stress between components of a member designed so that in resisting loads, the combined components act together as a single member (*MSJC Code*).

COMPOSITE MASONRY. Multiwythe masonry members acting with composite action.

COMPRESSIVE STRENGTH OF MASONRY. Maximum compressive force resisted per unit of net cross-sectional area of masonry, determined by the testing of masonry prisms or a function of individual masonry units, mortar and grout.

CONNECTOR. A mechanical device for securing two or more pieces, parts or members together, including anchors, wall ties and fasteners.

CONTRACT DOCUMENTS. Documents establishing the required Work, and including in particular, the Project Drawings and Project Specifications (*MSJC Specification*).

COVER. Distance between surface of reinforcing bar and edge of member.

DIAPHRAGM. A roof or floor system designated to transmit lateral forces to shear walls or other lateral load-resisting elements.

DIMENSIONS

> **Actual.** The measured dimension of a masonry unit or element.

> **Nominal.** A nominal dimension is equal to a specified dimension plus an allowance for the joints with which the units are to be laid. Thickness is given first, followed by height and then length.

Specified. The dimensions specified for the manufacture or construction of masonry, masonry units, joints or any other component of a structure.

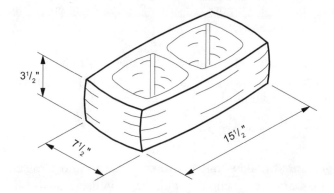

Figure 1.4 Nominal 8" x 4" x 16" (203 mm x 102 mm x 406 mm) slumped concrete block with actual dimensions of $7^1/_2$" x $3^1/_2$" x $15^1/_2$" (190 mm x 89 mm x 394 mm).

EFFECTIVE HEIGHT. For braced members, the effective height is the clear height between lateral supports and is used for calculating the slenderness ratio. The effective height for unbraced members is calculated in accordance with engineering mechanics.

EFFECTIVE PERIOD. Fundamental period of the structure based on cracked stiffness.

FIREPLACE. A hearth and fire chamber or similar prepared place in which a fire may be made and which is built in conjunction with a chimney.

FIREPLACE THROAT. The opening between the top of the firebox and the smoke chamber.

GLASS UNIT MASONRY. Nonload-bearing masonry composed of glass units bonded by mortar (*MSJC Code*).

GROUT LIFT. An increment of grout height within a total grout pour. A grout pour consists of one or more grout lifts (*MSJC Specification*).

GROUT POUR. The total height of masonry to be grouted prior to erection of additional masonry. A grout pour consists of one or more grout lifts (*MSJC Specification*).

GROUTED MASONRY

> **Grouted hollow-unit masonry.** That form of grouted masonry construction in which certain designated cells of hollow units are continuously filled with grout.

> **Grouted multiwythe masonry.** That form of grouted masonry construction in which the space between the wythes is solidly or periodically filled with grout.

HEAD JOINT. Vertical mortar joint placed between masonry units within the wythe at the time the masonry units are laid.

HEADER (Bonder). A masonry unit that connects two or more adjacent wythes of masonry.

HEIGHT, WALLS. The vertical distance from the foundation wall or other immediate support of such wall to the top of the wall.

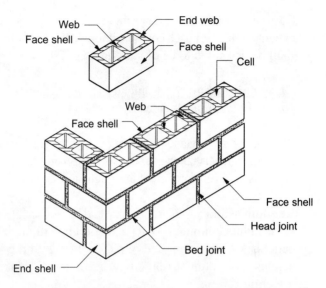

Figure 1.5 Head joint and bed joints, shell and web.

LOAD, DEAD. Dead weight supported by a member, as defined by the general building code (*MSJC Code*).

LOAD, LIVE. Live load specified by the general building code (*MSJC Code*).

LOAD, SERVICE. Load specified by the general building code (*MSJC Code*).

MASONRY. A built-up construction or combination of building units or materials of clay, shale, concrete, glass, gypsum, stone or other approved units bonded together with or without mortar or grout or other accepted method of joining.

Ashlar masonry. Masonry composed of various sized, rectangular units having sawed, dressed or squared bed surfaces, properly bonded and laid in mortar.

Coursed ashlar. Ashlar masonry laid in courses of stone of equal height for each course, although different courses shall be permitted to be of varying height.

Glass unit masonry. Nonload-bearing masonry composed of glass units bonded by mortar.

Plain masonry. Masonry in which the tensile resistance of the masonry is taken into consideration and the effects of stresses in reinforcement are neglected.

Random ashlar. Ashlar masonry laid in courses of stone set without continuous joints and laid up without drawn patterns. When composed of material cut into modular heights, discontinuous but aligned horizontal joints are discernible.

Reinforced masonry. Masonry construction in which reinforcement acting in conjunction with the masonry is used to resist forces.

Solid masonry. Masonry consisting of solid masonry units laid contiguously with the joints between the units filled with mortar.

MASONRY UNIT. Brick, tile, stone, glass block or concrete block conforming to the requirements specified in Section 2103.

Clay. A building unit larger in size than a brick, composed of burned clay, shale, fire clay or mixtures thereof.

Concrete. A building unit or block larger in size than 12 by 4 by 4 inches (305 mm by 102 mm by 102 mm) made of cement and suitable aggregates.

Hollow. A masonry unit whose net cross-sectional area in any plane parallel to the load-bearing surface is less than 75 percent of its gross cross-sectional area measured in the same plane.

Solid. A masonry unit whose net cross-sectional area in every plane parallel to the load-bearing surface is 75 percent or more of its gross cross-sectional area measured in the same plane.

MEAN DAILY TEMPERATURE. The average daily temperature of temperature extremes predicted by a local weather bureau for the next 24 hours.

MINIMUM/MAXIMUM (not less than.....not more than). Minimum or maximum values given in this Specification are absolute. Do not construe that tolerances allow lowering a minimum or increasing a maximum (*MSJC Specification*).

MORTAR. A plastic mixture of approved cementitious materials, fine aggregates and water used to bond masonry or other structural units.

MORTAR, SURFACE-BONDING. A mixture to bond concrete masonry units that contain hydraulic cement, glass fiber reinforcement with or without inorganic fillers or organic modifiers, and water.

OTHERWISE REQUIRED. Specified differently in requirements supplemental to this Specification (*MSJC Specification*).

OWNER. The public body or authority, corporation, association, partnership, or individual for whom the Work is provided (*MSJC Specification*).

PARTITION WALL. An interior wall without structural function (*MSJC Specification*).

PLASTIC HINGE. The zone in a structural member in which the yield moment is anticipated to be exceeded under loading combinations that include earthquakes.

PRISM. An assemblage of masonry units and mortar with or without grout used as a test specimen for determining properties of the masonry.

PROJECT DRAWINGS. The drawings that, along with the project specifications, complete the descriptive information for constructing the work required by the contract documents (*MSJC Code*).

PROJECT SPECIFICATIONS. The written documents that specify requirements for a project in accordance with the service parameters and other specific criteria established by the Owner or his agent (*MSJC Specification*).

QUALITY ASSURANCE. The administrative and procedural requirements established by the contract documents to assure that constructed masonry is in compliance with the contract documents (*MSJC Code*).

REINFORCEMENT. Nonprestressed steel reinforcement (*MSJC Code*).

REQUIRED STRENGTH. Strength of a member or cross-section required to resist factored loads.

RUBBLE MASONRY. Masonry composed of roughly shaped stones.

Coursed rubble. Masonry composed of roughly shaped stones fitting approximately on level beds and well bonded.

Random rubble. Masonry composed of roughly shaped stones laid without regularity of coursing but well bonded and fitted together to form well-divided joints.

Rough or ordinary rubble. Masonry composed of unsquared field stones laid without regularity of coursing but well bonded.

RUNNING BOND. The placement of masonry units such that head joints in successive courses are horizontally offset at least one-quarter the unit length.

SHEAR WALL

Detailed plain masonry shear wall. A masonry shear wall designed to resist lateral forces neglecting stresses in reinforcement, and designed in accordance with Section 2106.1.1.3.

Intermediate reinforced masonry shear wall. A masonry shear wall designed to resist lateral forces considering stresses in reinforcement, and designed in accordance with Section 2106.1.1.4.

Ordinary plain masonry shear wall. A masonry shear wall designed to resist lateral forces neglecting stresses in reinforcement, and designed in accordance with Section 2106.1.1.1.

Ordinary reinforced masonry shear wall. A masonry shear wall designed to resist lateral forces considering stresses in reinforcement, and designed in accordance with Section 2106.1.1.2.

Special reinforced masonry shear wall. A masonry shear wall designed to resist lateral forces considering stresses in reinforcement, and designed in accordance with Section 2106.1.1.5.

SHELL. The outer portion of a hollow masonry unit as placed in masonry.

SPECIFIED. Required by construction documents.

SPECIFIED COMPRESSIVE STRENGTH OF MASONRY, f'_m. Minimum compressive strength, expressed as force per unit of net cross-sectional area, required of the masonry used in construction by the construction documents, and upon which the project design is based. Whenever the quantity f'_m is under the radical sign, the square root of numerical value only is intended and the result has units of psi (MPa).

STACK BOND. The placement of masonry units in a bond pattern is such that head joints in successive courses are vertically aligned. For the purpose of this code, requirements for stack bond shall apply to masonry laid in other than running bond.

STIRRUP. Shear reinforcement in a beam or flexural member.

STONE MASONRY. Masonry composed of field, quarried, or cast stone units bonded by mortar.

Ashlar stone masonry. Stone masonry composed of rectangular units having sawed, dressed, or squared bed surfaces and bonded by mortar.

Rubble stone masonry. Stone masonry composed of irregular-shaped units bonded by mortar.

STRENGTH

Design strength. Nominal strength multiplied by a strength reduction factor.

Nominal strength. Strength of a member or cross-section calculated in accordance with these provisions before application of any strength reduction factors.

SUBMIT, SUBMITTED. Submit, submitted to the Architect/Engineer for review (*MSJC Specification*).

TIE, LATERAL. Loop of reinforcing bar or wire enclosing longitudinal reinforcement.

TIE, WALL. A connector which connects wythes of masonry walls together.

TILE. A ceramic surface unit, usually relatively thin in relation to facial area, made from clay or a mixture of clay or other ceramic materials, called the body of the tile, having either a "glazed" or "unglazed" face and fired above red heat in the course of manufacture to a temperature sufficiently high enough to produce specific physical properties and characteristics.

TILE, STRUCTURAL CLAY. A hollow masonry unit composed of burned clay, shale, fire clay or mixture thereof, and having parallel cells.

UNREINFORCED MASONRY. Masonry in which the tensile resistance of masonry is taken into consideration and the resistance of the reinforcing steel is neglected (*MSJC Code*).

WALL. A vertical element with a horizontal length to thickness ratio greater than 3, used to enclose space.

> **Cavity wall.** A wall built of masonry units or of concrete, or a combination of these materials, arranged to provide an air space within the wall, and in which the inner and outer parts of the wall are tied together with metal ties.

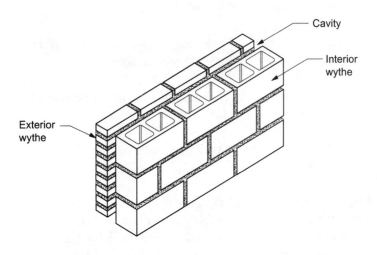

Figure 1.6 Cavity wall.

Composite wall. A wall built of a combination of two or more masonry units of different materials bonded together, one forming the backup and the other the facing element.

Dry-stacked, surface-bonded walls. A wall built of concrete masonry units where the units are stacked dry, without mortar on the bed or head joints, and where both sides of the wall are coated with a surface-bonding mortar.

Masonry-bonded hollow wall. A wall built of masonry units so arranged as to provide an air space within the wall, and in which the facing and backing of the wall are bonded together with masonry units.

Parapet wall. The part of any wall entirely above the roof line.

WALL FRAME. A moment frame of masonry beams and masonry columns within a plane, with special reinforcement details and connections that provide resistance to lateral and gravity loads.

WALL, LOADBEARING. Wall carrying vertical loads greater than 200 lb per lineal ft (2929 N/m) in addition to its own weight (*MSJC Code*).

WEB. An interior solid portion of a hollow-masonry unit as placed in masonry.

WHEN REQUIRED. Specified in requirements supplemental to this Specification (*MSJC Specification*).

WORK. The furnishing and performance of all equipment, services, labor, and materials required by the Contract Documents for the construction of masonry for the project or part of project under consideration (*MSJC Specification*).

WYTHE. Each continuous, vertical section of a wall, one masonry unit in thickness.

Materials

2.1 GENERAL

All materials used in reinforced concrete masonry construction must conform to standard requirements.

2.2 MATERIAL

Materials used in masonry shall conform to the requirements stated herein. If no requirements are specified in this section for a material, or if no published material standards exist, quality shall be based on generally accepted good practice, subject to the approval of the building official.

According to 2000 International Building Code, Section 2103, *Specification for Masonry Structures* (ACI 530.1-99/ASCE 6-99/TMS 602-99), Section 1.3 and the 1997 Uniform Building Code, Section 2102, masonry components shall meet the applicable industry quality Standards.

The Standards of the American Concrete Institute, the American Society for Testing and Materials and the U.S. Government referred to in this Specification are listed below:

2.2.1 Concrete Masonry Units

ASTM C 55 Standard Specification for Concrete Brick.

ASTM C 73 Standard Specification for Calcium Silicate Brick (Sand-Lime Brick).

ASTM C 90 Standard Specification for Loadbearing Concrete Masonry Units.

ASTM C 91 Standard Specification for Masonry Cement.

ASTM C 129 Standard Specification for Nonloadbearing Concrete Masonry Units.

ASTM C 140 Standard Test Methods for Sampling and Testing Concrete Masonry Units and Related Units.

ASTM C 426 Standard Test Method for Linear Drying Shrinkage of Concrete Masonry Units.

ASTM C 744 Standard Specification for Prefaced Concrete and Calcium Silicate Masonry Units.

2.2.2 Clay Masonry Units

ASTM C 34 Standard Specification for Structural Clay Loadbearing Wall Tile.

ASTM C 56 Standard Specification for Structural Clay Non-loadbearing Tile.

ASTM C 62 Standard Specification for Building Brick (Solid Masonry Units Made from Clay or Shale).

ASTM C 67 Standard Test Methods for Sampling and Testing Brick and Structural Clay Tile.

ASTM C 126 Standard Specification for Ceramic Glazed Structural Clay Facing Tile, Facing Brick, and Solid Masonry Units.

ASTM C 212 Standard Specification for Structural Clay Facing Tile.

ASTM C 216 Standard Specification for Facing Brick (Solid Masonry Units Made from Clay or Shale).

ASTM C 482 Standard Test Method for Bond Strength of Ceramic Tile to Portland Cement.

ASTM C 652 Standard Specification for Hollow Brick (Hollow Masonry Units Made from Clay or Shale).

ASTM C 1088 Standard Specification for Thin Veneer Brick Units Made from Clay or Shale.

2.2.3 Stone Masonry Units

ASTM C 97 Standard Test Methods for Absorption and Bulk Specific Gravity of Dimension Stone.

ASTM C 99 Standard Test Method for Modulus of Rupture of Dimension Stone.

ASTM C 120 Standard Method for Flexure Testing of Slate (Modulus of Rupture, Modulus of Elasticity).

ASTM C 121 Standard Test Method for Water Absorption of Slate.

ASTM C 170 Standard Test Method for Compressive Strength of Dimension Stone.

ASTM C 503 Standard Specification for Marble Dimension Stone (Exterior).

ASTM C 568 Standard Specification for Limestone Dimension Stone.

ASTM C 615 Standard Specification for Granite Dimension Stone.

ASTM C 616 Standard Specification for Quartz-Based Dimension Stone.

ASTM C 629 Standard Specification for Slate Dimension Stone.

2.2.4   Ceramic Tile

ANSI A 137.1 Standard Specification for Ceramic Tile.

2.2.5   Glass Unit Masonry

In accordance with Project Specifications.

2.2.6   Mortar

ASTM C 91 Standard Specification for Masonry Cement.

ASTM C 143 Standard Test Method for Slump of Hydraulic-Cement Concrete.

ASTM C 144 Standard Specification for Aggregate for Masonry Mortar.

ASTM C 150 Standard Specification for Portland Cement.

ASTM C 270 Standard Specification for Mortar for Unit Masonry.

ASTM C 780 Standard Test Method for Preconstruction and Construction Evaluation of Mortars for Plain and Reinforced Unit Masonry.

ASTM C 887 Standard Specification for Packaged, Dry, Combined Materials for Surface Bonding Mortar.

ASTM C 946 Standard Practice for Construction of Dry-Stacked, Surface-Bonded walls.

ASTM C 1329 Standard Specification for Mortar Cement.

2.2.7 Grout

ASTM C 476 Standard Specification for Grout for Masonry.

ASTM C 1019 Standard Test Method for Sampling and Testing Grout.

2.2.8 Reinforcement

2.2.8.1 Deformed Reinforcement

ACI 315 Details and Detailing of Concrete Reinforcement.

ASTM A 615/A 615M Standard Specification for Deformed and Plain Billet-Steel Bars for Concrete Reinforcement.

ASTM A 616/A 616M Standard Specification for Rail-Steel Deformed and Plain Bars for Concrete Reinforcement.

ASTM A 617/A 617M Standard Specification for Axle-Steel Deformed and Plain bars for Concrete Reinforcement.

ASTM A 706/A 706M Standard Specification for Low-Alloy Steel Deformed bars for Concrete Reinforcement.

ASTM A 767/A 767M Standard Specification for Zinc-Coated (Galvanized) Bars for Concrete Reinforcement.

ASTM A 775/A 775M Standard Specification for Epoxy-Coated Reinforcing Steel Bars.

ASTM A 996 Standard Specification for Rail-Steel and Axle-Steel Deformed Bars for Concrete Reinforcement.

2.2.8.2 Joint Reinforcement

ASTM A 884 Standard Specification for Epoxy-Coated Steel Wire and Welded Wire Fabric for Reinforcement.

ASTM A 951 Standard Specification for Masonry Joint Reinforcement.

2.2.8.3 Other Reinforcement/Metal Products

ASTM A 36/A 36M Standard Specification for Structural Steel.

ASTM A 82 Standard Specification for Steel Wire, Plain, for Concrete Reinforcement.

ASTM A 153/A 15M Standard Specification for Zinc Coating (Hot-Dip) on Iron and Steel Hardware.

ASTM A 167 Standard Specification for Stainless and Heat-Resisting Chromium-Nickel Steel Plate, Sheet and Strip.

ASTM A 185 Standard Specification for Steel Welded Wire, Fabric, Plain, for Concrete Reinforcement.

ASTM A 307 Standard Specification for Carbon Steel Bolts and Studs, 60,000 psi Tensile Strength.

ASTM A 366/A 366M Standard Specification for Steel, Sheet, Carbon, Cold-Rolled, Commercial Quality.

ASTM A 496 Standard Specification for Steel Wire, Deformed, for Concrete Reinforcement.

ASTM A 497 Standard Specification for Welded Deformed Steel Wire Fabric for Concrete Reinforcement.

ASTM A 580/A 580M Standard Specification for Stainless and Heat-Resisting Steel Wire.

ASTM A 641/A 641M Standard Specification for Zinc-Coated (Galvanized) Carbon Steel Wire.

ASTM A 653/A 653M Standard Specification for Steel Sheet, Zinc-Coated (Galvanized) by the Hot-Dip Process.

ASTM A 666 Standard Specification for Austenitic Stainless Steel, Sheet, Strip, Plate and Flat Bar for Structural Application.

ASTM A 899 Standard Specification for Steel Wire Epoxy-Coated.

ASTM E 488 Standard Test Methods for Strength of Anchors in Concrete and Masonry Elements.

2.2.9 Other Standards

ACI 117 Standard Specifications for Tolerances for Concrete Construction and Materials.

ASTM C 901   Standard Specification for Prefabricated Masonry Panels.

ASTM C 920 Standard Specification for Elastomeric Joint Sealants.

ASTM C 1314 Standard Method for Constructing and Testing Masonry Prisms Used to Determine Compliance with Specified Compressive Strength of Masonry.

ASTM D 994   Standard Specification for Preformed Expansion Joint Filler for Concrete (Bituminous Type).

ASTM D 1056 Standard Specification for Flexible Cellular Materials - Sponge or Expanded Rubber.

ASTM D 1187   Standard Specification for Asphalt-base Emulsion for Use as Protective Coating for Metal.

ASTM D 1227 Standard Specification for Emulsified Asphalt Used as Protective Coating for Roofing.

ASTM D 2000 Standard Classification System for Rubber Products in Automotive Applications.

ASTM D 2287 Standard Specification for Nonrigid Vinyl Chloride Polymer and Copolymer Molding and Extrusion Compounds.

Additionally, there are 20 Uniform Building Code Standards relating to masonry that are not listed here, with 14 printed in their entirety in Section 16.

2.3   CONCRETE MASONRY UNITS

2.3.1   General

The inspector's job site check of concrete masonry units should include a visual inspection. Significant quantities of broken or cracked units should be rejected. Unless noted in the specifications, minor cracks incidental to usual manufacturing, or minor chipping resulting from normal handling or shipping are not grounds for rejection. Inspection should also verify that colors and texture comply with the approved samples when required.

As an additional check, the inspector may break a unit, note the proportion of broken aggregate showing on the fractured face, and look for internal evidence of moisture. If no aggregate is broken, the inspector may recheck to be sure that the units have been tested in the laboratory and meet all required specifications. If moisture rings are apparent on the fractured face, the age of the units should be rechecked and the laboratory tests for moisture content should be verified.

2.3.2   Dimensions

Concrete masonry units (CMU) are commonly designated by their nominal dimensions, width, height and length (in that order), followed by a brief description, for example: 8" x 4" x 16" (203 mm x 102 mm x 406 mm) split face.

Specified unit dimensions, as defined in IBC Section 2102, *MSJC Code* Section 1.6 or UBC Section 2101, such as 7 $5/_8$" x 3 $5/_8$" x 15 $5/_8$", (194 mm x 92 mm x 397 mm) are generally $3/_8$" (10 mm) less than the nominal dimensions, which would be 8" x 4" x 16" (203 mm x 102 mm x 406 mm). A specified dimension is equal to the nominal dimension minus the mortar joint thickness. This allows for the typical $3/_8$" (10 mm) mortar joint used in CMU construction and retains a modular dimension increments of four inches (102 mm). See Figure 2.1.

31

Slumped block unit dimensions, illustrated in Figure 2.2, are generally $\frac{1}{2}$" (13 mm) less than the nominal dimensions and may vary depending on the characteristics of the particular units used.

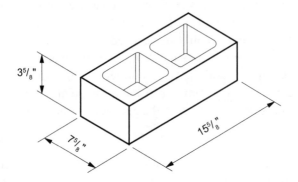

Figure 2.1 Precision concrete masonry unit.

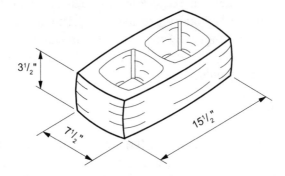

Figure 2.2 Slumped concrete masonry unit.

2.3.3   Wide Selection of Units

There is also a large variety of specialty concrete masonry units that have been developed for special purposes. Specialty units have been developed for sound control, energy-efficient use of insulation, rapid placing mortarless block systems, paving blocks, pilaster units, and others. Figure 2.3 shows some of these specialty units.

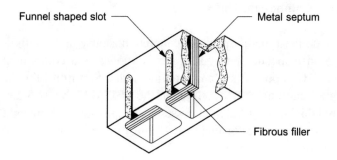

Funnel shaped slot

Metal septum

Fibrous filler

SLOTTED SOUND BLOCK

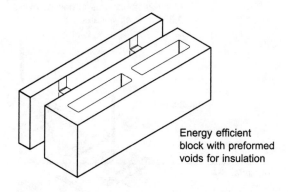

Energy efficient
block with preformed
voids for insulation

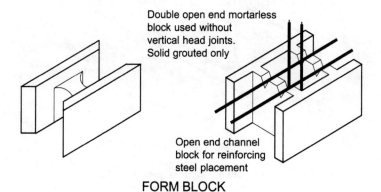

Double open end mortarless
block used without
vertical head joints.
Solid grouted only

Open end channel
block for reinforcing
steel placement

FORM BLOCK

Figure 2.3 Specialty concrete masonry units.

33

2.3.4. Component Units

Another type of specialty concrete masonry unit configuration an inspector may encounter is known as a component system. Component systems provide added versatility for the designer and engineer by allowing the wall to be built to any desired thickness. Wall thicknesses are usually range from eight inches (203 mm) to 24 inches (610 mm) in one inch (25 mm) increments. See Figure 2.4.

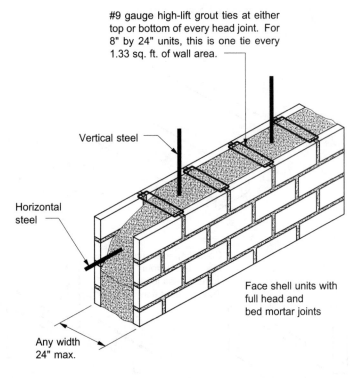

#9 gauge high-lift grout ties at either top or bottom of every head joint. For 8" by 24" units, this is one tie every 1.33 sq. ft. of wall area.

Vertical steel

Horizontal steel

Face shell units with full head and bed mortar joints

Any width 24" max.

Area: $^3/_{16}$" Dia. Wire = 0.0276 sq. in.

Area: Two 9 Ga. wires = 0.0346 sq. in.

Figure 2.4 Expandable component masonry system.

This system can be used in retaining walls, subterranean walls, structural building walls, or as forms for concrete walls.

The masonry components are solid concrete blocks conforming to ASTM C 55 with a 2500 psi (17,200 kPa) minimum compressive strength. An example is shown in Figure 2.5.

The components can be assembled with different architectural finishes and colors on each side. They may also be used as permanent forms for poured-in-place concrete.

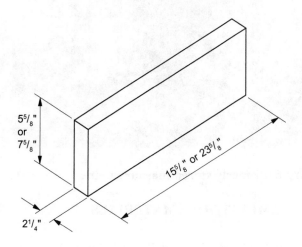

Figure 2.5 Component unit.

2.3.5   Storing Masonry Units

Care must be taken when storing concrete masonry units on the job site to ensure they are clean and dry when used, as shown in Figure 2.6. Concrete masonry units should not be wetted unless otherwise approved.

During inclement weather conditions proper storage includes covering the CMU to protect from rain. Subjecting the CMU to rain does not damage the units, but they must be allowed to dry adequately before laying.

Figure 2.6 Properly stored masonry units.

2.4 CEMENTITIOUS MATERIALS

For masonry units to function effectively in a wall, it is important that they be bonded together. This bonding is achieved with mortar and grout. The adhesion is obtained with the cementitious materials cement and lime.

Attempts have been made to increase the economy of block masonry by developing mortarless block systems that can interlock and be laid without mortar. Another approach has been to manufacture the units with very uniform bearing surfaces, often achieved by grinding the edges. The blocks are then laid with very thin high bond mortars.

2.4.1. Portland Cement

The classical definition of Portland cement is: "Portland cement is the product obtained by finely pulverizing a clinker made by calcining to incipient fusion an intimate and properly proportioned mixture of argillaceous and calcareous material with no additions subsequent to calcination except water and calcined or uncalcined gypsum."

Portland cement is the primary bonding agent used to glue together the grains of sand and pea gravel used in mortar and grout.

Portland cement must conform to the requirements of the ASTM C 150.

Portland cement must be properly stored off the ground and covered to prevent absorption of moisture. When the mortar joint color is critical, the same type and brand of cement and lime and aggregate must be used throughout the job. Sacks with hard lumps should be rejected. Usually Type I or Type II Portland cement is used for mortar and grout. In some instances, low alkali Portland cement, if available, can be used to reduce the possibility of efflorescence.

2.4.2 Plastic Cement

In some of the Southwestern areas of the United States, plastic cement is sometimes used for mortar. This is basically Type I Portland cement with approximately 12 percent plasticizing agent added. When plastic Portland cement is used in mortar, hydrated lime may be added, but not in excess of one-tenth of the volume of cement.

Plastic cement is generally used for small masonry projects and the "do it yourself" home masonry market since lime does not have to be used to obtain adequate plasticity. Mortar made with 1 part plastic cement and 3 parts sand is basically equivalent to a mix of 1 part Portland cement, 0.14 parts plasticizer and 3.4 parts sand which is richer than Type S, Portland cement, lime mortar.

It is important to note that plastic cement is not permitted for structural masonry in the code. The Uniform Building Code specifically excludes plastic cement in Seismic Zones 2, 3 and 4, and 2000 IBC simply does not provide for the use of plastic cement.

2.4.3   Mortar Cement

In some parts of the United States, Portland cement manufacturers and some masonry material suppliers may package a blend of Portland cement and hydrated lime or lime substitute and other ingredients. This blending may be in proportions by volume for Type M mortar, one part Portland cement and $^1/_4$ part lime or equivalent; for Type S mortar, one part Portland cement and $^1/_2$ part lime or equivalent; and for Type N mortar, one part Portland cement and one part lime or equivalent or prepackaged to specifications.

This packaged mortar cement conforms to the requirements of ASTM Standard C 1329 or UBC Standard 21-14. It is generally used for small projects or jobs where separate delivery of Portland cement and lime is inconvenient.

2.4.4   Masonry Cement

Masonry cement is a mixture of Portland cement, 30% to 60% plasticizer material, and added chemicals. This mixture is based on the requirements contained in ASTM C 91 *Standard Specification for Masonry Cement.*

These standards cover three types of masonry cement for use in mortar. There are Type M, S and N masonry cements that may be used for mortar with or without the addition of more Portland cement. The particular types of masonry cements are blended to produce mortar of the same type to conform to ASTM C 270 *Standard Specification for Mortar for Unit Masonry.*

2.4.5 Lime

The International Building Code and the Uniform Building Code permit the use of hydrated lime or lime putty in mortar. The use of lime putty has given way to convenient packaged hydrated lime that is delivered in sacks.

Hydrated limes are divided into two classes, as described in ASTM C 207, which are Type N and Type S hydrated limes. These are high calcium and dolomitic, high magnesium, hydrates. The Type S, special hydrated lime, is different from Type N, normal hydrated lime, principally by its ability to develop high early plasticity, higher water retentivity, and by its limitation on unhydrated oxide content.

Lime use in mortar improves the plasticity of the mix, improves water retention for longer board life, improves the water-tightness of the mortar joint, increases the bond between the mortar and the masonry unit, and contributes to the cementitious materials in the mortar mix.

Increasing the Portland cement content and reducing the lime content increases the compressive strength of mortar, but it also increases shrinkage, reduces workability, lowers water retentivitiy and causes rapid stiffening.

Conversely, increasing the lime improves workability, water retentivity and adhesion bond; it does not add to the compressive strength of mortar but it does aid waterproofing of the mortar. Figure 2.7 shows the relationship between various proportions of cement and lime and mortar strength and water retentivity.

The 2000 IBC, Table 2103.10 and 1997 UBC Table 21-B, *Grout Proportions by Volume* allows up to one-tenth part by volume hydrated lime. This allowance is believed to be a carry-over from when mortar was used as a slushing grout material. Although lime is not generally used in grout, it may occasionally be used as a lubricant to initially charge grout pumps.

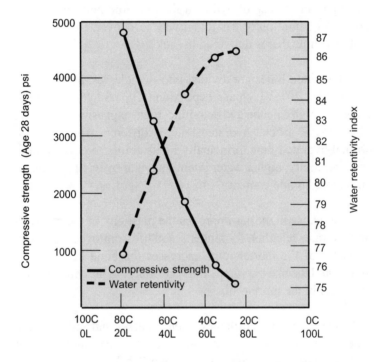

Proportion of cement (%) (C): Lime (L) in mortar
(C + L): sand: 1:3 by volume

Figure 2.7 Relations between mortar composition, compressive strength and water retentivity.

2.5   AGGREGATES FOR MORTAR AND GROUT

Aggregates for mortar and grout are composed of sand and pea gravel.

Aggregates should be stored in a level, dry, clean place from which they can be measured into the mixer with minimum handling and kept free from contamination by harmful substances.

Aggregates should be delivered to the job pregraded with the gradation certified by the supplier. The inspector need only check the certificate and observe the aggregate for consistent gradations. Field tests will need to be made when required by the project specifications. Field tests are generally sieve analysis tests.

2.6   REINFORCING STEEL

2.6.1   General

Reinforcing steel at the job site must be protected from accidental kinking or bending. It must also be kept free of dirt, mud, oil or other foreign matter detrimental to bond. Light surface rust or light mill scale is not detrimental to bond provided the unit weight after the specimen has been cleaned still meets minimum ASTM weight and height of deformation requirements.

Reinforcing steel must be placed as detailed on the plans and in the specifications. If, for any reason, the reinforcement cannot be placed as designed, the architect and/or engineer should be notified prior to construction.

The inspector must check the reinforcing bars to assure that they are the grade and size specified. Figure 2.8 shows the markings for identification of reinforcing bars.

Table 2-A and Table 2-B provide information on the properties of reinforcing bars.

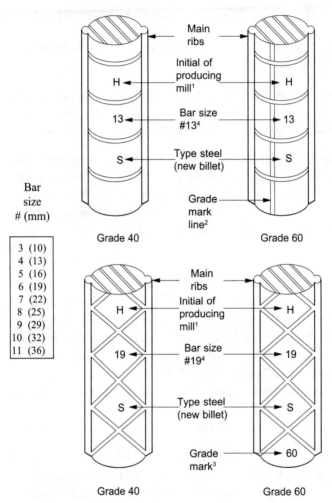

Bar size # (mm)
3 (10)
4 (13)
5 (16)
6 (19)
7 (22)
8 (25)
9 (29)
10 (32)
11 (36)

1. Bar identification marks may also be oriented to read horizontally (at 90° to those illustrated above).
2. Grade mark lines must be continued at least five deformation spaces.
3. Grade mark numbers may be placed within separate consecutive deformation spaces to read vertically or horizontally.
4. All bars are now stamped with metric size designations (in this case, #13 = $\frac{1}{2}$" bar and #19 = $\frac{3}{4}$" bar).

Note:
Grade 75 steel also available for masonry.
Bar size markings are given in metric which is indicated on reinforcement supplied for masonry use. Transition to all metric markings will be accomplished in the future.

Figure 2.8 Identification marks, line system of grade marks.

Table 2-A Properties of ASTM A 615 Steel Reinforcing Bars

Bar Designation No. [A]	Nominal Dimensions [B]				Deformation Requirements, in. [mm]		
	Nominal Weight, lb/ft [Nominal Mass, kg/m]	Diameter, in. [mm]	Cross-Sectional Area, in.² [mm²]	Perimeter, in. [mm]	Maximum Average Spacing	Minimum Average Height	Maximum Gap (Chord of 12.5% of Nominal Perimeter)
3 [10]	0.376 [0.560]	0.375 [9.5]	0.11 [71]	1.178 [29.9]	0.262 [6.7]	0.015 [0.38]	0.143 [3.6]
4 [13]	0.668 [0.994]	0.500 [12.7]	0.20 [129]	1.571 [39.9]	0.350 [8.9]	0.020 [0.51]	0.191 [4.9]
5 [16]	1.043 [1.552]	0.625 [15.9]	0.31 [199]	1.963 [49.9]	0.437 [11.1]	0.028 [0.71]	0.239 [6.1]
6 [19]	1.502 [2.235]	0.750 [19.1]	0.44 [284]	2.356 [59.8]	0.525 [13.3]	0.038 [0.97]	0.286 [7.3]
7 [22]	2.044 [3.042]	0.875 [22.2]	0.60 [387]	2.749 [69.8]	0.612 [15.5]	0.044 [1.12]	0.334 [8.5]
8 [25]	2.670 [3.973]	1.000 [25.4]	0.79 [510]	3.142 [79.8]	0.700 [17.8]	0.050 [1.27]	0.383 [9.7]
9 [29]	3.400 [5.060]	1.128 [28.7]	1.00 [645]	3.544 [90.0]	0.790 [20.1]	0.056 [1.42]	0.431 [10.9]
10 [32]	4.303 [6.404]	1.270 [32.3]	1.27 [819]	3.990 [101.3]	0.889 [22.6]	0.064 [1.63]	0.487 [12.4]
11 [36]	5.313 [7.907]	1.410 [35.8]	1.56 [1006]	4.430 [112.5]	0.987 [25.1]	0.071 [1.80]	0.540 [13.7]
14 [43][C]	7.650 [11.38]	1.693 [43.0]	2.25 [1452]	5.32 [135.1]	1.185 [30.1]	0.085 [2.16]	0.648 [16.5]
18 [57][C]	13.60 [20.24]	2.257 [57.3]	4.00 [2581]	7.09 [180.1]	1.58 [40.1]	0.102 [2.59]	0.864 [21.9]

[A]Bar numbers are based on the number of eighths of an inch included in the nominal diameter of the bars [bar numbers approximate the number of millimeters of the nominal diameter of the bar].

[B]The nominal dimensions of a deformed bar are equivalent to those of a plain round bar having the same weight [mass] per foot [meter] as the deformed bar.

[C]Not permitted in masonry construction. Maximum size bars for masonry are No. 11 for Working Stress Design and No. 9 for Strength Design (UBC) or No. 11 for any design method (IBC).

Table 2-B *Overall Diameter of Bars*

	Bar Size	Approx. dia. outside Deformations inches (mm)
	# 3	$^7/_{16}$ (11)
	# 4	$^9/_{16}$ (14)
	# 5	$^{11}/_{16}$ (17)
	# 6	$^7/_8$ (22)
	# 7	1 (25)
	# 8	$1^1/_8$ (29)
	# 9	$1^1/_4$ (32)
	# 10	$1^7/_{16}$ (37)
	# 11	$1^5/_8$ (41)

NOTE that diameters tabulated are approximate size outside of deformations, so clearance should be added for holes.

2.6.2   Reinforcing Bars

In the Western United States and particularly in California, deformed bars make up the majority of reinforcing steel used in masonry. The deformed bars range from #3 ($^3/_8$ inch (10 mm) in diameter) to a maximum of #11 bars ($1^3/_8$ inch (35 mm) in diameter). **Exception:** The maximum size of reinforcement is #9 for UBC strength design of masonry. This reinforcing steel conforms to ASTM A 615 which specifies the physical characteristics of the reinforcing steel. Reinforcing steel may be either Grade 40 with a minimum yield strength of 40,000 psi (300 MPa) or Grade 60 with a minimum yield strength of 60,000 psi (420 MPa).

Grade 40 steel bars are furnished in sizes 3, 4, 5 and 6. However, currently, Grade 60 steel is furnished in all sizes, and if Grade 40 is required, a special note must be made to ensure delivery.

2.6.3 Identification Marks

The ASTM specifications covering new billet steel, rail steel, axle steel and low alloy reinforcing bars (A 615, A 616, A 617 [or A 996], and A 706) require identification marks to be rolled into the surface of one side of the bar to denote the producer's mill designation, bar size and type of steel and for Grade 60, grade marks indicating yield strength. See Figure 2-8, Identification marks, line system of grade marks.

Grade 40 bars show only three marks (no grade mark) in the following order:

1st	-	Producing Mill (usually an initial)
2nd	-	Bar Size Number
3rd	-	Type S for New Billet, A for Axle, I for Rail, W for Low Alloy

Grade 60 bars must also show grade marks:

60 or one (1) Line for 60,000 psi (420 MPa) strength

Grade mark lines are smaller and between the two main longitudinal ribs which are on opposite sides of all U.S. made bars. Number grade marks are fourth in order.

2.6.4 Overall Bar Diameters

Bar diameters are nominal, with the actual diameter outside of deformations being somewhat greater. The outside diameter may be important when punching holes in structural steel members to accommodate bars or when allowing for the out-to-out width of a group of beam bars crossing and in contact with column verticals. Approximately $^1/_{16}$ inch (1.6 mm) for #3, #4, #5 bars, $^1/_8$ inch (3.2 mm) for #6, #7, #8, #9 bars, $^3/_{16}$ inch (5 mm) for #10 and #11 bars should be added to the nominal bar diameter for the height of the deformations. See Table 2-B.

2.7 JOINT REINFORCING STEEL

2.7.1 General

When high strength steel wire, in ladder or truss type configuration, is placed in the horizontal bed joints, it is called joint reinforcement.

High strength steel wire fabricated in ladder or truss systems, as illustrated in Figure 2.9a and 2.9b, is placed in the bed joints to reinforce the wall in the horizontal direction. The most common uses of joint reinforcement are:

(1)   to control shrinkage cracking in concrete masonry walls;

(2)   as part or all of the "minimum" steel required by the applicable Building Code; and;

(3)   as designed reinforcing steel that resists forces in the masonry, such as tension and shear. It can also be used as reinforcement in all types of masonry walls as a continuous tie system for veneer and cavity walls.

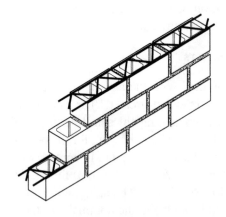

Truss joint reinforcement in concrete masonry wall spaced 16" (405 mm) o.c. vertically

Figure 2.9a Use of joint reinforcement.

Ladder joint reinforcement
tying brick veneer face to
concrete masonry
wall

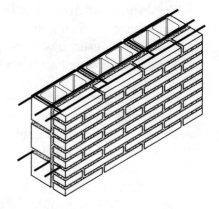

Figure 2.9b Use of joint reinforcement.

2.7.2 Description

Joint reinforcement consists of deformed longitudinal wires welded to cross wire in sizes suitable for placement in mortar joints between masonry courses (See Figure 2.9).

2.7.3 Configuration and Size of Longitudinal and Cross Wires

The requirements for configuration and size of longitudinal and cross wires are described in the ASTM A 951.

The distance between longitudinal wires and the configuration of cross wires connecting the longitudinal wires must conform to the design and requirements.

The diameter of longitudinal wires shall not be less than 0.148 inch (3.76 mm) or more than one-half the mortar joint thickness.

The diameter of cross wires shall not be less than (No. 9 gage) 0.148-inch (3.76 mm) diameter nor more than the diameter of the longitudinal wires. Cross wires shall not project beyond the outside longitudinal wires by more than $\frac{1}{8}$ inch (3.2 mm).

The width of joint reinforcement shall be the out-to-out distance between outside longitudinal wires. Variation in the width shall not exceed $\frac{1}{8}$ inch (3.2 mm).

The length of pieces of joint reinforcement shall not vary more than $\frac{1}{2}$ inch (13 mm) or 1.0 percent of the specified length, whichever is less.

2.7.4   Material Requirements

Additionally, the material requirements are described in ASTM A 951.

Wire of the finished product shall meet the following requirements:

Tensile strength, min, ksi (MPa)	80 (550)
Yield strength, min, ksi (MPa)	70 (485)
Reduction of area, min, %	30

For wire testing over 100,000 psi (689 MPa), the reduction of area shall not be less than 25 percent.

Wire shall not break or crack along the outside diameter of the bend when tested.

The least weld shear strength in pounds shall be not less than 25,000 multiplied by the specified area of the smaller wire in square inches.

2.7.5   Fabrication

The fabrication of joint reinforcement is described in ASTM A 951.

Wire shall be fabricated and finished in a workmanlike manner, shall be free from injurious imperfections and shall conform to the standard.

The wires shall be assembled by automatic machines or by other suitable mechanical means which will assure accurate spacing and alignment of all members of the finished product.

Longitudinal and cross wires shall be securely connected at every intersection by a process of electric-resistance welding.

Longitudinal wires shall be deformed. One set of two deformations shall occur around the perimeter of the wire at a maximum spacing of 0.7 times the diameter of the wire but not less than eight sets per inch (25 mm) of length. The overall length of each deformation within the set shall be such that the summation of gaps between the ends of the deformations shall not exceed 25 percent of the perimeter of the wire. The height or depth of the deformations shall be 0.012 inch (0.305 mm) for $^{3}/_{16}$ inch (4.76 mm) diameter or larger wire, 0.011 (0.28 mm) for 0.162-inch (4.11 mm) wire and 0.009 inch (0.23 mm) for 0.148-inch (3.76 mm) diameter wire.

2.8   WATER

Water used in masonry construction should be potable, (suitable for drinking) and free of harmful substances such as oil, acids, alkalis, and any other impurities that would classify the water as unfit for human consumption.

2.9   ADDITIVES AND ADMIXTURES

Sometimes it is desirable to have certain qualities, such as delayed setting, super plasticity, water reduction, integral water repellents, accelerated strength gain, etc. in the mortar or grout. These special qualities can be obtained by using special additives or admixtures. To use the additives, it is important to comply with the recommendations of the manufacturer to obtain satisfactory results after first obtaining approval of the local building official. Often, the building official will issue a general approval for additive use on all projects.

ASTM C 270 Standard Specification for Mortar for Unit Masonry and ASTM C 476 Standard Specification for Grout for Masonry provide general requirements.

Additives and admixtures to mortar or grout shall not be used unless specified and/or approved.

Antifreeze liquids, chloride salts or other substances should not be used in mortar or grout.

Air-entrainment substances shall not be used in mortar or grout unless tests are conducted to determine compliance with the requirements of this code.

2.10   MORTAR

2.10.1   General

Mortar is a basic component of reinforced and unreinforced masonry. Some claim that mortar holds the units apart, others claim it holds the masonry units together. It actually does both.

Mortar has been made from many different materials. Some ancient mortar mixtures were plain mud or clay, earth with ashes, ox blood and earth, and sand with lime.

Modern mortar consists of cementitious materials and well graded sand with sufficient fines. Mortar is used for the following purposes:

a. It is a bedding or seating material for the masonry unit.
b. It allows the unit to be leveled and properly placed.
c. It bonds the units together.
d. It provides compressive strength.
e. It provides shear strength, particularly parallel to the wall.
f. It allows some movement and elasticity between units.
g. It seals irregularities of the masonry unit and provides a weather-tight wall, prevents penetration of wind and water into and through the wall.
h. It can provide color to the wall by using mineral color additive.
i. It can provide an architectural appearance by using various types of joints, as shown in Figures 4.34 and 4.35.

Section 2103.7 of the 2000 International Building Code, Section 2102.2.8 of the 1997 Uniform Building Code and Section 2.1 of *MSJC Specification* state that mortar shall comply with the ASTM C 270 *Standard Specification for Mortar for Unit Masonry* or UBC Standard 21-15, Mortar for Unit Masonry.

Mortar and grout shall comply with the provisions of the applicable standard. Special mortars, grouts or bonding systems may be used, subject to satisfactory evidence of their capabilities when specified and/or approved.

Materials used as ingredients in mortar and grout shall conform to the applicable requirements. Cementitious materials for grout shall be Portland cement with the possible addition of lime. Cementitious materials for mortar shall be one or more of the following: lime, masonry cement, Portland cement and mortar cement. Cementitious materials or additives should not contain epoxy resins and derivatives, phenols, asbestos fiber or fireclays.

Water used in mortar or grout shall be clean and free of deleterious amounts of acid, alkalis or organic material or other harmful substances.

Mortar shall consist of a mixture of cementitious material and aggregate to which sufficient water and approved additives, if any, have been added to achieve a workable, plastic consistency.

2.10.2   Proportions of Mortar

Proportions of mortar may be based on laboratory testing based on prisms, cube strength, and cylinder strengths. Field experience based on history of performance with the mortar ingredients and masonry units for the project may be used as a basis for proportions.

Abundant experience has proved that mortar portions based on IBC Table 2103.7(1) and ASTM C 270, Table 1 Mortar Proportions by Volume for Unit Masonry, result in satisfactory performance.

Mortar with specified proportions of ingredients that differ from the mortar proportions of IBC Table 2103.7(1) may be approved for use when it is demonstrated that the mortar will conform to the property specifications. Water content shall be adjusted to provide proper workability under existing field conditions. When the proportion of ingredients are not specified, the proportions by mortar type shall be used as given in Table 2103.7(1).

IBC TABLE 2103.7(1) and ASTM C 270 Table 1 - MORTAR PROPORTIONS

Mortar	Type	Proportions by volume (cementitious materials)								Aggregate Measured in a damp, loose condition
		Portland[a] Cement or Blended Cement[b]	Masonry Cement[c] M	Masonry Cement[c] S	Masonry Cement[c] N	Mortar Cement[d] M	Mortar Cement[d] S	Mortar Cement[d] N	Hydrated lime or lime putty	
Cement-lime	M	1	-	-	-	-	-	-	$\frac{1}{4}$	Not less than $2\frac{1}{4}$ and not more than 3 times the sum of the separate volumes of cementitious materials.
	S	1	-	-	-	-	-	-	over $\frac{1}{4}$ to $\frac{1}{2}$	
	N	1	-	-	-	-	-	-	over $\frac{1}{2}$ to $1\frac{1}{4}$	
	O	1	-	-	-	-	-	-	over $1\frac{1}{4}$ to $2\frac{1}{2}$	
Mortar cement	M	1	-	-	-	-	-	1	-	
	M	-	-	-	-	1	-	-	-	
	S	$\frac{1}{2}$	-	-	-	-	-	1	-	
	S	-	-	-	-	-	1	-	-	
	N	-	-	-	-	-	-	1	-	
	O	-	-	-	-	-	-	1	-	
Masonry cement	M	1	-	-	1	-	-	-	-	
	M	-	1	-	-	-	-	-	-	
	S	$\frac{1}{2}$	-	-	1	-	-	-	-	
	S	-	-	1	-	-	-	-	-	
	N	-	-	-	1	-	-	-	-	
	O	-	-	-	1	-	-	-	-	

[a] Portland cement conforming to the requirements of ASTM C 150
[b] Blended cement conforming to the requirements of ASTM C 595
[c] Masonry cement conforming to the requirements of ASTM C 91
[d] Mortar cement conforming to the requirements of ASTM C 1329

The 1997 Uniform Building Code provides that in Seismic Zones 3 and 4, only Type M or Type S mortar can be used for the structural system. In Seismic Zones 0, 1 and 2, Types M, S or N can be used for the structural system.

Similarly, in IBC Seismic Design Categories D and E, only Type M or Type S Mortar can be used for the structural system. In Seismic Design Categories A, B and C, Types M, S or N can be used for the structural system.

The use of masonry cement and plastic cement is prohibited is Seismic Zones 2, 3 and 4 for the structural system, in accordance with the 1997 Uniform Building Code.

The *MSJC Code* does not recognize the use of plastic cement in masonry construction. It also does not permit the use of masonry cement in the lateral force-resisting system for Seismic Categories D and E.

Field practice is to use the range of proportions for each type of mortar that will result is a workable, smooth mortar that spreads easily and is plastic enough to be able to push the masonry unit into it when the unit is laid. It must also be stiff enough to support the masonry unit without deforming under the additional weight of masonry units.

For example, Type S mortar, made with Portland cement and hydrated lime can be proportioned with one part Portland cement, one-quarter to one-half part hydrated lime and 2.8 to 4.5 parts sand, depending on the amount of lime added. The variation in sand proportions allows an adjustment due to particle shape, size, and grading all of which affect workability and spreadability.

2.10.3 Mortar Aggregate—Sand

The aggregate used for mortar should be well graded with sufficient fine material passing the No. 100 sieve to impart smoothness to the mortar. Plaster sand is ideal for mortar for it has no particle larger than $^1/_8$ inch (3.2 mm) and it has sufficient fines for workability and smoothness.

Particle shape influences the workability of mortar. Round, spherical particles, well graded, are best for mortar while sharp, cubical or flat particles produce harsh mortar.

ASTM C 144, Aggregate for Masonry Mortar gives the grading requirements for sand.

ASTM C-144, Section 4		
Aggregate for use in masonry mortar shall be graded within the following limits, depending upon whether natural sand or manufactured sand is to be used:		
	Percent Passing	
Sieve Size	Natural Sand	Manufactured Sand
No. 4 (4.75 mm)	100	100
No. 8 (2.36 mm)	95 to 100	95 to 100
No. 16 (1.18 mm)	70 to 100	70 to 100
No. 30 (600-μm)	40 to 75	40 to 75
No. 50 (300-μm)	10 to 35	20 to 40
No. 100 (150-μm)	2 to 15	10 to 25
No. 200 (75-μm)	0 to 5	0 to 10

The aggregate shall not have more than 50% retained between any two consecutive sieves nor more than 25% between No. 50 (300-µm) and the No. 100 (150-µm) sieve.

If the fineness modulus varies by more than 0.20 from the value assumed in selecting proportions for the mortar, the aggregate shall be rejected unless suitable adjustments are made in proportions to compensate for the change in grading.

For heavy construction employing joints thicker than $1/_2$ inch (12.5 mm), a coarser aggregate may be desirable; for such work a fine aggregate conforming to Specification C 404 is satisfactory.

When an aggregate fails the gradation limits specified above, it may be used provided the mortar can be prepared to comply with the aggregate ratio, water retention, and compressive strength requirements of the property specifications of Specification C 270.

Concrete sand should not be used because the maximum grain sizes may be $3/_{16}$ inch (5 mm) to $1/_4$ inch (6 mm) and needed fines have been washed out resulting in a sand too harsh and coarse and unsuitable for mortar.

Aggregate, when stored, should be in a level, dry, clean place from which it can be measured into the mixer with minimum handling and kept free from contamination by harmful substances.

2.10.4 Mixing

Mortar mixing is best accomplished in a paddle type mixer. About one-half of the water and one quarter of the sand are put into the operating mixer first, then the cement, lime, color (if any) and the remaining water and sand are added. All materials should then mix for not less than three minutes and not more than ten minutes (UBC) or not less than 3 minutes and not more than 5 minutes (MSJC) in a mechanical mixer with the amount of water required to provide the desired workability. Small amounts of mortar can be hand mixed.

Figure 2.10 Plaster or paddle mortar mixer.

In a paddle mixer, shown in Figure 2.10, the drum is stationary and the blades rotate through the mortar materials for thorough mixing.

A drum or barrel mixer, shown in Figure 2.11, rotates the drum in which the materials are placed. The material is carried to the top of the rotation and drops down to achieve mixing.

Figure 2.11 Drum or barrel concrete mixer.

2.10.5 Silo Mixing System

Mortar can also be factory pre-blended and stored at the jobsite in silos. Some systems introduce water to the dry mortar mix in an auger screw at the base of the silo, while other systems discharge the dry mortar mix directly into a conventional mixer.

Pre-blended dry mortar is also available in sacks, which may be beneficial in keeping project debris at a minimum.

Dry mixes, pre-blended by the manufacturer should be mixed at the job site until workable, but not for more than 10 minutes (UBC).

When factory blended mortar is used, manufacturers certification of the type of mortar is recommended.

2.10.6 Retempering

Mortar may be retempered one time with water when needed to maintain workability. This should be done on mortar boards by forming a basin or hollow in the mortar, adding water and then reworking the mortar into the water. Splashing water over the top of the mortar is not permissible. Harsh mortar, mortar that has begun to stiffen or harden due to hydration, should be discarded. Mortar must be used within two-and-one-half hours after the initial water has been added to the dry ingredients at the job site.

2.10.7 Color

Mortar colors are generally mineral oxides or carbon black. Iron oxide is used for red, yellow and brown colors; chromium oxide is for green and cobalt oxide is for blue colors.

The amount of color additive depends on the color and intensity and typically ranges from 0.5% to 7.0% for the mineral oxides and a maximum of 2% for carbon black. The percent is based on weight of cement content. These maximum percentages are far greater than the normal amounts of color added, and specific code limitations are listed below, based on cement type.

There are commercially prepared colors for mortars that offer a wide variety of colors and shades.

MSJC Specification 2.6.A.2

2. When required, use mineral oxide or carbon black job site pigments. Limit the maximum percentage by weight of cement as follows:

a. Pigmented portland cement-lime mortar
  1) Mineral oxide pigment 10 percent
  2) Carbon black pigment 2 percent

b. Pigmented masonry cement mortar
  1) Mineral oxide pigment 5 percent
  2) Carbon black pigment 1 percent

c. Pigmented masonry cement mortar
  1) Mineral oxide pigment 5 percent
  2) Carbon black pigment 1 percent

The 1997 Uniform Building Code limits only carbon black color to a maximum of 3% of the weight of cement.

Mixing time should be long enough for a uniform, even color to be obtained in the mortar and should be the same length of time for every batch.

Mixing sequence should be the same for each batch and as specified in Section 2.10.4 "Mixing."

Retempering must be kept to a minimum when coloring is used, and for best results should not be done at all.

The source of materials, manufacturer and amount of each ingredient should remain the same for all colored mortar on the project so as to obtain uniform color throughout. Prepackaged mineral color additives that can be added to the mix based on full sacks of Portland cement provide a consistent batching for quality control of mortar color.

2.10.8 Proprietary Mortars

Proprietary mortars such as masonry cement mortars, delayed set mortars and ready mix mortars must be approved by the engineer or architect and accepted by the building official, where applicable. Handling and use of these materials should be in strict compliance with the manufacturer's recommendations.

2.10.9 Mortar Admixtures

There are retarding admixtures that delay the set and stiffening of mortar. Retardation can be obtained for 36 hours or more.

There are also admixtures used to replace lime. These admixtures usually add air to the mortar mix to provide workability.

Integral water repellents can be added to mortar for improved resistance of water penetration to the mortar joints.

Admixtures must be approved by the architect or engineer and be acceptable to the building official, as applicable.

2.11   GROUT

2.11.1 General

Grout is a fluid mixture of cement, sand, and frequently pea gravel; it is very plastic concrete with a required slump of eight to eleven inches (203 mm to 279 mm). This high slump is necessary for the grout to flow into all the grout spaces and joints and completely surround the steel. The excess water is immediately absorbed into the masonry units, thereby reducing the initial water/cement ratio of the grout. The absorbed water in the concrete masonry units aids in curing the grout and increasing the strength gain.

Grout shall consist of a mixture of cementitious materials and aggregate to which water has been added such that the mixture will flow without segregation of the constituents. Grout shall have a minimum compressive strength f'_g of 2,000 pounds per square inch (14.0 MPa) at 28 days. Higher grout strength may be required by the designer and must be specified in the project documents.

2.11.2 Type of Grout

Fine Grout: Fine grout, or sand grout, may be used in grout spaces in multiwythe masonry as small as $^3/_4$ inch (19 mm) or larger in least clear horizontal dimension and in grout spaces in hollow unit construction $1^1/_2$ inches by 2 inches (38 mm x 51 mm) or more in least clear horizontal dimension.

Coarse Grout: Coarse grout which uses pea gravel may be used in grout spaces in multiwythe masonry $1^1/_2$ inches (38 mm) or larger in least clear horizontal dimension and in grout spaces in hollow unit construction $1^1/_2$ inches by 3 inches (38 mm x 76 mm) or more in least clear horizontal dimension.

2.11.3 Proportions

Grout may be proportioned by laboratory design mixed based on testing or field experience or in accordance with 2000 IBC Table 2103.10, ASTM C 476, Table 1, or UBC Table 21-B. The testing values would be based on masonry prism tests or grout specimen tests made in accordance with field experience based on a history of performance with the same masonry units and grout materials and mix proportions used for the project. The use of 70% sand and 30% pea gravel requires six sacks of Portland cement per cubic yard and results in a pumpable grout that will provide the strength required. Grout must have adequate strength for satisfactory f'_m values, for bonding reinforcing steel, for embedment of anchor bolts and for proper bond to transfer the stress to the reinforcing bar.

Extensive research and experience documents that grout proportions based on the grout proportion tables listed above are successful for regular load-bearing concrete masonry.

Adjust the water content at grout to provide proper workability and to enable proper placement under existing field conditions, without segregation.

IBC TABLE 2103.10[1] - GROUT PROPORTIONS BY VOLUME[2] FOR MASONRY CONSTRUCTION (*ASTM C 476*)

Type	Parts by Volume of Portland Cement or Blended Cement	Parts by Volume of Hydrated Lime or Lime Putty	Aggregate Measured in a Damp Loose Condition	
			Fine	Course
Fine grout	1	0 to $^1/_{10}$	$2\,^1/_4$ to 3 times the sum of the volumes of the cementious materials	
Coarse grout	1	0 to $^1/_{10}$	$2\,^1/_4$ to 3 times the sum of the volumes of the cementious materials	1 to 2 times the sum of the volumes of the cementious materials

[1] ASTM C 476, Table 1; 1997 UBC Table 21-B.
[2] Grout shall attain a minimum compressive strength at 28 days of 2,000 psi (13.8 Mpa).

2.11.4 Aggregate for Grout

Aggregate for grout is required to conform to the grading requirements of ASTM C 404, Table 1.

2.11.5 Mixing

Grout prepared at the job site shall be mechanically mixed for at least three minutes to assure thorough blending of all ingredients, but not more than 10 minutes (UBC) or a minimum of 5 minutes if using ASTM C 476 as the governing standard. Enough water must be used in the mixing process to achieve a high slump of eight to eleven inches (203 to 279 mm). This high slump is necessary for the grout to flow into relatively small cells of the concrete masonry. Excess water is immediately absorbed into the masonry, thereby aiding the curing process.

2.11.6 Grout Admixtures

Admixtures used in grout render desired properties. When admixtures are used, they should be approved by the architect or the engineer and be acceptable to the building official. Three types of admixtures used in masonry grout are:

a. Shrinkage compensating admixtures counteract the loss of water and the shrinkage of Portland cement by creating an expansive gas in the grout.

b. Super plasticizer admixtures obtain high slump with reduced water in the grout. Grout with a 4 inch (102 mm) slump can go to a 10 inch (254 mm) slump with the use of a super plasticizer.

c. Cement replacement such as fly ash can be used in grout. Current provisions allow a maximum of 15% to 20% by weight of Portland cement to be replaced by fly ash. The maximum amount is dependent on the fly ash, Portland cement and strength gain characteristics.

ASTM C 404 - TABLE 1 - GRADING REQUIREMENTS

Amounts Finer than Each Laboratory Sieve (Square Openings), Weight %

Sieve Size	Size No. 1	Fine Aggregate Size No. 2		Coarse Aggregate	
		Natural	Manufactured	Size No. 8	Size No. 89
1/2-in. (12.5-mm)	...	...	...	100	100
3/8-in. (9.5-mm)	100	...	...	85 to 100	90 to 100
No. 4 (4.75-mm)	95 to 100	100	100	10 to 30	20 to 55
No. 8 (2.36-mm)	80 to 100	95 to 100	95 to 100	0 to 10	5 to 30
No. 16 (1.18-mm)	50 to 85	70 to 100	70 to 100	0 to 5	0 to 10
No. 30 (600-µm)	25 to 60	40 to 75	40 to 75	...	0 to 5
No. 50 (300-µm)	10 to 30	10 to 35	20 to 40	...	...
No. 100 (150-µm)	2 to 10	2 to 15	10 to 25	...	...
No. 200 (75-µm)	0 to 5	0 to 5	0 to 10	...	...

Fly ash is a pozzolanic material obtained from combustion of coal which is collected in electrostatic precipitators or bag houses. It is classified by precise particle size and by chemical composition as Class N, F or C.

Class N fly ash consists of raw or calcined natural pozzolans such as diatomaceous earths; opaline cherts and shales; tuffs and volcanic ashes or pumicities. It is not typically used in masonry grout.

Class F fly ash is obtained from the combustion of anthracite, bituminous or sub-bituminous coal. It is low in lime, less than 7%, and contains greater than 70% silica, alumina and iron.

Class C fly ash comes from burning lignite of sub-bituminous coal and has more than 15% lime.

Class N, F and C ash are siliceous or siliceous and aluminous material which in itself possesses little or no cementitious value but will, in finely divided form and in the presence of moisture, react with calcium hydroxide at ordinary temperatures to form compounds possessing cementitious properties.

Fly ash, because of its fine, spherical particles, increases workability and cohesiveness. It reduces water demand and improves pumpability of grout.

When fly ash is used as a cement replacement, it is necessary to have assurance that the required strength will be obtained in the stated period of time.

2.11.7 Anti-Freeze Compounds

Most anti-freeze admixtures are actually accelerators that increase the temperature by speeding up the hydration process.

Some anti-freeze admixtures use alcohol to lower the freezing point; however, it requires a significant amount and this will reduce both the compressive strength and bond strength of mortar.

ASTM C 270 and ASTM C 476 state that the use of Anti-freeze liquids, chloride salts or other such substances are severely restricted in mortar or grout.

2.11.8 Ready Mixed Grout

On large commercial projects, grout is often batched at a concrete plant and shipped to the job site in transit mix trucks. This process introduces water to the cement and aggregates at the plant and mixes the grout while in transit. At the job site, the grout is normally pumped in the wall by means of a grout pump.

Common practice is to batch this grout to the predetermined quantities of a mix design. The mix design may be a standard mix design which is known to yield a certain specified strength or a special mix design meeting the criteria for a specific project.

The requirements for ready mixed grout such as an 8 inch to 11 inch (203 mm to 279 mm) slump, are the same as previously detailed in Section 2.11.

Grout should be placed within $1^1/_2$ hours after the initial water is introduced to the dry ingredients, however, the Uniform Building Code does not include this restriction for transit mixed grout. For transit mixed grout it is reasonable to follow the commentary guidelines of ACI 318, which allows for placement of transit mixed material provided the material has not hydrated to the extent that the curing process is adversely affected.

SECTION 3

Quality Control, Sampling and Testing

3.1 QUALITY CONTROL

To assure that materials are in accordance with the International Building Code, the Uniform Building Code, the *MSJC Code Specification* and the particular project specifications, tests may be required on the mortar, grout, masonry units, and prisms. The following code excerpts mandate the implementation of a quality assurance program.

IBC Section 2105

QUALITY ASSURANCE

2105.1 General. A quality assurance program shall be used to ensure that the constructed masonry is in compliance with the construction documents.

The quality assurance program shall comply with the inspection and testing requirements of Chapter 17.

> ## UBC Section 2105.1
> ## QUALITY ASSURANCE
>
> **2105.1 General.** Quality assurance shall be provided to ensure that materials, construction and workmanship are in compliance with the plans and specifications, and the applicable requirements of this chapter. When required, inspection records shall be maintained and made available to the building official.

The scope of the quality assurance program should include verification of f'_m by the Prism Test Method, the Unit Strength Method, or Testing Prisms from Constructed Masonry. The Uniform Building Code also allows verification by using historic Masonry Prism Test Records. Tests may also include units, mortar or grout, however these tests are unnecessary and redundant when testing masonry assemblages.

3.2   SAMPLING AND TESTING

Testing should be done in compliance with specifications and verified prior to the start of work. Job site tests, when required, should then be made to confirm the continuing acceptable quality of materials used.

3.2.1   Cone Penetration Test for Consistency of Mortar

The cone penetration test as outlined in ASTM C 780 *Standard Test Method for Preconstruction and Construction Evaluation of Mortars for Plain and Reinforced Unit Masonry* provides a technique for determining the consistency or plasticity of mortar.

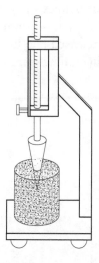

Figure 3.1 Cone penetrometer.

Consistency determinations by cone penetration allow controlling additions for all mortars included in the pre-construction test series. Although mortar consistency as measured at the construction site may be a higher penetration value than the pre-construction tests, the cone penetration test serves to standardize water additions for mortar mixes being considered before construction. A cone penetrometer is illustrated in Figure 3.1.

Consistency retention by cone penetration using mortar samples provides a means of establishing the early age setting and stiffening characteristics of the mortar.

The cone penetration test method determines the consistency by measuring the penetration of a conical plunger into a mortar sample (see Figure 3.2). A cylindrical measure, having an inside diameter of 3 inches (76 mm) and a depth of $3^{15}/_{32}$ inches $\pm$ $^{1}/_{16}$ inches (88 mm $\pm$ 1.6 mm), is filled with mortar in three equal layers.

Each layer is spaded 20 times with a metal spatula. The top is leveled and a cone $1^5/_8$ inch (41 mm) in diameter and $3^5/_8$ inches (92 mm) long is released into the mortar. The depth of penetration is measured in millimeters.

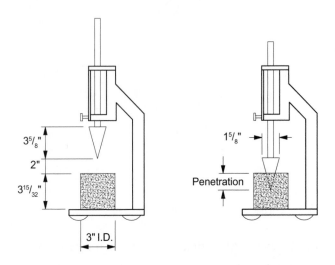

Figure 3.2 Cone penetration to test consistency of mortar.

Consistency or plasticity of mortar for hollow unit concrete masonry is generally stiffer with a lower cone penetration value than mortar for brick, which generally will be a softer, more plastic mortar. This is because hollow concrete units are heavy and stiff mortar must hold the unit in position without squeezing down. Brick units are light and can be easily moved into position in the plastic mortar.

3.2.2 Field Test for Mortar Strength

It is sometimes necessary to know the properties of mortar and strength of grout actually used on the project. Therefore, specimens can be made in the field, using job site materials and made as directed by International Building Code Sections 2105.4 and 2105.5. Figure 3.3 depicts the mortar specimen preparation procedure as outlined in UBC Standard 21-16. ASTM C 780 contains similar test specimen procedure methods without the requirement of placing the mortar on a masonry unit prior to mortar placement in the cylinder.

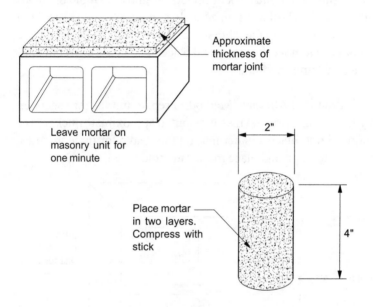

Figure 3.3 Preparing and making field test mortar specimens.

IBC Section 2105.4

2105.4 Mortar Testing. When required, mortar testing shall be tested in accordance with the property specifications of ASTM C 270 or evaluated in accordance with ASTM C 780.

UBC Section 2105.4

2105.4 Mortar Testing. When required, mortar shall be tested in accordance with UBC Standard 21-16.

3.2.3   Field Compressive Test Specimens for Mortar

Spread mortar on the masonry units $^1/_2$ inch to $^5/_8$ inch (13 mm to 16 mm) thick, and allow to stand for one minute, then remove mortar and place in a 2 inch by 4 inch (51 mm by 102 mm) cylinder in two layers, compressing the mortar into the cylinder using a flat-end stick or fingers. Lightly tap mold on opposite sides, level off and immediately cover molds and keep them damp until taken to the laboratory. After 48-hours' set, have the laboratory remove the molds and place them in the fog room until tested in damp condition.

Proposed Alternate Method: Prepare mortar for specimen by spreading mortar on masonry unit to approximate thickness of mortar joint, place another unit on top, leave for three minutes, remove top unit and place mortar in mold (see Figure 3.4).

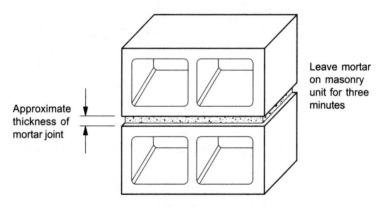

Figure 3.4 Alternate method of preparing field mortar for test specimens.

3.2.4   Mortar Strength Requirements

1997 UBC Standard 21-16 requires that each such mortar test specimen shall exhibit a minimum ultimate compressive strength of 1,500 pounds per square inch (10 340 kPa).

It is recommended that each mortar test specimen exhibit a minimum 28-day ultimate compressive strength as set forth in Table 3-A.

Table 3-A *Compressive Strength of Mortar (psi)*

Mortar Type	2" x 4" (51 mm x 102 mm) Cylinder Specimen		2" Cube (51 mm) Specimen	
M	2100	(14,500 kPa)	2500	(17,200 kPa)
S	1500	(10,300 kPa)	1800	(12,400 kPa)
N	625	(4,300 kPa)	750	(5,200 kPa)

Lesser periods of time for testing may be used provided the relation between early tested strength and the 28-day strength of the mortar is established.

The strength requirement for mortar is based on a 2 inch (51 mm) cube, while field test specimens are based on 2 inch x 4 inch (51 mm x 102 mm) cylindrical specimens. The 2 inch (51 mm) cube is typically used for laboratory prepared mortar with a specified flow while the 2 inch x 4 inch (51 mm x 102 mm) cylindrical specimen is used for field mortar.

To obtain an equivalency of a 2 inch x 4 inch (51 mm x 102 mm) cylinder field test specimen to a 2 inch (51 mm) cube specimen, divide the compression test result of the cylinder specimen by 0.85.

If mortar tests are required, the following schedule is suggested.

Take one test per day for three successive work days at the start of the job and store in a moist climate until tested. One test shall consist of three specimens.

After the first three tests, specimens for continuing quality control shall be taken once a week, or for every 5000 square foot (465 m²) of wall, whichever occurs first.

Mortar compressive strength shall be at least 50% of the 28-day strength after seven days and at least equal to the specified strength after 28 days.

The strength of mortar has some influence on the compressive strength of the masonry prism and wall. It is a convenient control test to assure minimum standards and adequate cementing materials are used in the mortar to provide bond.

3.2.5   Field Tests for Grout

Grout significantly contributes to the strength of the masonry wall and bonds the reinforcing steel into the structural system. Specimens are made in such a way as to duplicate the condition of grout in the wall.

3.2.6.   Field Compressive Test Specimens for Grout

IBC Section 2105.5
2105.5 Grout Testing. When required, grout shall be tested in accordance with ASTM C 1019.

UBC Section 2105.5
2105.5 Grout Testing. When required, grout shall be tested in accordance with UBC Standard 21-18.

ASTM C 1019 outlines the method of making a grout specimen to achieve similarity to grout in the wall. An absorptive paper toweling prevents bond of grout to the unit and allows the excess moisture to be absorbed into the unit. Refer to Figure 3.5.

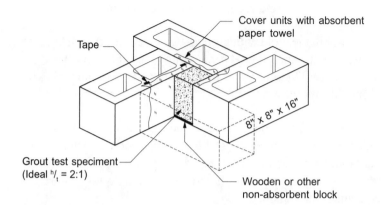

Figure 3.5 Arrangement of masonry units for making a grout test specimen.

Requirements of ASTM C 1019 are to:

● Select a level location where the molds can remain undisturbed for 48 hours.

● Construct the mold space to replicate the grout location in the wall. If the grout is placed between two different types of masonry units, both types should be used to construct the mold.

● Form a square prism space, nominally 3 inches (76.2 mm) or larger on each side, twice as high as its width, by stacking masonry units of the same type and moisture condition as those being used in the construction. Place wooden blocks, cut to proper size and of the proper thickness or quantity, at the bottom of the space to achieve the necessary height of specimen. Tolerance on space and specimen dimensions shall be within 5 percent of the specimen width.

● Line the masonry surfaces that will be in contact with the grout specimen with a permeable material, such as paper towel, to prevent bond to the masonry units.

• Measure and record the slump of the grout.

• Fill the mold with grout in two layers. Rod each layer 15 times with the tamping rod penetrating $^1/_2$ inch (12.7 mm) into the lower layer. Distribute the strokes uniformly over the cross section of the mold.

• Level the top surface of the specimen with a straight-edge and cover immediately with a damp absorbent material such as cloth or paper towel. Keep the top surface of the sample damp by wetting the absorbent material and do not disturb the specimen for 48 hours.

• Protect the sample from freezing and variations in temperature. Store a maximum-minimum indicating thermometer with the sample and record the maximum and minimum temperatures experienced prior to the time the specimens are placed in the moist laboratory room.

• Remove the masonry units between 24 and 48 hours after casting specimens (UBC requires a minimum of 48 hours). Transport field specimens to the laboratory, keeping the specimens damp and in a protective container.

Alternate Methods: Some laboratories and inspectors prepare grout specimens by pouring the grout into the concrete block cells, as shown in Figure 3.6. After the grout has set for a few days, the masonry shells and webs are broken off. The grout specimens are:

a. tested as is and an adjustment made for height and area,

b. sawed into $3^3/_{16}$ inch x $3^{13}/_{16}$ inch x $7^5/_8$ inch (81 mm x 97 mm x 194 mm) prismatic specimens and tested, or

c. cored into a 3 inch or 4 inch (76 mm or 102 mm) diameter specimen drilled from the grout cell and then tested.

The alternate method is not recommended since the breaking, sawing and coring will negatively impact the strength of the sample, thereby yielding distorted test results.

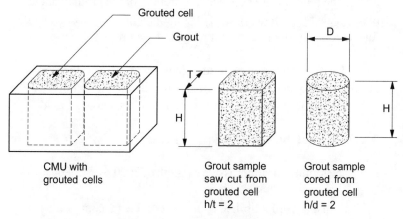

CMU with
grouted cells

Grout sample
saw cut from
grouted cell
h/t = 2

Grout sample
cored from
grouted cell
h/d = 2

Figure 3.6   Alternate grout test specimens.

Another method that could be used is to pour grout into a special concrete block that has three 4 inch (102 mm) diameter cells, as shown in Figure 3.7. After the grout has set for several days, the block is broken away and three 4 inch x 8 inch (102 mm x 203 mm) grout specimens are obtained.

Field sampling of grout using
ABC grout sample block

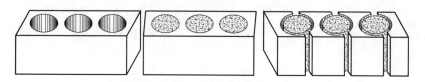

Block is nominal 6" x 8" x 16"
with three 4" diameter holes.

Figure 3.7   Proprietary grout sample block.

The alternate methods of making a grout specimen closely relate to actual field conditions. Comparison specimens can be made for both the alternate method and standard method to establish the relationship between the strength of the grout of specimens made by each method. This relationship, once established for the job, can then be used throughout the project.

Use of an alternate method of making grout specimens may be subject to question should the test results do not comply with specification requirements and comparison tests are not made.

3.2.7   Grout Strength Requirements

The minimum compressive strength of 2000 psi (13,800 kPa) is to:
   a. insure compatibility with the concrete masonry units.
   b. provide adequate bond strength of the grout to the reinforcing bars.
   c. provide compressive strength capacity to the wall assemblage.

The minimum value is satisfactory for masonry construction in which the design strength $f'_m = 1500$ psi (10,300 kPa) and the masonry unit has a compressive strength of 1900 psi (13,100 kPa).

ASTM C 476 requires grout to be specified by the required compressive strength for a particular project (minimum 2,000 psi (13,800 kPa)) based on a mix design or by the proportions stated in ASTM C 476, Table 1 (see Section 2.11.)

It is recommended that the compressive strength of grout in concrete masonry construction be at least equal to 1.25 to 1.33 times the design strength of the masonry assemblage, f'_m.

An example of this is that 2000 psi (13,800 kPa) grout is required for a masonry assemblage strength f'_m of 1500 psi (10,300 kPa).

If grout tests are required, the following schedule is suggested.

At the start of grouting operations, take one test per day for the first three days. The tests shall consist of three specimens which are made in accordance with ASTM C 1019 Section 5, Test Specimens.

After the first three tests, specimens for continuing quality control shall be taken once a week or for every 30 cubic yards (23 m³) of grout or for every 5000 square feet (465 m²) of wall, whichever comes first.

For minimum grout strength as required by ASTM C 476, historical laboratory test data may justify that a seven day compressive strength of 1,200 psi (6,900 kPa) will extrapolate to 2,000 psi (13,800 kPa) at 28 days. For higher strength grout, it is appropriate to rely more on actual 28 day strength test results instead of seven day extrapolated results.

3.3   CONCRETE MASONRY UNITS

While most of the tests on concrete masonry units are performed prior to start of work, some random sampling at the job site may be required of concrete masonry units by project specifications or by request of the building official, architect or other authorized person. These samples should be truly random, representative, average samples.

The tests that should be conducted are based on the requirements of ASTM C 90 *Standard Specification for Load Bearing Concrete Masonry Units* and should meet the requirements for compressive strength, water absorption and thickness for face shells and webs. In addition, the linear shrinkage of the unit, must not exceed 0.065% at time of delivery.

The test procedures for compressive strength, absorption, weight, moisture content and dimensions are given in ASTM C 140 *Standard Test Methods for Sampling and Testing Concrete Masonry Units and Related Units*.

See Section 14, Masonry Units, for some of the numerous sizes and types of hollow concrete masonry units.

3.4   PRISM TESTING

3.4.1   General

Prism testing is primarily used when strengths are required higher than the conventional assumed design values allow. Unusual conditions are frequently involved, therefore, it is important that adequate time be allowed for preparing these prisms since retesting could be required. The test is to determine how well different materials work together. The full strength developed depends on many factors, including workmanship and materials.

The procedure for making samples, curing and testing is specified in ASTM C 1314, *Standard Test Method for Compressive Strength of Masonry Prisms*. The method consists essentially of making sample assemblies of the materials to be used in the construction and then testing the assemblages to see what capacities that combination of materials will develop. Typically, three samples (one set) are made and tested prior to starting the work. Subsequent sets of three are taken at 5,000 square foot (465 m²) intervals during construction using the same masonry units, mortar, grout and masons used in the construction of the wall.

Care must be exercised in handling the prisms in order to prevent damage before testing. The prisms should be left undisturbed and under moist cover for two days after grouting before being moved to the laboratory. They are then cured moist, as specified, and tested at 28 days. In addition, the Uniform Building Code provides that three and/or seven-day tests can be taken if the relationship of these strengths to the 28-day strengths is known. When three or seven-day tests are made, extrapolation can determine whether results are satisfactorily meeting the 28-day strength requirement.

Construct the prisms on a flat, level base. Masonry units used in the prism shall be representative of the units used in the corresponding construction. Build each prism shall in an opened moisture-tight bag which is large enough to enclose and seal the completed prism. The orientation of the units, where top and bottom cross sections vary due to taper of the cells, or where the architectural surface of either side of the unit varies, shall be the same orientation as used in the corresponding construction. Construct prism a single wythe in thickness and lay up in stack bond (see Figure 3-8).

If architectural features, such as flutes or ribs, are part of the unit and project more than $\frac{1}{2}$ inch (12.7 mm) from the surface at the unit, cut the projections off to give the unit an even face.

The length of masonry prisms may be reduced by saw cutting; however, prisms composed of regular shaped hollow units require at least one complete cell with one full-width cross web on either end. Prisms composed of irregular-shaped units need to be cut to obtain a cross section as symmetrical as possible. The minimum length of saw-cut prisms shall be 4 inches (102 mm).

Masonry prisms shall be laid in full mortar bed (mortar bed on both webs and face shells). Mortar shall be representative of that used in the corresponding construction. Mortar joint thickness and the method of positioning and aligning units shall be representative of the corresponding construction. ASTM requires mortar joints to be flush cut while UBC Standard 21-17 provides for tooling of mortar joints to match actual jobsite conditions.

Prisms shall be a minimum of two units in height, but the total height shall not be less than 1.3 times the least actual thickness or more than 5.0 times the least actual thickness. Immediately following the construction of the prism, the moisture-tight bag is drawn around the prism and sealed.

Where the corresponding construction is solid grouted, prisms are solid grouted. Grout shall be representative of grout used in the corresponding construction. Place grout not less than one day nor more than two days following the construction of the prism. Grout consolidation shall be representative of that used in the construction. Place additional grout in the prism after reconsolidation and settlement due to water loss, but prior to the grout setting. Screed off excess grout and level with the top of the prism. When open-end units are used, additional masonry units shall be used as forms to confine the grout during placement. Masonry unit forms shall be sufficiently braced to prevent displacement during grouting. Immediately following the grouting operation, the moisture-tight bag is drawn around the prism and resealed.

Where the corresponding construction is partially grouted, construct two sets of prisms; one set is grouted solid and the other set is not grouted.

The Uniform Building Code Standard requires ungrouted, single wythe prisms for prism testing in multi-wythe masonry construction. ASTM C 1314 contains the same requirement when the wythes have different units or mortar; however, when units and mortar of the two wythes are the same and grouted, then ASTM C 1314 requires that the two wythes be constructed and grouted replicating the actual well configuration.

Prisms shall be left undisturbed for at least two days after construction.

3.4.2 Standard Prism Tests

The Test Method for Compressive Strength of Masonry Prisms is based on the ASTM C 1314 *Standard Test Method for Compressive Strength of Masonry Prisms*. The test requires a prism two-units high with at least one mortar joint, as shown in Figure 3.8.

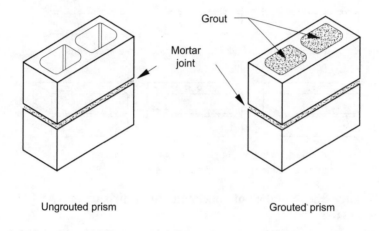

Ungrouted prism

Grouted prism

Figure 3.8 Masonry prism construction for 8 inch (200 mm) high units.

ASTM E 447 *Standard Test Method for Compressive Strength of Laboratory Constructed Masonry Prisms* was once used as a field standard, but has been replaced by ASTM C 1314. ASTM C 1314 is consistent with 1997 UBC Standard 21-17.

3.4.3   Tests of Masonry Prisms

When masonry prisms are required in accordance with IBC Section 2105.2.2.2 or the *MSJC Specification*, the prisms shall be tested in accordance with ASTM C 1314. Refer to Figure 3.9.

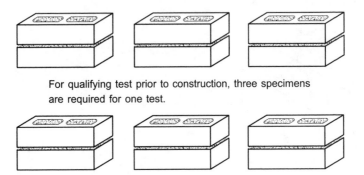

For qualifying test prior to construction, three specimens are required for one test.

For field control as the project is being constructed three specimens are required for one test.

Figure 3.9   Number of specimens for a prism test (ASTM C 1314).

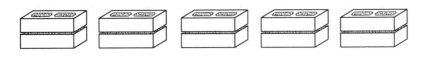

For qualifying test prior to construction, five specimens are required for one test.

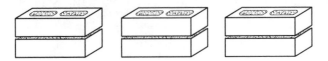

For field control as the project is being constructed three specimens are required for one test.

Figure 3.10   Number of specimens for a prism test (UBC Standard 21-17).

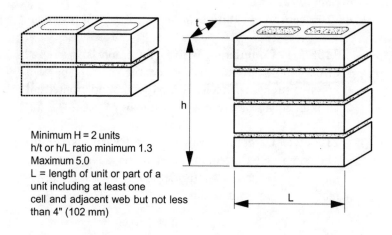

Minimum H = 2 units
h/t or h/L ratio minimum 1.3
Maximum 5.0
L = length of unit or part of a
unit including at least one
cell and adjacent web but not less
than 4" (102 mm)

Figure 3.11 Size of prism specimen.

3.4.4   Specified Compressive Strength, f'_m

The value of the specified compressive strength (f'_m) must be verified based upon either the provisions of IBC Section 2105.2.2.1, Unit Strength Method or 2105.2.2.2, Prism test Method. The Unit Strength Method uses IBC Tables 2105.2.2.1.1 and 2105.2.2.1.2 to determine compressive strength values of clay and concrete masonry respectively. These are similar to the values contained in Tables 1 and 2 of the *MSJC Specification*.

2105.2 Acceptance relative to strength requirements.

2105.2.1 Compliance with f'_m. Compressive strength of masonry shall be considered satisfactory if the compressive strength of each masonry wythe and grouted collar joint equals or exceeds the value of f'_m.

2105.2.2 Determination of compressive strength. The compressive strength for each wythe shall be determined by the unit strength method or by the prism test method as specified herein.

2105.2.2.1 Unit strength method.

2105.2.2.1.1 Clay masonry. The compressive strength of masonry shall be determined based on the strength of the units and the type of mortar specified using Table 2105.2.2.1.1, provided:

1. Units conform to ASTM C 62, ASTM C 216, or ASTM C 652 and are sampled and tested in accordance with ASTM C 67.

2. Thickness of bed joints does not exceed $5/8$ inch (15.9 mm).

3. For grouted masonry, the grout meets one of the following requirements:

3.1. Grout conforms to ASTM C 476.
3.2. Minimum grout compressive strength equals f'_m but not less than 2,000 psi (13.79 MPa). The compressive strength of grout shall be determined in accordance with ASTM C 1019.

TABLE 2105.2.2.1.1
COMPRESSIVE STRENGTH OF CLAY MASONRY

NET AREA COMPRESSIVE STRENGTH OF CLAY MASONRY UNITS (psi)		NET AREA COMPRESSIVE STRENGTH OF MASONRY (psi)
Type M or S mortar	**Type N mortar**	
2,400	3,000	1,000
4,400	5,500	1,500
6,400	8,000	2,000
8,400	10,500	2,500
10,400	13,000	3,000
12,400	-----	3,500
14,400	-----	4,000

For SI: 1 pound per square inch = 0.00689 MPa.

2105.2.2.1.2 Concrete masonry. The compressive strength of masonry shall be determined based on the strength of the unit and type of mortar specified using Table 2105.2.2.1.2, provided:

1. Units conform to ASTM C 55 or ASTM C 90 and are sampled and tested in accordance with ASTM C 140.
2. Thickness of bed joints does not exceed $^5/_8$ inch (15.9 mm).
3. For grouted masonry, the grout meets one of the following requirements:

3.1. Grout conforms to ASTM C 476.
3.2. Minimum grout compressive strength equals f'_m but not less than 2,000 psi (13.79 MPa). The compressive strength of grout shall be determined in accordance with ASTM C 1019.

TABLE 2105.2.2.1.2
COMPRESSIVE STRENGTH OF CONCRETE MASONRY

NET AREA COMPRESSIVE STRENGTH OF CONCRETE MASONRY UNITS (psi)		NET AREA COMPRESSIVE STRENGTH OF MASONRY (psi)[a]
Type M or S mortar	Type N mortar	
1,250	1,300	1,000
1,900	2,150	1,500
2,800	3,050	2,000
3,750	4,050	2,500
4,800	5,250	3,000

For SI: 1 inch = 25.4 mm, 1 pound per square inch = 0.006895 MPa.
[a] For units of less than 4 inches in height 85 percent of the values listed

2105.2.2.2 Prism test method.

2105.2.2.2.1 General. The compressive strength of masonry shall be determined by the prism test method:
1. Where specified in the construction documents.
2. Where masonry does not meet the requirements for application of the unit strength method in Section 2105.2.2.1.

2105.2.2.2.2 Number of prisms per test. A prism test shall consist of testing three prisms in accordance with ASTM C 1314.

2105.2.2.2.3 Compressive strength determination. The compressive strength of masonry shall be taken as the average strength of three prisms, as modified in ASTM C 1314, but not more than the strength of the masonry units used in prism construction.

In the event that verification of f'_m is not confirmed, the IBC provides for testing prisms from constructed masonry. This method is based on the established method of Section 2105.3.5 of the 1997 Uniform Building Code. Inadequate test results can be a result of improper casting, handling, or testing of the original masonry prisms, therefore, this is a logical step in lieu of rejecting the masonry.

IBC Section 2105.3

2105.3 Testing prisms from constructed masonry. When approved by the building official, acceptance of masonry which does not meet the requirements of Sections 2105.2.2.1 or 2105.2.2.2 shall be permitted to be based on tests of prisms cut from the masonry construction in accordance with Sections 2105.3.1, 2105.3.2 and 2105.3.3.

2105.3.1 Prism sampling and removal. A set of three prisms that are at least 28 days old shall be saw cut from the masonry for each 5,000 square feet (465 m²) of the wall area that is in question but not less than one set of three masonry prisms for the project. The length, width and height dimensions of the prisms shall comply with the requirements of ASTM C 1314. Transporting, preparation and testing of prisms shall be in accordance with ASTM C 1314.

2105.3.2 Compressive strength calculations. The compressive strength of prisms shall be the value calculated in accordance ASTM C 1314, except that the net cross-sectional area of the prism shall be based on the net mortar bedded area.

2105.3.3 Compliance. Compliance with the requirements for the specified compressive strength of masonry, f'_m, shall be considered satisfied provided the modified compressive strength equals or exceeds the specified f'_m. Additional testing of specimens cut from locations in question shall be permitted.

Similarly, UBC has comprehensive methods for verifying compliance with the compressive strength of masonry, f'_m.

UBC Section 2105.3
2105.3 Compliance with f'_m.

2105.3.1 General. Compliance with the requirements for the specified compressive strength of masonry f'_m shall be in accordance with one of the sections in this subsection.

2105.3.2 Masonry prism testing. The compressive strength of masonry determined in accordance with UBC Standard 21-17 for each set of prisms shall equal or exceed f'_m. Compressive strength of prisms shall be based on tests at 28 days. Compressive strength at seven days or three days may be used provided a relationship between seven-day and three-day and 28-day strength has been established for the project prior to the start of construction. Verification by masonry prism testing shall meet the following:

1. A set of five masonry prisms shall be built and tested in accordance with UBC Standard 21-17 prior to the start of construction. Materials used for the construction of the prisms shall be taken from those specified to be used in the project. Prisms shall be constructed under the observation of the engineer or special inspector or an approved agency and tested by an approved agency.

2. When full allowable stresses are used in design, a set of three prisms shall be built and tested during construction in accordance with UBC Standard 21-17 for each 5,000 square feet (465 m²) of wall area, but not less than one set of three masonry prisms for the project.

3. When one half the allowable masonry stresses are used in design, testing during construction is not required. A letter of certification from the supplier of the materials used to verify the f'_m in accordance with Section 2105.3.2, Item 1, shall be provided atthe time of, or prior to, delivery of the materials to the jobsite to ensure the materials used in construction are representative of the materials used to construct the prisms prior to construction.

2105.3.3 Masonry prism test record. Compressive strength verification by masonry prism test records shall meet the following:

1. A masonry prism test record approved by the building official of at least 30 masonry prisms which were built and tested in accordance with UBC Standard 21-17. Prisms shall have been constructed under the observation of an engineer or special inspector or an approved agency and shall have been tested by an approved agency.

2. Masonry prisms shall be representative of the corresponding construction.

3. The average compressive strength of the test record shall equal or exceed $1.33 f'_m$.

4. When full allowable stresses are used in design, a set of three masonry prisms shall be built during construction in accordance with UBC Standard 21-17 for each 5,000 square

feet (465 m²) of wall area, but not less than one set of three prisms for the project.

5. When one half the allowable masonry stresses are used in design, field testing during construction is not required. A letter of certification from the supplier of the materials to the jobsite shall be provided at the time of, or prior to, delivery of the materials to assure the materials used in construction are representative of the materials used to develop the prism test record in accordance with Section 2105.3.3, Item 1.

2105.3.4 Unit strength method. Verification by the unit strength method shall meet the following:

1. When full allowable stresses are used in design, units shall be tested prior to construction and test units during construction for each 5,000 square feet (465 m²) of wall area for compressive strength to show compliance with the compressive strength required in Table 21-D; and

EXCEPTION: Prior to the start of construction, prism testing may be used in lieu of testing the unit strength. During construction, prism testing may also be used in lieu of testing the unit strength and the grout as required by Section 2105.3.4, Item 4.

2. When one half the allowable masonry stresses are used in design, testing is not required for the units. A letter of certification from the manufacturer of the units shall be provided at the time of, or prior to, delivery of the units to the jobsite to assure the units comply with the compressive strength required in Table 21-D; and

3. Mortar shall comply with the mortar type required in Table 21-D; and

4. When full stresses are used in design for concrete masonry, grout shall be tested for each 5,000 square feet (465 m²) of wall area, but not less than one test per project, to show compliance with the compressive strength required in Table 21-D, Footnote 4.

5. When one half the allowable stresses are used in design for concrete masonry, testing is not required for the grout. A letter of certification from the supplier of the grout shall be provided at the time of, or prior to, delivery of the grout to the jobsite to assure the grout complies with the compressive strength required in Table 21-D, Footnote 4; or

6. When full allowable stresses are used in design for clay masonry, grout proportions shall be verified by the engineer or special inspector or an approved agency to conform with Table 21-B.

7. When one half the allowable masonry stresses are used in design for clay masonry, a letter of certification from the supplier of the grout shall be provided at the time of, or prior to, delivery of the grout to the jobsite to assure the grout conforms to the proportions of Table 21-B.

2105.3.5 Testing prisms from constructed masonry. When approved by the building official, acceptance of masonry which does not meet the requirements of Section 2105.3.2, 2105.3.3 or 2105.3.4 shall be permitted to be based on tests of prisms cut from the masonry construction in accordance with the following:

1. A set of three masonry prisms that are at least 28 days old shall be saw cut from the masonry for each 5,000 square feet (465 m²) of the wall area that is in question but not less than one set of three masonry prisms for the project. The

length, width and height dimensions of the prisms shall comply with the requirements of UBC Standard 21-17. Transporting, preparation and testing of prisms shall be in accordance with UBC Standard 21-17.

2. The compressive strength of prisms shall be the value calculated in accordance with UBC Standard 21-17, Section 21.1707.2, except that the net cross-sectional area of the prism shall be based on the net mortar bedded area.

3. Compliance with the requirement for the specified compressive strength of masonry, f'_m, shall be considered satisfied provided the modified compressive strength equals or exceeds the specified f'_m. Additional testing of specimens cut from locations in question shall be permitted.

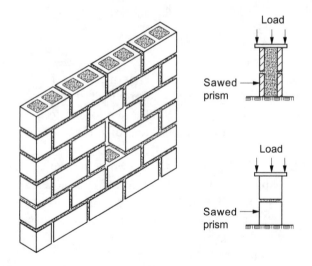

Figure 3.12 Test prism sawed from wall.

The MSJC Specification also contains language relative to the verification of compressive strength of masonry.

MSJC Specification, Section 1.4B

1.4 B. *Compressive strength determination*

1. *Alternatives for determination of compressive strength* – Determine the compressive strength for each wythe by the unit strength method or by the prism test method as specified herein.

2. *Unit strength method*
   a. Clay masonry – Determine the compressive strength of masonry based on the strength of the units and the type of mortar specified using Table 1. The following articles must be met:

   1) Units conform to ASTM C 62, ASTM C 216, or ASTM C 652 and are sampled and tested in accordance with ASTM C 67.
   2) Thickness of bed joints does not exceed $5/_8$ in. (15.9 mm).
   3) For grouted masonry, the grout meets one of the following requirements:

   a) Grout conforms to ASTM C 476.
   b) Grout compressive strength equals f'_m but compressive strength is not less than 2,000 psi (13.79 MPa). Determine compressive strength of grout in accordance with ASTM C 1019.

   b. Concrete masonry – Determine the compressive strength of masonry based on the strength of the unit and type of mortar specified using Table 2. The following Articles must be met:

   1) Units conform to ASTM C 55 or ASTM C 90 and are sampled and tested in accordance with ASTM C 140.

2) Thickness of bed joints does not exceed $^5/_8$ in. (15.9 mm).

3) For grouted masonry, the grout meets one of the following requirements:

a) Grout conforms to ASTM C 476.

b) Grout compressive strength equals f'_m but compressive strength is not less than 2,000 psi (13.79 Mpa). Determine compressive strength of grout in accordance with ASTM C 1019.

3. *Prism test method*

a. Determine the compressive strength of masonry by the prism test method for the following conditions:

1) When required.

2) When masonry does not meet the requirements for application of the unit strength method.

b. A prism test set shall consist of testing three prisms in accordance with ASTM C 1314.

c. The compressive strength of the masonry is calculated in accordance with ASTM C 1314.

Since the derived values among the three codes are slightly different, it is imperative that all parties involved in the project are aware of the applicable code.

MSJC Specification 1.4 B

Table 1 - Compressive strength of masonry based on the compressive strength of clay masonry units and type of mortar used in construction.

Net Area of compressive strength of clay masonry units, psi (MPa)		Net area compressive strength of masonry, psi (MPa)
Type M or S Mortar	Type N Mortar	
1,700 (11.72)	2,100 (14.48)	1,000 (6.90)
3,300 (23.10)	4,150 (28.61)	1,500 (10.34)
4,950 (34.13)	6,200 (42.75)	2,000 (13.79)
6,600 (45.51)	8,250 (56.88)	2,500 (17.24)
8,250 (56.88)	10,300 (71.02)	3,000 (20.69)
9,900 (68.26)	-----	3,500 (24.13)
13,200 (91.01)	-----	4,000 (27.58)

Table 2 - Compressive strength of masonry based on the compressive strength of concrete masonry units and type of mortar used in construction

Net area of compressive strength of concrete masonry units, psi (MPa)		Net area compressive strength of masonry, psi[1] (MPa)
Type M or S Mortar	Type N Mortar	
1,250 (8.62)	1,300 (14.48)	1,000 (6.90)
1,900 (13.10)	2,150 (28.61)	1,500 (10.34)
2,800 (19.31)	3,050 (42.75)	2,000 (13.79)
3,750 (25.86)	4,050 (56.88)	2,500 (17.24)
4,800 (33.10)	5,250 (71.02)	3,000 (20.69)

[1] For units of less than 4 in. (102 mm) height, 85 percent of values listed

3.5   CORE TESTING

The California Division of the State Architect recognizes core testing as an acceptable method to determine compressive strength. Cores are drilled from the face of the wall to the opposite site, avoiding the reinforcing steel.

California Building Code, Section 2105A.3.1

2105A.3.1 *Masonry core testing*. Not less than two cores having a diameter of 6 inches (152 mm) shall be taken from each project. Two cores shall be taken from each building for each 5,000 square feet (465 m^2) of the greater of the masonry wall area of the floor area or fraction thereof. The architect or structural engineer in responsible charge of the project or his/her representative (inspector) shall select the areas for sampling. One half of the number of cores taken shall be tested in shear. The shear wall loadings shall test both joints between the grout core and the outside wythes of the masonry. Core samples shall not be soaked before testing. Materials and workmanship shall be such that for all masonry when tested in compression, cores shall show an ultimate strength at least equal to the f'_m assumed in design, but not less than 1,500 psi (10.34 MPa). When tested in shear, the unit shear on the cross section of the core shall not be less than 2.5 f'_m psi.

Shear testing apparatus shall be of a design approved by the enforcement agency. Visual examination of all cores shall be made to ascertain if the joints are filled.

The project inspector or testing agency shall inspect the coring of the masonry walls and shall prepare a report of the coring operations for the testing laboratory files and mail one copy to the enforcement agency. Such reports shall include the total number of cores cut, the location, and the condition of all cores cut on each project, regardless of whether the core specimens failed during the cutting operation. All cores shall be submitted to the laboratory for examination.

Quite often, the opposite face shell or wythe of the wall separates from the grout during the process. This is usually caused by the excessive vibration and force from the drilling process. Cores containing separated wall elements should not be tested.

This section of the California Building Code has been applied to all masonry walls, however, when one looks closely at the code language and considers the construction of different masonry elements, the application appears to be intended for double wythe wall systems.

The first paragraph of Section 2105A.3.1 correctly refers to testing shear wall loadings between the grout and the outside wythes of the masonry. By definition, a wythe is one masonry unit of thickness, therefore, it is clear that this section does apply to double wythe walls where the brick faces on each side of the wall are not homogeneous units. In this application, the bond is a significant issue.

Reinforced hollow unit masonry, however, has the face shells connected by cross webs and are an integral unit. In addition to any bond afforded by the grout, the homogeneous makeup of the unit virtually eliminates the possibility the face shell could separate from the wall even under the most extreme loading conditions. Naturally, this assumes that the design and construction of the masonry is code compliant.

The method of core testing to verify the compressive strength of masonry, f'_m, is an option of minimal destructive testing that may be desirable when other non-destructive test methods have not produced satisfactory results.

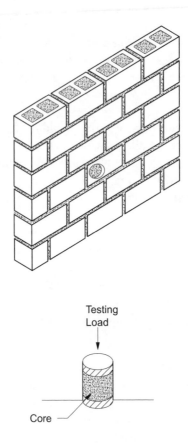

Testing
Load

Core

Figure 3.13   Compressive test of core from wall.

3.6.   SUMMARY

Specifications and verification requirements for the State of California , Title 24, the International Building Code, *MSJC Code*, *MSJC Code Specification* and the 1997 Uniform Building Code are summarized in Table 3-B. Table 3-C is a summary of masonry inspection requirements, and Table 3-D summarizes mortar mix design requirements.

Table 3-B Specification and Verification Requirements[1] for Masonry/Masonry Materials[2]

Material Category	Material Type & Property	Specification Requirements 1997 UBC	Specification Requirements ASTM	Additional Verification Requirements[3]			
				CAC T24	1997 UBC	2000 IBC	ACI-530.1-99
Building, Facing Hollow Brick	Burned Clay Brick	UBC Std. 21-1 (ASTM C 62, C 216, C 652)	ASTM C 62 C 216 C 652	Test Prior to Use Grade NW Not Permitted	Not Required	Not Required	Not Required
Sand-Lime Brick	Sand-Lime Brick	UBC Std. 21-2 (ASTM C 73)	ASTM C 73	Material Not Permitted	Not Required	Not Required	Not Required
Clay Load Bearing Tile	Burned Hollow Clay Tile	ASTM C 34 & C 212	ASTM C 34 C 212	Material Not Permitted	Not Required	Not Required	Not Required
Structural Clay, Non Load Brg. Tile	Burned Hollow Clay Tile	ASTM C 56	ASTM C 56	Material Not Permitted	Not Required	Not Required	Not Required
Cast Stone	Portland Concrete Trim & Facing	ACI 704	ASTM C 744	Test Prior to Use	Not Required	Not Required	Not Required
Unburned Clay Units	Adobe Block	UBC Std. 21-9		Material Not Permitted	Not Required	Not Required	Not Required
Wire	Steel Wire	UBC Std. 21-10 (ASTM A 82)	ASTM A 82, A 185, A 496, A 497, A 461	Test Prior to Use[4]	Not Required	Not Required	Not Required

Table 3-B Specification and Verification Requirements[1] for Masonry/Masonry Materials[2] (Cont'd)

Material Category	Material Type & Property	Specification Requirements 1997 UBC	Specification Requirements ASTM	Additional Verification Requirements[3]				
				CAC T24	1997 UBC	2000 IBC	ACI-530.1-99
Quicklime	Unslaked Lime	UBC Std. 21-12 (ASTM C 5)	ASTM* C 270→C 5	Test as Required	Not Required	Not Required	Not Required
Hydrated Lime	Slaked Lime	UBC Std. 21-13 (ASTM C 207)	ASTM* C 270→C 207	Test as Required	Not Required	Not Required	Not Required
Grout	Portland Cement Grout	UBC Sec. 2103.4, T-24, Sec. 2103A.4 (ASTM C 1019, C 476) UBC Stds. 21-18 and 21-19	ASTM C 476 C 1019	Proportioned per Code Field Test for Compressive Strength Required	Not Required	Proportioned per Code[5]	Not Required
Masonry Cement	Cement (Any Binder)	UBC Std. 21-11 (ASTM C 91)	ASTM C 270→C 91	Material Not Permitted	Not Permitted in Seismic Zones 2, 3 or 4	Material Not Permitted in Seismic Design Categories D and E	Material not Permitted in Seismic Category D and E

* Footnote → Arrow means sub-reference

Table 3-B *Specification and Verification Requirements[1] for Masonry/Masonry Materials[2] (Cont'd)*

Material Category	Material Type & Property	Specification Requirements 1997 UBC	Specification Requirements ASTM	Additional Verification Requirements[3]			
				CAC T24	1997UBC	2000 IBC	ACI-530.1-99
Cores	Sample of Masonry	T-24 Sec. 2105A.3.1	Not Noted	Compression & Shear Tests per Sec. 2105A.3.1[6]	Not Required	Not Required	Not Required
Admixtures		UBC Section 2103.5, T-24, Section 2103A.5	ACI 530.1/2.2.2.3 ASTM C 270/4.1.4 ACI 530.1/4.2.1 ASTM C 476	See Footnotes 7 & 8	See Footnotes 7 & 8	Refer to ACI 530.1-99	See Footnote 9
Portland Cement	Portland Cement	(ASTM C 150)	ASTM C 270→C 150 C 476→C 150	Test as Required	Not Required	Not required	Not Required
Metal Ties & Anchors	Steel Connectors	UBC Section 2102.2.7	ASTM A 123, A 153, A 167, A 366, A 525	Not Required	Not Required	Not Required	Not Required
Water	Water	UBC Section 2103.2	ASTM C 670/4.1.3 C 476/3.1.4	Not Required	Not Required	Not Required	Not Required

Table 3-B *Specification and Verification Requirements[1] for Masonry/Masonry Materials[2] (Cont'd)*

Material Category	Material Type & Property	Specification Requirements 1997 UBC	Specification Requirements ASTM	Additional Verification Requirements[3]			
				CAC T24	1997 UBC	2000 IBC	ACI-530.1-99
Aggregate for Grout	Aggregates for Grout	ASTM C 404	ASTM C 404	Test Prior to Use	Not Required	Not Required	Not Required
Aggregate for Mortar	Aggregate for Mortar	ASTM C 144	ASTM C 144	Test Prior to Use	Not Required	Not Required	Not Required
Mortar	Proportion Spec. or Property Spec.	UBC Std. 21-15 (ASTM C 161 & C 270)	ASTM C 270	Proportioned per Code Field Test for Compressive Strength Required[10]	By Proportioning per Code or Properties Verified by Complete Tests Prior to Use[5]		As Noted by Quality Assurance Table 2 or 3
Mortar	Ready Mix	UBC Std. 21-15	ASTM C 270	Subject to Prior Approval of Agency	Subject to Prior Approval of Building Official		As Noted by Quality Assurance Table 2 or 3
Mortar	Field Test	UBC Std. 21-16		Per Section 2103A.3[10]	As Required by Building Official		Method not Noted

Table 3-B *Specification and Verification Requirements[1] for Masonry/Masonry Materials[2] (Cont'd)*

Material Category	Material Type & Property	Specification Requirements 1997 UBC	Specification Requirements ASTM	Additional Verification Requirements[3]			
				CAC T24	1997UBC	2000 IBC	ACI-530.1-99
Concrete Masonry Units	Hollow Load Bearing	UBC Std. 21-4 (ASTM C 90)	ASTM C 90	Grade S Not Permitted Complete Test Prior to Use	Not Required	Not Required	Not Required
Concrete Masonry Units	Non Load Bearing	UBC Std. 21-5 (ASTM C 129)	ASTM C 129	Complete Test Prior to Use	Not Required	Not Required	Not Required
Masonry Prisms	Qualification Testing	UBC Std. 21-17 (ASTM C 1314)	ASTM C 1314	Prism Tests if Spec. f'_m is greater than 1500 psi with Approved Quality Control Methods	Determine f'_m Unless Values in Table 21-D are used. Field Tests per Every 5000 sq. ft. of Wall, 1 min	Frequency as required	Frequency as Required Noted by QA Table 2 or 3
Cement	Plastic	UBC Std. 25-1 Also Conforming to UBC Std. 21-11 when in lieu of masonry cement	Not Noted	Special Approval is Necessary Sec. T24, 2102A.2.2.2	Plasticizing Agents Require Approval Prior to Use	Not Recognized	Conform to ASTM C91, C 150 or C 1329 Not Permitted in SPC D,E

Table 3-B *Specification and Verification Requirements[1] for Masonry/Masonry Materials[2] (Cont'd)*

Material Category	Material Type & Property	Specification Requirements 1997 UBC	Specification Requirements ASTM	Additional Verification Requirements[3]				
				CAC T24	1997 UBC	2000 IBC	ACI-530.1-99
Concrete Brick	Concrete Building Brick	UBC Std. 21-3 (ASTM C 55)	ASTM C 55	Complete Test Prior to Use	Not Required	Not Required	Not Required
Ceramic Structural Facing Tile	Load Bearing Tiles	ASTM C 126	ASTM C 126	Complete Test Prior to Use	Not Required	Not Required	Not Required
Brick	Sampling and Testing	ASTM C 67	ASTM C 67	Not Required	Not Required	Not Required	Not Required
Gypsum Concrete	Gypsum Concrete		Not Covered	Complete Test Prior to Use	Not Permitted for Use in Resistance to Lateral Forces	Not Recognized	

Footnotes to Table 3-B

1 The specifications listed fall into one classification. The UBC Standards are requirements generally mandated by the building code enforcement agency and are essentially ASTM Standards modified to conform to such requirements. The ASTM Standards and the ACI Standards are industry standards used to inform the buyer of the conditions under which materials are furnished.

2 Based on *Sub-Committee Testing Guidelines for Construction Materials* by Nezih Gunal, P.E., Chairman, Report No. 2, Masonry and Masonry Materials, 1986, Structural Engineers Association of Southern California, Los Angeles, California.

3 Additional verification requirements are specific tests and/or analyses required by the building code enforcement agency in addition to the ASTM specification requirements. These tests and/or analyses are generally based on the ASTM specification indicated, and are generally conducted by independent agents such as testing laboratories.

4 Tensile and bend tests per each 10 tons or fraction thereof of each size of reinforcement in each lot. Where manufacturer's name, or heat identification number, or manufacturer's chemical analysis is unknown, testing frequency must be increased to each $2^1/_2$ tons or fraction thereof.

5 Field tests for compressive strength may be required, by jurisdiction or specifications.

6 Two cores minimum, with at least one core taken from every 5,000 square feet of floor area, or fraction thereof.

7 Admixtures require prior approval by the building official before addition to grout or mortar.

8 For color, only pure mineral oxides, carbon black limited to 3%, or synthetic colors are permitted.

9 For portland cement-lime mortar, color is limited to 10% for mineral oxide pigment and 2% for carbon black pigment. For masonry cement mortar, color is limited to 5% for mineral oxide pigment and 1 % for carbon black pigment.

10 Test sampling consists of at least one sample taken on each of three consecutive working days at beginning of masonry work, and at least one at weekly intervals thereafter

Table 3-C1 *Summary of Inspection Requirements*

MASONRY INSPECTION REQUIREMENTS	
CAC Title 24 Part 2	1997 UBC, Section 1701 and 2105
1. Continuous inspection during laying and grouting of masonry including placing of reinforcement and taking test samples. Check all materials, details of construction and construction procedures. 2. Continuous inspection during placing of reinforced gypsum concrete including placing of reinforcement and taking test samples. Check all materials, details of construction and construction procedures.	1. Called inspections of masonry construction may be required by the building official. 2. Continuous inspection by a special inspector is required during the preparation of masonry wall prisms, sampling and placing (laying) of all masonry units, placing of reinforcement, inspection of grout space immediately prior to closing cleanouts and all grouting operations. This special inspection includes assurance that all materials meet the applicable quality standards, proportioning and mixing of mortar and grout, construction details, procedures and workmanship, and the placement of reinforcement including splices. (Special inspection need not be provided when design stresses have been adjusted to permit noncontinuous inspection—one-half stress or less with maximum limits (2107.1.2). Some inspections may be made on a periodic basis and satisfy the requirements of continuous inspection, provided this periodic scheduled inspection is performed as outlined in the project plans and specifications and approved by the building official. NOTE: The plans shall describe the required strengths of masonry materials and inspection requirements of which all parts of the structure were designed.

Table 3-C2 *MSJC Level 1 Quality Assurance*

MINIMUM TESTS AND SUBMITTALS	MINIMUM INSPECTION
Certificates for materials used in masonry construction indicating compliance with the contract documents	Verify compliance with the approved submittals

Table 3-C3 *MSJC Level 2 Quality Assurance*

MINIMUM TESTS AND SUBMITTALS	MINIMUM INSPECTION
Certificates for materials used in masonry construction indicating compliance with the contract documents Verification of f'_m prior to construction, except where specifically exempted by this Code	As masonry construction begins, verify the following are in compliance: • proportions of site-prepared mortar • construction of mortar joints • location of reinforcement and connectors Prior to grouting verify the following are in compliance: • grout space • placement of reinforcement and connectors • proportions of site-prepared grout • construction of mortar joints Verify grout placement is in compliance Observe preparation of grout specimens, mortar specimens, and/or prisms Verify compliance with the required inspection provisions of the contract documents and the approved submittals

Table 3-C4 *MSJC Level 3 Quality Assurance*

MINIMUM TESTS AND SUBMITTALS	MINIMUM INSPECTION
Certificates for materials used in masonry construction indicating compliance with the contract documents Verification of f'_m: • prior to construction • every 5000 sq. ft (464.5 m²) during construction Verification of proportions of materials in mortar and grout as delivered to the site	From the begining of masonry construction and continuously during construction of masonry, verify the following are in compliance: • proportions of site-mixed mortar and grout • placing of masonry units and construction of mortar joints • placement of reinforcement and connectors • grout space prior to grouting • placement of grout Observe preparation of grout specimens, mortar specimens, and/or prisms Verify compliance with the required inspection provisions of the contract documents and the approved submittals

Table 3-D *Mortar Mix Design Requirements*

1997 UBC[1,3]	MSJC Specification[2,3]
1 Proportions established by laboratory or field experience with the mortar ingredients and masonry units to be used. Compressive strength must comply with UBC Standard No. 21-16.	1 In accordance with materials and proportions established by ASTM C 270, Table 1.
2 In accordance with the materials and proportions in Table 21-A. Compressive strength must comply with UBC Standard 21-16.	2 In accordance with property specifications in ASTM C 270.
3 In accordance with property specifications in UBC Standard 21-15.	

[1]The mixing of mortar in a mechanical mixer shall be for a period of 3-10 minutes.
[2]The mixing of mortar in a mechanical mixer shall be for a period of 3-5 minutes.
[3]Mortar may be re-tempered.

IBC Section 1704.5

TABLE 1704.5.1—LEVEL 1 SPECIAL INSPECTION

INSPECTION TASK	Continuous during task listed	Periodically during task listed	IBC Section	ACI 530/ ASCE 5/ TMS 402	ACI 530/ ASCE 5/ TMS 402
1. As masonry construction begins, the following shall be verified to ensure compliance:					Article
a. Proportions of site prepared mortar.	--	X	--	--	2.6A
b. Construction of mortar joints.		X			3.3B
c. Location of reinforcement and connectors.		X			3.4
2. The inspection program shall verify:					Article
a. Size and location of structural elements.		X			3.3G
b. Type, size and location of anchors, including other details of anchorage of masonry to structural members, frames or other construction.		X		Section 1.15.4, 2.1.2	
c. Specified size, grade and type of reinforcement.			Section 2108.9.2.11 Item 2		
d. Welding of reinforcing bars.		X		1.12	2.4, 3.4
e. Protection of masonry during cold weather (temperature below 40°F) or hot weather (temperature above 90°F).	X	X	2104.3, 2104.4	8.5.7 8.5.7.2	1.8
3. Prior to grouting, the following shall be verified to ensure compliance:					Article
a. Grout space is clean.		X			3.2D
b. Placement of reinforcement and connectors.	--	X	--	Section 1.12	3.4
c. Proportions of site-prepared grout.		X			2.6B
d. Construction of mortar joints		X			3.3B
4. Grout Placement shall be verified to ensure compliance with code and construction document provisions.	X	--	--	--	Article 3.5
5. Preparation of any required grout specimens, mortar specimens and/or prisms shall be observed.	X	--	Section 2105.3, 2105.4, 2105.5	--	Article 1.4
6. Compliance with required inspection provisions of the construction documents and the approved submittals shall be verified.	--	X	--	--	Article 1.5

IBC Section 1704.5

TABLE 1704.5.3—LEVEL 2 SPECIAL INSPECTION

INSPECTION TASK	FREQUENCY OF INSPECTION		REFERENCE FOR CRITERIA		
	Continuous during task listed	Periodically during task listed	IBC Section	ACI 530/ ASCE 5/ TMS 402	ACI 530/ ASCE 5/ TMS 402
1. From the beginning of masonry construction, the following shall be verified to ensure compliance:					
a. Proportions of site mixed mortar and grout.		X	--	Ch. 8	Article 2.6A
b. Placement of masonry units and construction of mortar joints.		X			3.3B
c. Placement of reinforcement and connectors.					3.4
d. Grout space prior to grouting.		X			3.2D
e. Placement of grout.	X X				3.5
2. The inspection program shall verify:					
a. Size and location of structural elements.		X			Article 3.3G
b. Type, size and location of anchors, including other details of anchorage of masonry to structural members, frames or other construction.	X			Section 1.15.4, 2.1.2	
c. Specified size, grade and type of reinforcement.					
d. Welding of reinforcing bars.		X	Section 2108.9.2.11 Item 2	1.12	2.4, 3.4
e. Protection of masonry during cold weather (temperature below 40°F) or hot weather (temperature above 90°F).	X	X	2104.3, 2104.4	8.5.7 8.5.7.2	1.8
3. Preparation of any required grout specimens, mortar specimens and/or prisms shall be observed	X	--	Section 2105.3, 2105.4, 2105.5	--	Article 1.4
4. Compliance with required inspection provisions of the construction documents and the approved submittals shall be verified.	--	X	--	--	Article 1.5

General Construction Practice and Layout

4.1 GENERAL

Inspection is most important during actual construction. The inspector's job is to assure that all work performed is done according with the applicable building code and the approved plans and specifications, and the materials are as specified and used correctly.

4.2 PREPARATION OF FOUNDATION AND SITE

Prior to laying the first course of concrete masonry, the concrete surfaces shall be clean and free of laitance, loose aggregate, dirt, mud, grease or anything that will prevent the mortar from bonding properly. It must be rough to provide good bond between the foundation concrete and the mortar and grout.

Concrete abutting structural masonry walls in UBC Seismic Zones 3 and 4, such as at starter courses or at wall intersections not designed as true separation joints, contain special code provisions to obtain the maximum shear interface between the concrete foundation and masonry wall.

UBC Section 2106.1.12.4

4. Concrete abutting structural masonry. Concrete abutting structural masonry, such as at starter courses or at wall intersections not designed as true separation joints, shall be roughened to a full amplitude of $^1/_{16}$ inch (1.6 mm) and shall be bonded to the masonry in accordance with the requirements of this chapter as if it were masonry. Unless keys or proper reinforcement is provided, vertical joints as specified in Section 2106.1.4 shall be considered to be stack bond and the reinforcement as required for stack bond shall extend through the joint and be anchored into the concrete.

Surfaces should be level and at a correct grade so that the initial bed joint is not less than $^1/_4$ inch (6.4 mm) nor more than $^3/_4$ inch (19.1 mm) in height. UBC allows the initial bed joint to be a maximum of 1 inch (25.4 mm).

IBC Section 2104.1.2.1

2104.1.2.1 Bed and head joints. Unless otherwise required or indicated on the construction documents, head and bed joint shall be $^3/_8$ inch (9.5 mm) thick, except that the thickness of the bed joint of the starting course placed over foundations shall not be less than $^1/_4$ inch (6.4 mm) and not more than $^3/_4$ inch (19.1 mm).

MSJC Specification, Section 3.3 B

3 B. *Placing mortar and units*

1. *Bed and head joints* – Unless otherwise required, construct $^3/_8$ inch (9.5 mm) thick bed and head joints except at foundation or with glass unit masonry. Construct bed joint of the starting course of foundation with a thickness of not less than $^1/_4$ inch (6.4 mm) and not more than $^3/_4$ inch (19.1 mm).

> **UBC Section 2106.1.6**
>
> **2106.1.6 Vertical support.** Structural members providing vertical support of masonry shall provide a bearing surface on which the initial bed joint shall not be less than $\frac{1}{4}$ inch (6 mm) or more than 1 inch (25 mm) in thickness and shall be of noncombustible material, except where masonry is a nonstructural decorative feature or wearing surface.

Reinforcing steel dowels shall be properly placed. The specified size and length shall be checked and if they need to be bent, they may be bent at a slope of no more than 1 inch (25.4 mm) horizontally per 6 inches (152 mm) of height. This provision is extrapolated from concrete which allows the 6:1 ratio in UBC Section 1907.8.1.1 or ACI 318-95 Section 7.8.1.1.

If any of the site conditions or layout are improper, masonry work should not begin until corrected.

The first course on the foundation should have all webs and face shells set in mortar for full bearing. The mortar, however, must not project more than $\frac{1}{2}$ inch (13 mm) into the cells that are to contain grout, as shown in Figure 4.1. Inverted bond beam units may be used on initial course to maximize grout contact with foundation. The grout must have direct contact and bearing on the foundation or slab.

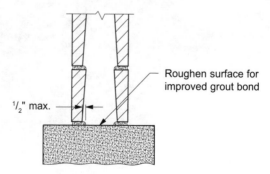

Figure 4.1 First course mortar joint.

Figure 4.2 Proper storage of masonry units.

Figure 4.3 Reinforcing steel.

Figure 4.4 Concrete masonry units should normally not be wetted.

Figure 4.5 Properly stored sacked material.

Figure 4.6 Mortar (plaster) mixer.

Figure 4.7 Pre-blended mortar silo setup.

4.3   MATERIALS, HANDLING, STORAGE AND PREPARATION

Figures 4.2 through 4.7 illustrate the requirements contained in *MSJC Specification* Section 1.7 for delivery, storage and handling of material.

MSJC Specification, Section 1.7

1.7 – Delivery, storage and handling

1.7 A. Do not use damaged masonry units, damaged components of structure, or damaged packaged material.

1.7 B Protect moisture-controlled concrete masonry units and cementitious materials from precipitation or ground water.

1.7 C. Do not use masonry units that are contaminated.

1.7 D. Store different aggregates separately.

1.7 E. Protect reinforcement, ties, and metal accessories from permanent distortions and store them off the ground.

4.4   PLACEMENT AND LAYOUT

4.4.1   General

All dimensions, locations of all wall openings, positions of vertical reinforcing steel, methods of grouting, mortar mixes, patterns of bond, and the general sequence of operation should be determined prior to laying the first course of masonry.

Where no bond pattern is shown, the wall should be laid in straight uniform courses with alternate vertical joints aligning (called running bond or common bond, shown in Figure 4.8). Proper alignment of the vertical cells gives maximum size openings for pouring grout in vertically reinforced cells and reduces ledges or projections that may impede the flow of grout.

Figure 4.8 Running or common bond masonry.

In bearing and nonbearing walls, except veneer walls, if the units in any transverse vertical plane lap the ends of the units above and below a distance less than one fourth the length of the unit, the wall shall be considered laid in stack bond.

If units are laid in stack bond, shown in Figure 4.9, give particular attention to proper type and placement of reinforcing steel or metal ties and joint reinforcement used to provide the mechanical bond.

Unless specified otherwise, vertical and horizontal mortar joints for precision units should be $3/_8$ inch (10 mm) $\pm$ $1/_8$ inch (3 mm), and for slumped units should be $1/_2$ inch (13 mm) $\pm$ $1/_4$ inch (6 mm).

Figure 4.9 Masonry laid up in stack bond.

4.4.2 Installation

4.4.2.1 Placing Masonry Units - IBC

All building codes contain some language on installation requirements. The IBC, through MSJC Specifications, contains language on construction tolerances for masonry installation.

IBC Section 2104.1

SECTION 2104
CONSTRUCTION

2104.1 Masonry construction. Masonry construction shall comply with the requirements of Sections 2104.1.1 through 2104.5 and with ACI 530.1/ASCE 6/TMS 602.

2104.1.1   Tolerances. Masonry, except masonry veneer, shall be constructed within the tolerances specified in ACI 530.1/ASCE 6/TMS 602.

2104.1.2   Placing mortar and units. Placement of mortar and units shall comply with Sections 2104.1.2.1 through 2104.1.2.5.

2104.1.2.1   Bed and head joints. Unless otherwise required or indicated on the construction documents, head and bed joint shall be $^3/_8$ inch (9.5 mm) thick, except that the thickness of the bed joint of the starting course placed over foundations shall not be less than $^1/_4$ inch (6.4 mm) and not more than $^3/_4$ inch (19.1 mm).

2104.1.2.1.1 Open-end units. Open-end units with beveled ends shall be fully grouted. Head joints of open-end units with beveled ends need not be mortared. The beveled ends shall form a grout key that permits grouts within $^5/_8$ inch (15.9 mm) of the face of the unit. The units shall be tightly butted to prevent leakage of the grout.

2104.1.2.2   Hollow units. Hollow units shall be placed such that face shells of bed joints are fully mortared; webs are fully mortared in all courses of piers, columns, pilasters, in the starting course on foundations where adjacent cells or cavities are to be grouted, and where otherwise required; and head joints are mortared a minimum distance from each face equal to the face shell thickness of the unit.

2104.1.2.3   Solid units. Unless otherwise required or indicated on the construction documents, solid units shall be placed in fully mortared bed and head joints. The ends of the units shall be completely buttered. Head joints shall not be filled by slushing with mortar. Head joints shall be constructed by shoving mortar tight against the adjoining unit. Bed joints shall not be furrowed deep enough to produce voids.

2104.1.2.4 Glass unit masonry. Glass units shall be placed so head and bed joints are filled solidly. Mortar shall not be furrowed.

Unless otherwise required, head and bed joints of glass unit masonry shall be $\frac{1}{4}$ inch (6.4 mm) thick, except that vertical joint thickness of radial panels shall not be less than $\frac{1}{8}$ inch (3.2 mm). The bed joint thickness tolerance shall be minus $\frac{1}{16}$ inch (1.6 mm) and plus $\frac{1}{2}$ inch (3.2 mm). The head joint thickness tolerance shall be plus or minus $\frac{1}{8}$ inch (3.2 mm).

2104.1.2.5 All units. Units shall be placed while the mortar is soft and plastic. Any unit disturbed to the extent that the initial bond is broken after initial positioning shall be removed and relaid in fresh mortar.

4.4.2.2 Tolerances

The tolerances contained in *MSJC Specification* are based on structural requirements (eccentricities) for performance, not aesthetics. It is, however, reasonable to use these tolerance values for aesthetic acceptance of the project. Consideration should also be given to the ASTM distance viewing requirements for aesthetic acceptance.

MSJC Specification, Section 3.3 G
3.3 G. *Site Tolerances* – Erect masonry within the following tolerances from the specified dimensions.
 1. Dimension of elements
   a. In cross section or elevation
   ....-$\frac{1}{4}$ in. (6.4 mm), +$\frac{1}{2}$ in. (12.7 mm)

MSJC Specification, Section 3.3 G

3.3 G. *Site Tolerances* – Erect masonry within the following tolerances from the specified dimensions.
1. Dimension of elements
    b. Mortar Joint Thickness
       bed...$\pm^1/_8$ in. (3.2 mm)
       head..............................-$^1/_4$ in. (6.4 mm), +$^3/_8$ in. (9.5 mm)
       collar............................-$^1/_4$ in. (6.4 mm), +$^3/_8$ in. (9.5 mm)

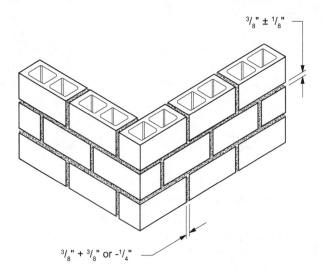

$^3/_8$" ± $^1/_8$"

$^3/_8$" + $^3/_8$" or -$^1/_4$"

Figure 4.10 Permissible variations in mortar joint thickness.

MSJC Specification, Section 3.3 G

3.3 G. *Site Tolerances* – Erect masonry within the following tolerances from the specified dimensions.
1. Dimension of elements
    c. Grout space or cavity width, except for masonry walls passing framed construction
       ....-$^1/_4$ in. (6.4 mm), +$^3/_8$ in. (9.5 mm)

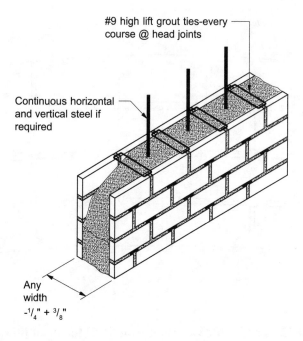

Figure 4.11 Permissible variation of grout space.

MSJC Specification, Section 3.3 G
3.3 G. *Site Tolerances* – Erect masonry within the following tolerances from the specified dimensions.
   2. Elements
      a. Variation from level
      bed joints
      ....$\pm^{1}/_{4}$ in. (6.4 mm) in 10 ft. (3.05 m)
      ....$\pm^{1}/_{2}$ in (12.7 mm) maximum
      top surface of bearing walls
      ....$\pm^{1}/_{4}$ in. (6.4 mm) in 10 ft. (3.05 m)
      ....$\pm^{1}/_{2}$ in (12.7 mm) maximum

127

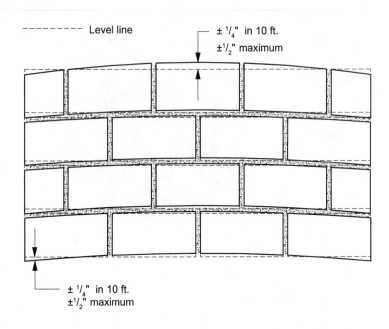

Figure 4.12 Permissible variation from level for head joints.

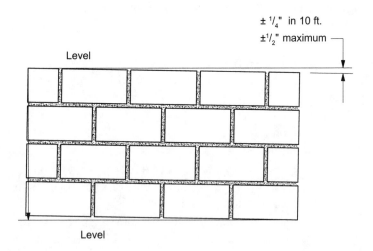

Figure 4.13 Permissible variation from level, top surface of bearing walls

MSJC Specification, Section 3.3 G

3.3 G. *Site Tolerances* – Erect masonry within the following tolerances from the specified dimensions.
   2. Elements
     b. Variation from plumb
     ....$\pm^1/_4$ in. (6.4 mm) in 10 ft. (3.05 m)
     ....$\pm^3/_8$ in. (9.5 mm) in 20 ft. (6.10 m)
     ....$\pm^1/_2$ in (13 mm) maximum

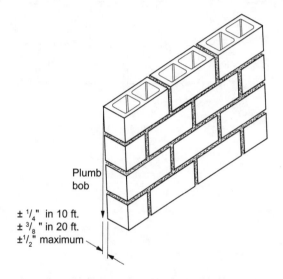

Figure 4.14 Permissible variation from plumb.

MSJC Specification, Section 3.3 G

3.3 G. *Site Tolerances* – Erect masonry within the following tolerances from the specified dimensions.
   2. Elements
     c. True to line
     ....$\pm^1/_4$ in. (6.4 mm) in 10 ft. (3.05 m)
     ....$\pm^3/_8$ in. (9.5 mm) in 20 ft. (6.10 m)
     ....$\pm^1/_2$ in (12.7 mm) maximum

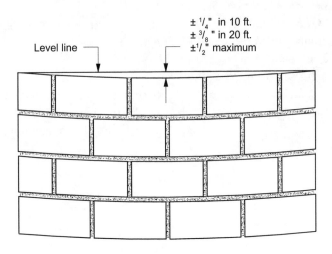

Level line

± ¼" in 10 ft.
± ³/₈ " in 20 ft.
±½" maximum

Elevation View

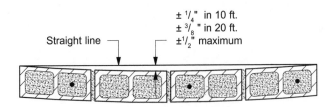

Straight line

± ¼" in 10 ft.
± ³/₈ " in 20 ft.
±½" maximum

Plan View

Figure 4.15 Permissible variation from true to line.

130

MSJC Specification, Section 3.3 G

3.3 G. *Site Tolerances* – Erect masonry within the following tolerances from the specified dimensions.

2. Elements

d. Alignment of columns and walls (bottom vs. top)

....$\pm^1/_2$ in. (12.7 mm) for bearing walls

................................$\pm^3/_4$ in. (19.7 mm) for nonbearing walls

3. Location of elements.

a. Indicated in plan

................................$\pm^1/_2$ in. (12.7 mm) in 20 ft. (6.10 m)

....$\pm^3/_4$ in (19.1 mm) maximum

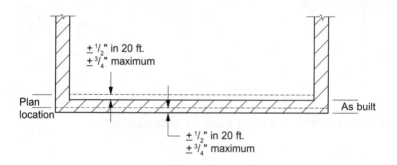

Figure 4.16 Permissible variation of element indicated in the plan.

3.3 G. *Site Tolerances* – Erect masonry within the following tolerances from the specified dimensions
   3. Location of elements
     b. Indicated in elevation
      ....$\pm^1/_4$ in. (6.4 mm) in story height
      ....$\pm^3/_4$ in (19.1 mm) maximum

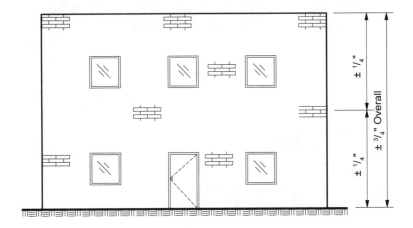

Figure 4.17   Permissible variation of element indicated in elevation.

4.4.2.3 Placing Masonry Units - UBC

UBC Section 2104.4
2104.4 Placing Masonry Units.

2104.4.1 Mortar. The mortar shall be sufficiently plastic and units shall be placed with sufficient pressure to extrude mortar from the joint and produce a tight joint. Deep furrowing which produces voids shall not be used.

The initial bed joint thickness shall not be less than $^1/_4$ inch (6 mm) or more than 1 inch (25 mm); subsequent bed joints shall not be less than $^1/_4$ inch (6 mm) or more than $^5/_8$ inch (16 mm) in thickness.

2104.4.2 Surfaces. Surfaces to be in contact with mortar or grout shall be clean and free of deleterious materials.

2104.4.3 Solid masonry units. Solid masonry units shall have full head and bed joints. (See Figure 4.18).

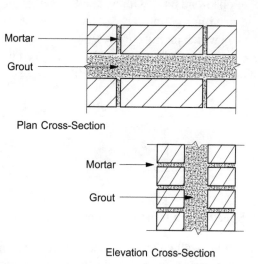

Plan Cross-Section

Elevation Cross-Section

Figure 4.18 Grout flows into head joint and bed joint for full joints in concrete bricks.

UBC Section 2104.4.4
2104.4.4 Hollow-masonry units. All head and bed joints shall be filled solidly with mortar for a distance in from the face of the unit not less than the thickness of the shell. (See Figure 4-19).

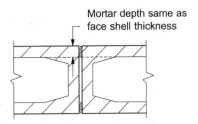

Figure 4.19 Hollow masonry unit head joints

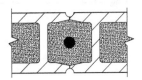

Figure 4.20 Speed block mortarless head joints.

Pilasters (in the wall columns) are laid up at the same time as the wall, taking care to place the pilaster ties as required.

No unit should be moved after setting as this breaks the mortar bond. Should moving of a unit be necessary, the mortar should be removed and the unit set in fresh mortar.

4.4.3 Typical Layout of CMU Walls

A. Corner Details are Illustrated in Figures 4.21 and 4.22.

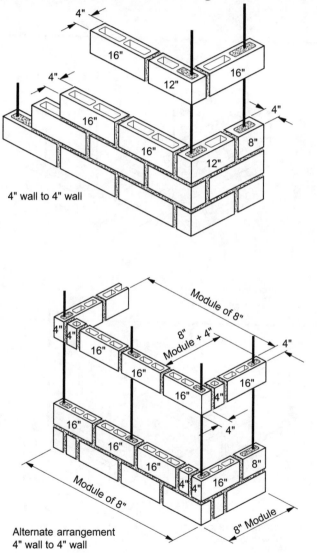

Figure 4.21 Arrangement of masonry units for corners.

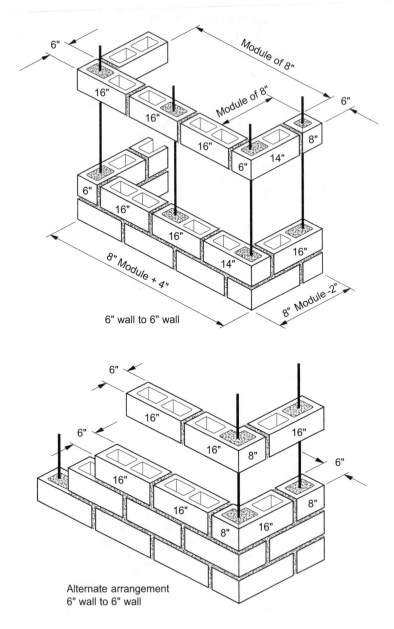

Figure 4.21 (Cont'd).

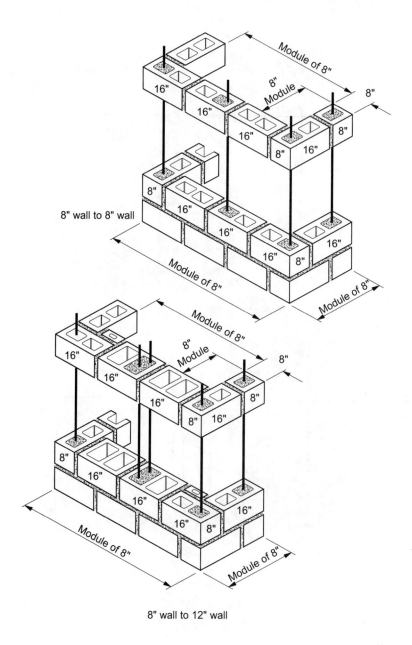

Figure 4.22 Arrangement of masonry units for corners.

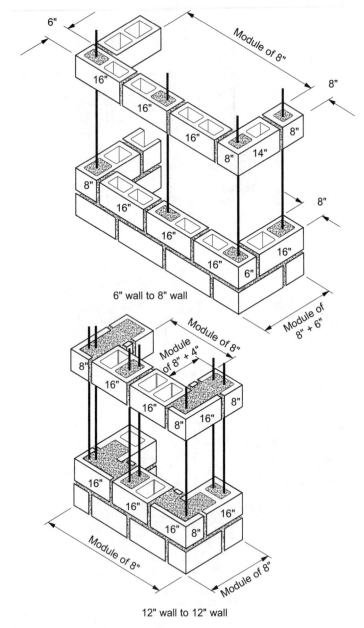

6" wall to 8" wall

12" wall to 12" wall

Figure 4.22 (Cont'd).

B. **Typical Layout of Pilasters is shown in Figures 4.23 through 4.25.**

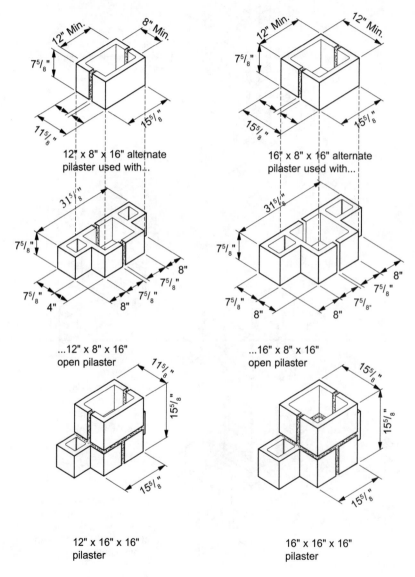

12" x 8" x 16" alternate pilaster used with...

16" x 8" x 16" alternate pilaster used with...

...12" x 8" x 16" open pilaster

...16" x 8" x 16" open pilaster

12" x 16" x 16" pilaster

16" x 16" x 16" pilaster

Figure 4.23 Arrangement of units for pilaster.

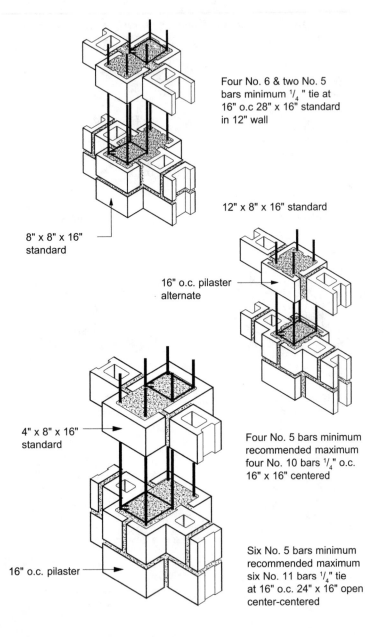

Four No. 6 & two No. 5 bars minimum $\frac{1}{4}$" tie at 16" o.c 28" x 16" standard in 12" wall

12" x 8" x 16" standard

8" x 8" x 16" standard

16" o.c. pilaster alternate

4" x 8" x 16" standard

Four No. 5 bars minimum recommended maximum four No. 10 bars $\frac{1}{4}$" o.c. 16" x 16" centered

16" o.c. pilaster

Six No. 5 bars minimum recommended maximum six No. 11 bars $\frac{1}{4}$" tie at 16" o.c. 24" x 16" open center-centered

Figure 4.24 Pilaster details.

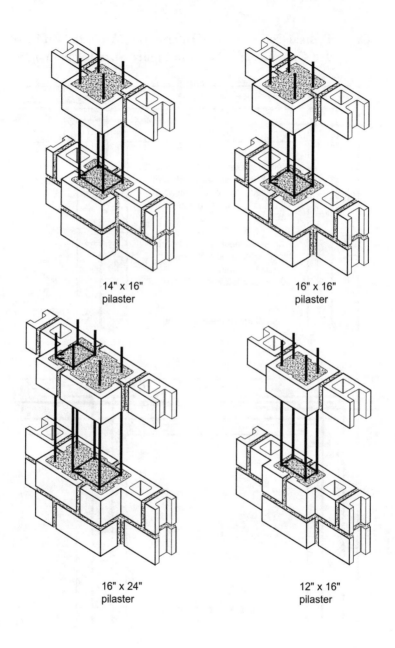

14" x 16"
pilaster

16" x 16"
pilaster

16" x 24"
pilaster

12" x 16"
pilaster

Figure 4.25 Pilaster details.

C.   Typical Connections of Intersecting Walls and Embedded Columns are shown in Figures 4.26 through 4.28.

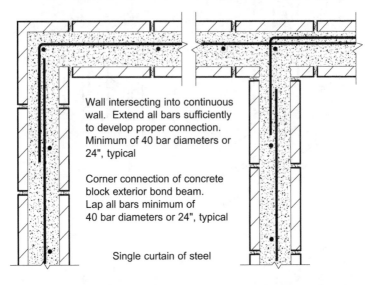

Wall intersecting into continuous wall. Extend all bars sufficiently to develop proper connection. Minimum of 40 bar diameters or 24", typical

Corner connection of concrete block exterior bond beam. Lap all bars minimum of 40 bar diameters or 24", typical

Single curtain of steel

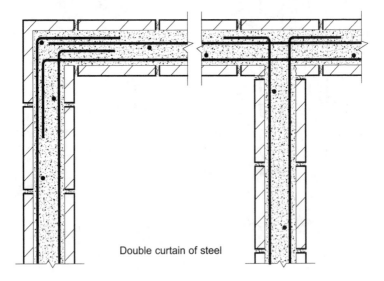

Double curtain of steel

Figure 4.26 Typical intersecting wall connections.

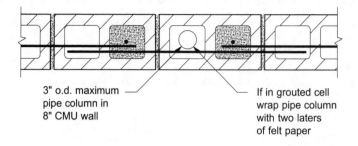

3" o.d. maximum
pipe column in
8" CMU wall

If in grouted cell
wrap pipe column
with two laters
of felt paper

Figure 4.27 Embedded steel columns in masonry wall.

D.   Lintel and Bond Beam.

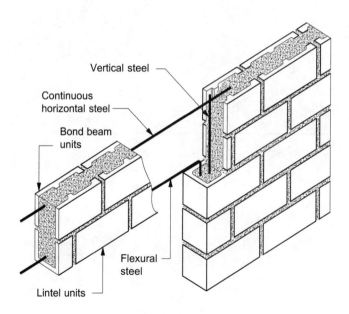

Vertical steel

Continuous
horizontal steel

Bond beam
units

Flexural
steel

Lintel units

Figure 4.28 Lintel and bond beam detail.

143

E.   **Arrangement of Open End Units is Shown in Figures 4.29 and 4.30.**

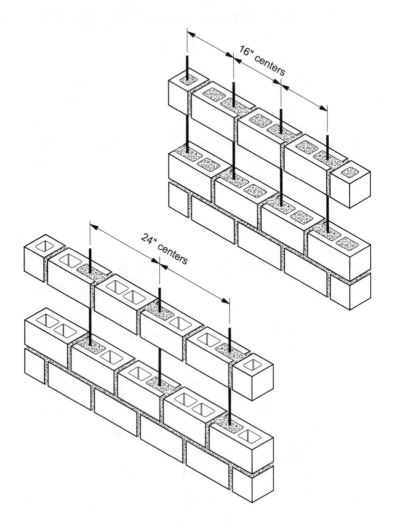

Figure 4.29 Typical arrangement of steel and open end units—16 inch (406 mm) and 24 inch (610 mm) spacing.

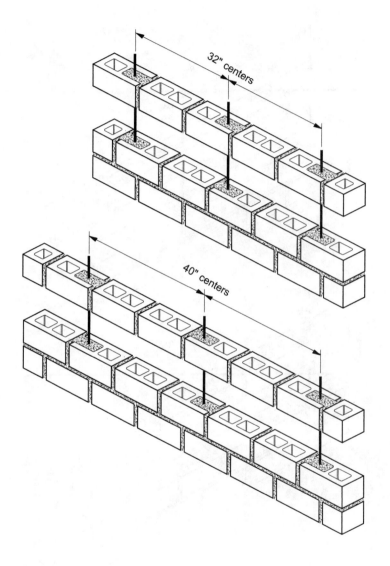

Figure 4.30 Typical arrangement of steel and open end units—32 inch (813 mm), and 40 inch (1016 mm).

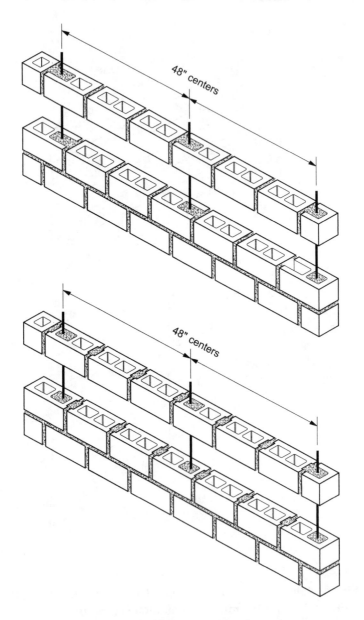

Figure 4.30 (Cont'd). Typical arrangement of steel and open-end units-48 inch (1219 mm) spacing.

F.   Typical Wall Assembly is Shown in Figure 4.31.

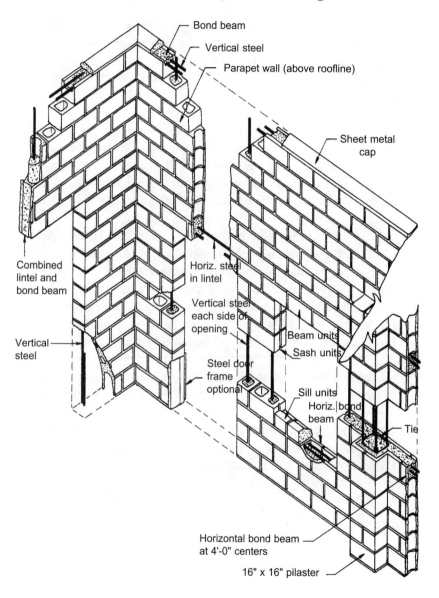

Figure 4.31 Wall assembly and terminology.

4.5   RACKING and TOOTHING

Occasionally, a section of wall cannot be sequentially constructed due to project conditions. An example would be constructing a wall next to a door frame, but the door frame has not been installed, causing an interruption in the masonry construction.

Given this condition, it may be necessary to "rack back" the wall. This method is shown in Figure 4.32. When the condition causing the interruption has been eliminated, then the mason can return and continue to construct the masonry wall. The racking method is preferred over the toothing method.

There are times when racking is not practical. An example would be the adjoining of new construction to old with a design that integrates the masonry units. Another example would be filling in a pre-existing door or window opening. Under these conditions, the method of construction would be toothing the block, as shown in Figure 4.33. Consent from the Architect or Engineer should be obtained before toothing is performed.

When toothing, careful consideration must be given to the mortar joints. While placing units into the existing "tooth", the mason must properly compact the mortar to ensure a full and tightly compressed joint. Inserting steel and grouting the toothed cells must also be done with care to assure full contact between the reinforcement and the grout.

Figure 4.32 Racked masonry.

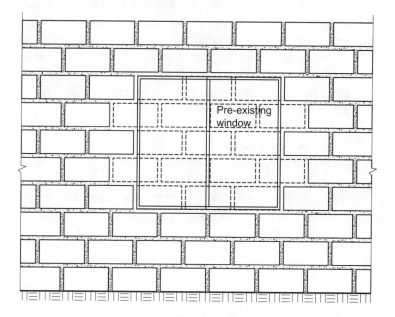

Figure 4.33 Toothed masonry - window infill.

4.6   MORTAR JOINTS

Mortar is used in the joints between masonry units. The horizontal joint is the bed joint and the vertical joint is the head joint. Mortar is the bedding material that allows the units to be placed level, plumb and in proper position. Mortar is also the sealing material between masonry units. The exposed surface of the mortar can be finished in a number of ways, as illustrated in Figures 4.34 and 4.35.

Concave, V-joints and weathered joints are recommended for exterior masonry. Tooling the joints requires pressure, which compresses the mortar, creating a tight bond between the mortar and the unit thus providing a dense surface for weatherproofing and sealing the interface between mortar and masonry unit.

Mortar joints for interiors may be the same as exterior joints or they may be raked, extruded or weeping, struck or flush cut. These joints increase the chance for water leakage in weather exposed masonry since the small ledges allow water to collect and migrate into the wall at the mortar unit interface and they are usually not compressed by tooling. These joints require special attention and tooling to improve water tightness and are not recommended for exterior work.

Flush cut joints should be used where the finished surface is to be plastered or texture covered.

Special effect joints that are sometimes used are beaded and grapevine. These are for simulating old style masonry.

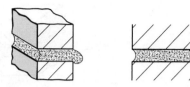

a) Concave joint

Most common joint used, tooling works the mortar tight into the joint to produce a good weather joint. Pattern is emphasized and small irregularities in laying are concealed.

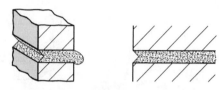

b) "V" joint

Tooling works the mortar tight and provides a good weather joint. Used to emphasize joints and conceal small irregularities in laying and provide a line in center of mortar joint.

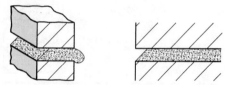

c) Weather joint

Use to emphasize horizontal joints. Acceptable weather joint with proper tooling.

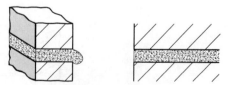

d) Flush joint

Use where wall is to be plastered or where it is desired to hide joints under paint. Special care is required to make joint weatherproof.

Figure 4.34 Types of recommended mortar joints.

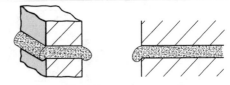

e) Squeeze joint
Provides a rustic, high texture look. Satisfactory indoors and exterior fences. Not recommended for exterior building walls.

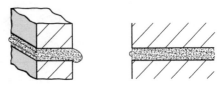

f) Beaded joint
Special effect, poor exterior weather joint because of exposed ledge - Not recommended for exterior use.

g) Raked joint
Strongly emphasizes joints. Poor weather joint - Not recommended if exposed to weather unless tooled at bottom of mortar joint.

h) Struck joint
Use to emphasize horizontal joints. Poor weather joint. Not recommended as water will penetrate on lower ledge.

Figure 4.35 Types of non-weather mortar joints, for special effects only.

Reinforcing Steel

5.1   GENERAL

Reinforcing steel is the material that imparts ductility, added strength and toughness to masonry structures. It is one of the primary components for lateral force-resistant design and construction.

5.2   MAXIMUM SIZE/AMOUNT OF REINFORCING STEEL

Building codes impose the maximum size and amount of reinforcing steel that can be placed in a masonry wall depending on the applicable code and the design method. Tables 5.A and 5.B summarize the requirements.

Table 5.A – Maximum Size of Reinforcement		
	Working Stress Design	Strength Design
IBC (2000)	Lesser of: $^1/_8$ of nominal wall thickness, *or* $^1/_4$ of least cell dimension	Lesser of: #11 bar, *or* $^1/_8$ of nominal wall thickness, *or* $^1/_4$ of least cell dimension
MSJC (1999)	#11	---
UBC (1997)	#11	#9

Table 5.B – Maximum Amount of Reinforcement

	Working Stress Design	Strength Design
IBC (2000)	Refer to MSJC Code	4% of cell area except at splices-no more than 2 bars per cell
MSJC (1999)	One half least clear dimension of cell	---
UBC (1997)	6% of cell area, 12% of cell area at splices	Diameter not to exceed ¼ least dimension of cell-no more than 2 bars per cell

5.2.1 Maximum Size/Amount of Reinforcing Steel-Working Stress Design

IBC sets forth maximum reinforcement size based on cell dimension, whereas, the MSJC Code and UBC base maximum reinforcement size based on a specific bar size.

The maximum size and amount of reinforcing steel reduces the congestion and facilitates grouting of the cells. Splices increase the congestion and should therefore be staggered whenever possible.

IBC Section 2107.2.4
2107.2.4 ACI 530/ASCE 5/TMS 402, maximum bar size. The bar diameter shall not exceed one-eighth of the nominal wall thickness and shall not exceed one-quarter of the least dimension of the cell, course or collar joint in which it is placed.

MSJC Code Section 1.12.2
1.12.2 *Size of reinforcement*
  1.12.2.1 The maximum size of reinforcement used in masonry shall be No. 11 (M #36).

UBC Section 2107.2.2.1
2107.2.2.1 Maximum reinforcement size. The maximum size of reinforcement shall be No. 11 bars. Maximum reinforcement area in cells shall be 6 percent of the cell area without splices and 12 percent of the cell area with splices.

  The Uniform Building Code goes one step further to limit the use of plain bars in masonry to a maximum of $^1/_4$ inch (6.4 mm). The IBC and MSJC do not address this issue and it is conceivable that smooth reinforcing steel could be furnished in accordance with ASTM A 615, *Specification for Deformed and Plain Billet-Steel Bars for Concrete Reinforcement*, although that would be contrary to the intent of the Code.

UBC Section 2106.3.2
2106.3.2 Plain Bars. The use of plain bars larger than $^1/_4$ inch (6.4mm) in diameter is not permitted.

5.2.2 Maximum Size/Amount of Reinforcing Steel-Strength Design

  The Strength Design provisions of the 2000 International Building Code allow for reinforcement bar size of No. 11 (M #36) and smaller, however, the maximum area of reinforcement in a cell is limited to 4%, except where splices occur.

IBC Section 2108.9.2

2108.9.2   Reinforcement requirements and details.
2108.9.2.1 Reinforcing bar size. Reinforcing bars used in masonry shall not be larger than a No. 11 bar. The bar diameter shall not exceed one-eighth of the nominal wall thickness and shall not exceed one-fourth of the least dimension of the cell, course or collar joint in which it is placed. The area of reinforcing bars placed in a cell, or in a course, of hollow unit construction shall not exceed 4 percent, except where splices occur, of the cell area. No more than two bars shall be placed in a cell of a wall or a wall frame.

UBC Section 2108.2.2

2108.2.2   Reinforcement requirements and details.
2108.2.2.1 Maximum Reinforcement. The maximum size of reinforcement shall be No. 9. The diameter of a bar shall not exceed one-fourth the least dimension of a cell. No more than two bars shall be placed in a cell of a wall or a wall frame.

5.3   SPACING OF STEEL IN WALLS

Placing steel reinforcement in the proper location is critical. For a masonry structure to resist wind, seismic and other loads, the steel reinforcement must be positioned where it can function properly. The Codes provide specific language addressing this important issue.

MSJC Specification Section 3.4B

3.4 B *Securing reinforcement* - Support and fasten reinforcement together to prevent displacement beyond the tolerances allowed by construction loads or by placement of grout or mortar.

UBC Section 2104.5

2104.5 Reinforcement Placing. Reinforcement details shall conform to the requirements of this chapter. Metal reinforcement shall be located in accordance with the plans and specifications.

The Codes also provide language on clear distances between bars. This language is graphically presented in Figures 5.1 and 5.2.

IBC Section 2108.9.2.3 (Strength Design)

2108.9.2.3 Clear distance between parallel bars.
The clear distance between parallel reinforcing bars shall not be less than the nominal diameter of the bars nor less than 1 inch (25.4 mm).

MSJC Code Section 1.12.3

1.12.3 *Placement limits for reinforcement*
1.12.3.1 The clear distance between parallel bars shall not be less than the nominal diameter of the bars, nor less than 1 in. (25.4 mm).

UBC Section 2106.3.3

2106.3.3 Spacing of longitudinal reinforcement.
The clear distance between parallel bars, except in columns, shall not be less than the nominal diameter of the bars or 1 inch (25 mm), except that bars in a splice may be in contact. This clear distance requirement applies to the clear distance between a contact splice and adjacent splices or bars.

Table 5-C *UBC Maximum Amount of Reinforcement in CMU Cells¹ (Walls)*

Nominal Thickness of CMU (mm)	Approx. Cell Size (mm x mm)	Approx. Cell Area (mm²)	Max. Steel Area—6% of Cell Area (mm²)	Bar Selection	Suggested Maximum Steel Area—4% of Cell Area (mm²)	Bar Selection
4" (102)	1¾"x5½" (44 x 140)	10 sq. in. (6450)	0.6 sq. in. (387)	1-#7 (2-15M)	0.4 sq. in. (258)	1-No. 6 (1-20M)
6" (152)	3¼" x5½" (83 x 140)	18 sq. in. (11 610)	1.1 sq. in. (710)	1-#9 (1-30M)	0.7 sq. in. (452)	1-No. 8 (1-25M)
8" (203)	5" x 5¼" (127 x 133)	26 sq. in. (16 775)	1.6 sq. in. (1032)	1-#11² (1-35M)	1.0 sq. in. (645)	1-No. 9 (1-30M)
10" (254)	7"x5¼" (178 x 133)	37 sq. in. (23 870)	2.2 sq. in (1419)	2-#9 (2-30M)	1.5 sq. in (968)	1 No. 11² or 2 No. 7 (1-35M)
12" (305)	9" x 5¼" (229 x 133)	47 sq. in (30 325).	2.8 sq. in. (1807)	2-#10² (2-35M)	1.9 sq. in. (1226)	2-No. 9 (2-30M)

¹ Area of steel in cells may be doubled for lapped spliced bars.
² Maximum allowable reinforcement size for Strength Design is #9.

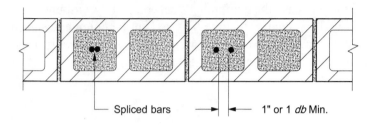

Figure 5.1 Spacing of vertical reinforcing in cell.

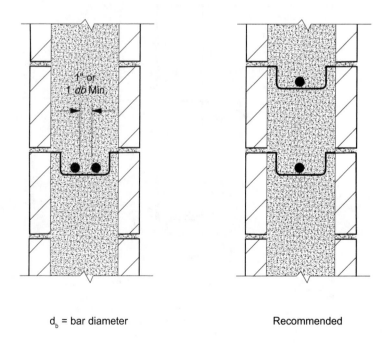

d_b = bar diameter   Recommended

Figure 5.2 Spacing of horizontal reinforcement in masonry wall.

5.4   CLEARANCES OF STEEL IN MASONRY

For a reinforced masonry wall to function properly it is essential to have the reinforcing steel completely surrounded by grout. This requires that the bars be kept a minimum distance from the masonry to allow the grout to flow around the steel and bond the concrete block and steel together.

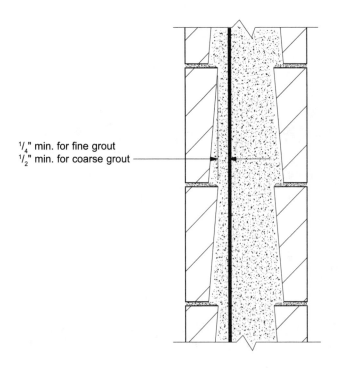

$1/4$" min. for fine grout
$1/2$" min. for coarse grout

Figure 5.3 Clearance of reinforcing steel.

MSJC Code Section 1.12.3

1.12.3.5 Reinforcement embedded in grout shall have a thickness of grout between the reinforcement and masonry units not less than $^1/_4$ in. (6.4 mm) for fine grout and $^1/_2$ in. (12.7 mm) for coarse grout.

MSJC Specification Section 3.4 C

3.4 C.2 Maintain clear distance between reinforcing bars and any face of masonry unit or formed surface, but not less than $^1/_4$ in. (6.4 mm) for fine grout and $^1/_2$ in. (12.7 mm) for coarse grout.

UBC Section 2106.3.3

The clear distance between the surface of a bar and any surface of a masonry unit shall not be less than $^1/_4$ in. (6.4 mm) for fine grout and $^1/_2$ in. (12.7 mm) for coarse grout. Cross webs of hollow units may be used as support for horizontal reinforcement.

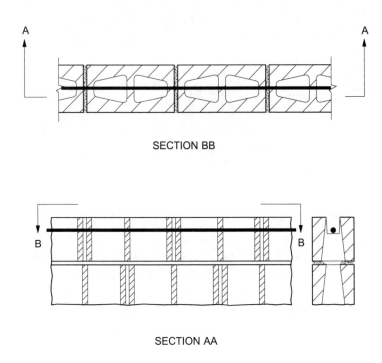

Figure 5.4 Support of reinforcing steel.

IBC Section 2108.9.2.7 (Strength Design)

2108.9.2.7 Reinforcing bar cover. Reinforcing bars shall have a minimum masonry cover not less than $2\,^1/_2\,d_b$ nor less than the following:

    1. Where the masonry face is exposed to earth or weather, 2 inches (51 mm) for bars larger than No. 5 and $1\,^1/_2$ inches (38 mm) for No. 5 bar or smaller.

    2. Where the masonry is not exposed to earth or weather, $1\,^1/_2$ inches (38 mm).

MSJC Code Section 1.12.4

1.12.4 Protection for reinforcement

    1.12.4.1 Reinforcing bars shall have a masonry cover not less than the following:

    (a) Masonry face exposed to earth or weather: 2 in. (50.8 mm) for bars larger than No. 5 (M #16); $1\,^1/_2$ in. (38.1 mm) for No. 5 (M #16) bars or smaller.

    (b) Masonry not exposed to earth or weather: $1\,^1/_2$ in. (38.1 mm).

UBC Section 2107.2.2.2

2107.2.2.2 Cover. All reinforcing bars, except joint reinforcement, shall be completely embedded in mortar or grout and have a minimum cover, including the masonry unit, of at least 3/4 inch (19 mm), $1\,^1/_2$ inches (38 mm) of cover when the masonry is exposed to weather and 2 inches (51 mm) of cover when the masonry is exposed to soil.

(See Figure 5.5)

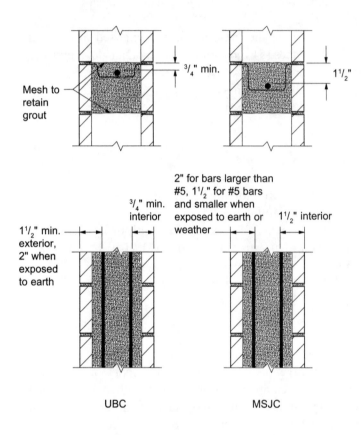

Figure 5.5 Minimum cover over reinforcing steel.

Wiring the vertical steel to dowels projecting from the foundation is satisfactory if the dowels are in the prescribed location. If they are not, the dowels can be bent to properly position them, as shown in Figure 5.6. However, the vertical steel can lap the dowels without the bars being wired together. In fact, they can be separated by several inches and transmit force between them.

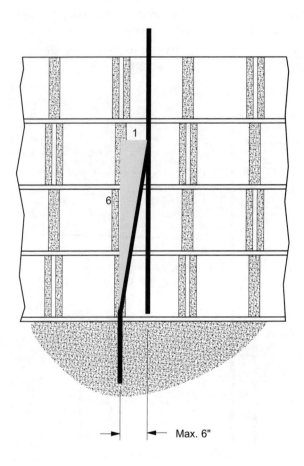

Figure 5.6 Slope for bending reinforcing steel into position.

If necessary, due to improper location or failure to install dowels, new dowels may be required. These can be installed by several methods, such as drilling, then dry packing mortar or epoxying around a reinforcing bar; or drilling, then installing anchored dowels, using cinch anchors, anchor shields or similar method.

Vertical steel may be held in place by reinforcing bar positioners. These wire positioners will locate the bar in the proper position, e.g. center, to one side, one bar on each side, etc., and will also secure it from moving during grouting of the wall (see Figure 5.7 and Figure 5.8).

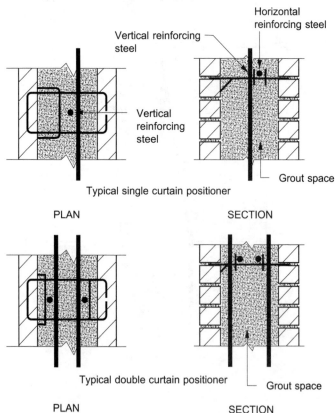

Figure 5.7 Bar positioners used to locate and hold vertical and horizontal steel.

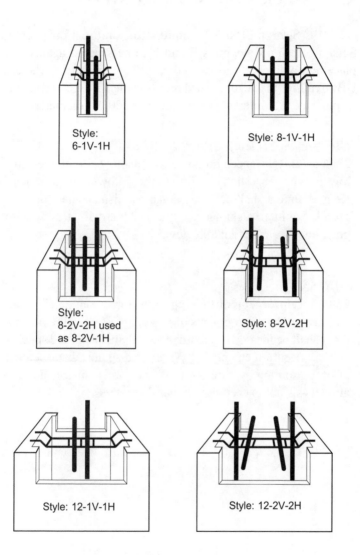

Common cradle positioner styles and configurations

Figure 5.8 Reinforcing bar positioners for concrete masonry.

5.5   SECURING REINFORCING STEEL

IBC Section 2106.6.2 requires structural reinforcement in Seismic Design Categories E and F to be secured against displacement at intervals not exceeding 112 bar diameters, whereas, UBC requires that all deformed reinforcement be secured against displacement at intervals not exceeding 200 bar diameters.

IBC Section 2106.6.2.2 (SDC E & F)

2106.6.2.2 Reinforced hollow unit masonry. Reinforced hollow unit masonry shall conform to the following requirement. Reinforcement shall be secured against displacement prior to grouting at intervals not exceeding 112 bar diameters by wire positioners or other suitable devices.

UBC Section 2104.5

2104.5 Reinforcement Placing. Reinforcement details shall conform to the requirements of this chapter. Metal reinforcement shall be located in accordance with the plans and specifications. Reinforcement shall be secured against displacement prior to grouting by wire positioners or other suitable devices at intervals not exceeding 200 bar diameters.

Table 5.D Maximum Intervals for Securing Reinforcing Bars (IBC, SDC E & F)			
Bar Size	Maximum Secured Intervals	Bar Size	Maximum Secured Intervals
#3	3'-6" (1.1 m)	#8	9'-4" (2.8 m)
#4	4'-8" (1.4 m)	#9	10'-6" (3.2 m)
#5	5'-10" (1.8 m)	#10	11'-8" (3.6 m)
#6	7'-0" (2.1 m)	#11	12'-10" (3.9 m)
#7	8'-2" (2.5 m)	#14	Not Permitted

Table 5.E Maximum Intervals for Securing Reinforcing Bars (UBC)			
Bar Size	Maximum Secured Intervals	Bar Size	Maximum Secured Intervals
#3	6'-3" (1.9 m)	#8	16'-8" (5.1 m)
#4	8'-4" (2.5 m)	#9	18'-9" (5.7 m)
#5	10'-5" (3.2 m)	#10	20'-10" (6.3 m)
#6	12'-6" (3.8 m)	#11	22'-11" (7.0 m)
#7	14'-7" (4.4 m)	#14	Not Permitted

As noted in Sections 4.2 and 5.4, using the Code requirements set forth in the Concrete Section, reinforcing dowels may be bent at a slope of no more than one inch (25.4 mm) horizontally per six inches (152 mm) of height.

UBC Section 1907.8.1
1907.8.1 Offset bars. Offset bent longitudinal bars shall conform to the following:
1907.8.1.1 Slope of inclined portion of an offset bar with axis of column shall not exceed 1 in 6.

5.6   LOCATION TOLERANCES OF BARS

Proper location of structural reinforcing steel is important for safe and adequate performance. To assure proper location, Model Building Codes provide tolerances permitted for placement of bars.

MSJC Specification Section 3.4 E
3.4 E   *Placement Tolerances*
1.Tolerances for the placement of steel in walls and flexural elements shall be $\pm \frac{1}{2}$ in. (12.7 mm) when the distance from the centerline of steel to the opposite face of masonry, d, equal to 8 in. (203 mm) or less, ± 1 in. (25.4 mm) for d equal to 24 in. (610 mm) or less but greater than 8 in. (203 mm), and $\pm 1\frac{1}{4}$ in. (31.8 mm) for d greater than 24 in. (610 mm).

2. Place vertical bars within 2 in. (50.8 mm) of the required location along the length of the wall. (See Tables 5-C and Figure 5.9)

3. If it is necessary to move bars more than one bar diameter or a distance exceeding the tolerance stated above to avoid interference with other reinforcing steel, conduits, or embedded items, notify the Architect/Engineer for acceptance of the resulting arrangement of bars.

UBC Section 2104.5

Tolerances for the placement of reinforcement in walls and flexural elements shall be $\pm \frac{1}{2}$ in. (13 mm) for d equal to 8 in. (200 mm) or less, ± 1 in. (25 mm) for d equal to 24 in. (600 mm) or less but greater than 8 in. (200 mm), and $\pm 1\frac{1}{4}$ in. (32 mm) for d greater than 24 in. (600 mm).

Tolerance for longitudinal location of reinforcement shall be ± 2 inches (51 mm). (See Table 5-F and Figure 5.9).

Table 5-F *Tolerances for Placing Reinforcement*

Distance, d, from face of CMU to the Center of Reinforcing	Allowable Tolerance
$d \leq 8"$ (200 mm)	$\pm \frac{1}{2}"$ (13 mm)
$8"$ (200 mm) $< d \leq 24"$ (600 mm)	$\pm 1"$ (25 mm)
$24"$ (600 mm) $< d$	$\pm 1\frac{1}{4}"$ (32 mm)

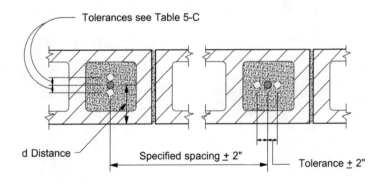

Figure 5.9 Typical tolerances for placement of reinforcing bars in a cell for an 8" (200 mm) CMU.

5.7   LAP SPLICES, REINFORCING BARS

Reinforcing bars and joint reinforcing steel are typically delivered to construction job sites in uniform lengths which can be easily handled by one person. When reinforcing bars meet in a wall they must be connected in some fashion so that all of the stresses can be transferred from one bar to the other. This is usually accomplished by lapping or splicing the bars.

Splices may be made only at such points and in such a manner that the structural strength of the member will not be reduced. Lapped splices must provide sufficient lap to transfer the working stress of the reinforcement by bond and shear.

Bars that are not spliced shall be in the same cell as the bar to be spliced and not in an adjacent cell.

IBC Section 2108.9.2.11 (Strength Design)
2108.9.2.11 Splices. Reinforcement splices shall comply with one of the following:

1. The minimum length of lap for bars shall be 15 in. (380 mm) or the length determined by Equation 21-25, whichever is greater.

$$l_d = l_{de} / \phi \qquad \textbf{(Equation 21-25)}$$

where:
l_d = Required development length of reinforcement, inches (mm).
l_{de} = Embedment length of reinforcement, inches (mm).
ϕ = Strength reduction factor; ϕ = 0.8 for Equation 21-25.

Reinforcing bars larger than No. 9 in size shall be spliced using mechanical connectors in accordance with Section 2108.9.2.11, Item 3.

Bars spliced by noncontact lap splices shall be spaced transversely a distance not greater than one fifth the required length of lap nor more than 8 inches (203 mm).

2. A welded splice shall have the bars butted and welded to develop in tension 125 percent of the yield strength of the bar, f_y. Welding shall conform to AWS D1.4.

3. Mechanical splices shall have the bars connected to develop in tension or compression, as required, at least 125 percent of the yield strength of the bar, f_y.

MSJC Code Section 2.1.8.6 (Working Stress Design)

2.1.8.6 *Splices of reinforcement* - Lap splices, welded splices, or mechanical connections are permitted in accordance with the provisions of this section. All welding shall conform to AWS D1.4

2.1.8.6.1 *Lap Splices*

2.1.8.6.1.1 The minimum length of lap for bars in tension or compression shall be determined by Eq. (2-9), but not less than 12 in. (305 mm).

$$l_d \qquad d_b F_s \qquad\qquad (2\text{-}9)$$

l_d = embedment length or lap length of straight reinforcement, in. (mm).

d_b = nominal diameter of reinforcement, in. (mm).

F_s = allowable tensile or compressive stress in reinforcement, psi (MPa).

When epoxy-coated bars are used, lap length determined by Eq. (2-9) shall be increased by 50 percent.

2.1.8.6.1.2 Bars spliced by noncontact lap splices shall not be spaced transversely farther apart than one-fifth the required length of lap nor more than 8 in. (203 mm).

2.1.8.6.2 *Welded splices* - Welded splices shall have the bars butted and welded to develop in tension at least 125 percent of the specified yield strength of the bar.

2.1.8.6.3 *Mechanical connections* - Mechanical connections shall have the bars connected to develop in tension or compression, as required, at least 125 percent of the specified yield strength of the bar.

UBC Section 2107.2.2.6 (Working Stress Design)

2107.2.2.6 Splices. The amount of lap of lapped splices shall be sufficient to transfer the allowable stress of the reinforcement as specified in Sections 2106.3.4, 2107.2.2.3 and 2107.2.12. In no case shall the length of the lapped splice be less than 30 bar diameters for compression or 40 bar diameters for tension.

Welded or mechanical connections shall develop 125 percent of the specified yield strength of the bar in tension.

EXCEPTION: For compression bars in columns that are not part of the seismic-resisting system and are not subject to flexure, only the compressive strength need be developed.

When adjacent splices in grouted masonry are separated by 3 inches (76 mm) or less, the required lap length shall be increased 30 percent.

EXCEPTION: Where lap slices are staggered at least 24 bar diameters, no increase in lap length is required.

See Section 2107.2.12 for lap splice increases.

2107.2.2.3 Development length. The required development length l_d for deformed bars or deformed wire shall be calculated by:

$$l_d = 0.002\, d_b f_s \text{ for bars in tension} \qquad (7\text{-}9)$$
For **SI:** $l_d = 0.29\, d_b f_s$ for bars in tension

$$l_d = 0.0015\, d_b f_s \text{ for bars in compression} \qquad (7\text{-}10)$$
For **SI:** $l_d = 0.022\, d_b f_s$ for bars in compression

Development length for smooth bars shall be twice the length determined by Formula (7-9).

UBC Section 2108.2.2.7 (Strength Design)
2108.2.2.7 Splices. Reinforcement splices shall comply with one of the following:

1. The minimum length of lap for bars shall be 12 inches (305 mm) or the length determined by Formula (8-14).

$$l_d = l_{de} / \phi \qquad (8\text{-}14)$$

Bars spliced by noncontact lap splices shall be spaced transversely a distance not greater than one fifth the required length of lap or more than 8 inches (203 mm).

2. A welded splice shall have the bars butted and welded to develop in tension 125 percent of the yield strength of the bar, f_y.

3. Mechanical splices shall have the bars connected to develop in tension or compression, as required, at least 125 percent of the yield strength of the bar, f_y.

Uniform Building Code requires that if two bars are both spliced in one cell and are less than 3 inches (76 mm) apart, the splice length is required to be 30% longer. See Figure 5.10. Staggering the splices by 24 bar diameters eliminates this 30% increase in lap length.

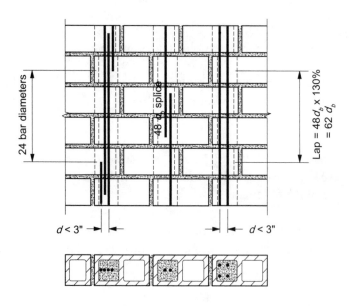

Figure 5.10 Lap splice of steel in cell for Grade 60 steel (UBC).

MSJC Code Section 2.1.8

2.1.8 *Development of reinforcement embedded in grout*

2.1.8.1 *General* - The calculated tension or compression in the reinforcement at each section shall be developed on each side of the section by embedment length, hook or mechanical device, or a combination thereof. Hooks shall not be used to develop bars in compression.

2.1.8.2 *Embedment of bars and wires in tension* - The embedment length of bars and wire shall be determined by

Eq. (2-8), but shall not be less than 12 in. (305 mm) for bars and 6 in. (152 mm) for wire.

$$l_d = 0.0015 \, d_b F_s \qquad\qquad (2\text{-}8)$$

When epoxy-coated bars or wires are used, development length determined by Eq. (2-8) shall be increased by 50 percent.

UBC Section 2106.3.4

The tension or compression in any bar at any section shall be developed on each side of that section by the required development length. The development length of the bar may be achieved by a combination of an embedment length, anchorage or, for tension only, hooks.

Based on the UBC equations 7-9 and 7-10, the development length for deformed bars must be as follows with a minimum length of 12 inches (305 mm).

For Grade 40 reinforcing bar in tension $\qquad l_d = 40 \, d_b$

For Grade 40 reinforcing bar in compression $\qquad l_d = 30 \, d_b$

For Grade 60 reinforcing bar in tension $\qquad l_d = 48 \, d_b$

For Grade 60 reinforcing bar in compression $\qquad l_d = 36 \, d_b$

where d_b = diameter of the reinforcing bar.

Refer to Table 5-G, Length of Lap (inches).

Table 5-G   Length of Lap (inches)¹

| Bar Size | | Grade 40 | | Grade 60 | | | | UBC Concrete | |
No.	Dia. (mm)	UBC Masonry 30 Dia. Min. (mm)	UBC Masonry 40 Dia. Min. (mm)	36 Dia. (mm)	48 Dia. (mm)	50 Dia. (mm)	60 Dia. (mm)	Dev. Lgth (mm)	Top Bars (mm)
3	0.375 (10)	12 (305)	15 (381)	14 (356)	18 (457)	19 (483)	23 (584)	12 (305)	12 (305)
4	0.500 (13)	15 (381)	20 (508)	18 (457)	24 (610)	25 (635)	30 (762)	12 (305)	12 (305)
5	0.625 (16)	19 (483)	25 (635)	23 (584)	30 (762)	31 (787)	38 (965)	12 (305)	16 (406)
6	0.750 (19)	23 (584)	30 (762)	27 (686)	36 (914)	38 (965)	45 (1143)	16 (406)	22 (559)
7	0.875 (22)	27 (686)	35 (889)	32 (813)	42 (1067)	44 (1118)	51 (1295)	22 (559)	30 (762)
8	1.000 (25)	30 (762)	40 (1016)	36 (914)	48 (1219)	50 (1270)	60 (1524)	28 (711)	39 (991)
9	1.128 (29)	34 (864)	45 (1143)	41 (1041)	54 1372	56 (1422)	68 (1727)	36 (914)	50 (1270)
10 □	1.270 (32)	39 (991)	50 (1270)	45 (1143)	61 (1549)	64 (1626)	76 (1930)	44 (1118)	62 (1575)
11 □	1.410 (36)	43 (1092)	56 (1422)	50 (1270)	68 (1727)	71 (1803)	85 (2159)	56 (1422)	78 (1981)

¹Working Stress Design
²Not permitted for UBC Strength Design

5.8   JOINT REINFORCEMENT

> *UBC Section 2106.1.5.4*
> **2106.1.5.4 Joint reinforcement.** Prefabricated joint reinforcement for masonry walls shall have at least one cross wire of at least No. 9 gage steel for each 2 square feet (0.19 m²) of wall area. The vertical spacing of the joint reinforcement shall not exceed 16 inches (406 mm). The longitudinal wires shall be thoroughly embedded in the bed joint mortar. The joint reinforcement shall engage all wythes.

5.8.1   Lap Splices, Joint Reinforcement

> *UBC Section 2104.8*
> **2104.8 Joint Reinforcement.** Wire joint reinforcement used in the design as principal reinforcement in hollow-unit construction shall be continuous between supports unless splices are made by lapping:
>
> 1. Fifty-four wire diameters in a grouted cell, or
>
> 2. Seventy-five wire diameters in the mortared bed joint, or
>
> 3. In alternate bed joints of running bond masonry a distance not less than 54 diameters plus twice the spacing of the bed joints, or
>
> 4. As required by calculation and specific location in areas of minimum stress, such as points of inflection.

***Table 5-H** Length of Lap of Wire Joint Reinforcement (in.)*

Wire Size					UBC[3]
No.	Dia (mm)	54 Dia.[1] (mm)	75 Dia.[2] (mm)	Vertical Spacing 8" (mm)	Vertical Spacing 16" (mm)
9	.1483 (3.77)	8 (203)	12 (305)	24 (610)	40 (1016)
8	.1620 (4.11)	9 (229)	13 (330)	25 (635)	41 (1041)
$^3/_{16}$"	.1875 (4.76)	11 (279)	14 (356)	26 (660)	42 (1067)

[1] Grouted Cell
[2] Mortared Joint
[3] Alternate Bed Joints

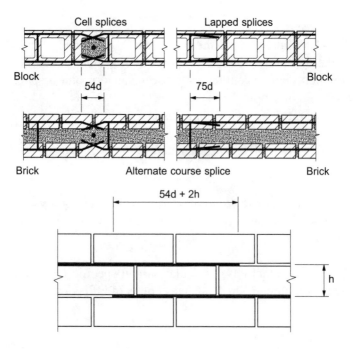

Figure 5.11 Typical splice arrangement for ladder type joint reinforcement. When calculations show that shorter splices are adequate in areas of minimum stress (e.g. inflection points) shorter splices may be used.

5.8.2   Coverage and Layout of Joint Reinforcing Steel

A. Coverage. All longitudinal wires shall be completely embedded in mortar. Joint reinforcement embedded in horizontal mortar joints shall have not less than $^5/_8$ inch (16 mm) mortar coverage from the exposed face. Refer to Figure 5.12.

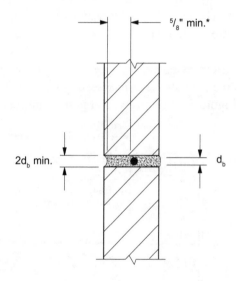

*MSJC Code allows $^1/_2$" cover with interior exposure

Figure 5.12 Cover over joint reinforcement.

MSJC Code, Section 1.12.4.2
1.12.4.2 Longitudinal wires of joint reinforcement shall be fully embedded in mortar or grout with a minimum cover of $^5/_8$ inch (15.9 mm) when exposed to earth or weather and $^1/_2$ inch (12.7 mm) when not exposed to earth or weather. Joint reinforcement in masonry exposed to earth or weather shall be corrosion resistant or protected from corrosion by coating.

UBC Section 2106.1.8

2106.1.8 Protection of ties and joint reinforcement. A minimum of $^5/_8$ inches (16 mm) mortar cover shall be provided between ties or joint reinforcement and any exposed face. The thickness of grout or mortar between masonry units and joint reinforcement shall not be less than $^1/_4$ inch (6 mm), except that $^1/_4$ inch (6 mm) or smaller diameter reinforcement or bolts may be placed in bed joints which are at least twice the thickness of the reinforcement or bolts.

B. Layout of Intersecting Walls. Figure 5.13 illustrates a plan for joint reinforcement showing intersecting walls and alternative lapping. Figure 5.14 shows typical joint reinforcement.

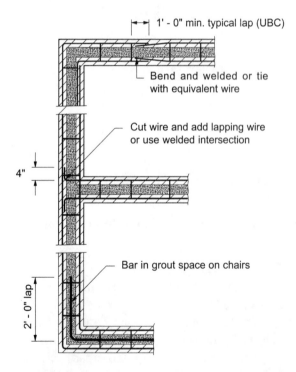

Figure 5.13 Plan of joint reinforcement showing intersection and alternate lapping.

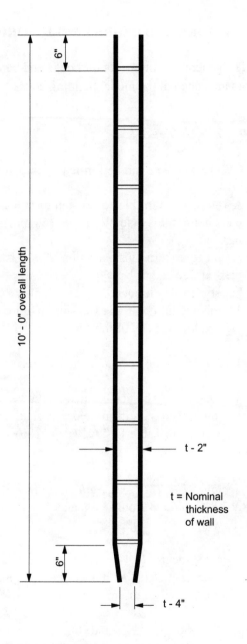

6"

10' - 0" overall length

t - 2"

t = Nominal
thickness
of wall

6"

t - 4"

Figure 5.14 Typical joint reinforcement.

5.9 HOOKS AND BENDS IN REINFORCING BARS

The general requirements for hooks and bends in reinforcing bars are stated in the model building codes.

MSJC Code, Section 1.12.5

1.12.5 *Standard hooks*

Standard hooks shall be formed by one of the following methods:

(a) A 180 degree turn plus extension of at least 4 bar diameters but not less than $2^1/_2$ inches (64 mm) at free end of bar.

(b) A 90 degree turn plus extension of at least 12 bar diameters at free end of bar.

(c) For stirrup and tie anchorage only, either a 90 degree or a 135 degree turn plus an extension of at least 6 bar diameters at the free end of the bar.

1.12.6 *Minimum bend diameter for reinforcing bars*

The diameter of bend measured on the inside of reinforcing bars, other than for stirrups and ties, shall not be less than values specified in Table 1.12.6.1 (Page 186).

IBC Section 2108.9.2.8 (Strength Design)

2108.9.2.8 Standard Hooks. A standard hook shall be one of the following:

1. A 180-degree (3.14 rad) turn plus extension of at least 4 bar diameters, but not less than $2^1/_2$ inches (63 mm) at the free end of the bar.

2. A 135-degree (2.56 rad) turn plus an extension of at least 6 bar diameters at the free end of the bar.

3. A 90-degree (1.57 rad) turn plus an extension of at least 12 bar diameters at the free end of the bar.

4. For stirrup and tie anchorage only, either a 135-degree or a 180-degree (2.56 rad or 3.14 rad) turn plus an extension of at least 6 bar diameters at the free end of the bar.

5. The equivalent embedment length for standard hooks in tension, l_{dh}, shall be as follows:

$$l_{dh} = 13d_b \qquad \text{(Equation 21-22)}$$

where:

d_b = Diameter of reinforcement, inches (mm).
l_{dh} = Equivalent development length for a standard hook, inches (mm).

2108.9.2.9 Minimum bend diameter for reinforcing bars.
The diameter of bend measured on the inside of the bar, other than for stirrups and ties, shall not be less than values specified in Table 2108.9.2.9.

UBC Section 2107.2.2.5 (Working Stress Design)
2107.2.2.5 Hooks.
1. The term "standard hook" shall mean one of the following:
    1.1 A 180-degree turn plus extension of at least four bar diameters, but not less than $2^1/_2$ inches (63 mm) at free end of bar.
    1.2 A 90-degree turn plus extension of at least 12 bar diameters at free end of bar.
    1.3 For stirrup and tie anchorage only, either a 90-degree or 135-degree turn, plus an extension of at least six bar diameters, but not less than $2^1/_2$ inches (63 mm) at the free end of the bar.

2. Inside diameter of bend of the bars, other than for stirrups and ties, shall not be less than that set forth in Table 21-I.

3. Inside diameter of bend for No. 5 or smaller stirrups and ties shall not be less than four bar diameters. Inside diameter of bend for No. 5 or larger stirrups and ties shall not be less than that set forth in Table 21-I.

UBC Section 2108.2.2.4 (Strength Design)

2108.2.2.4 Standard hooks. A standard hook shall be one of the following:

1. A 180-degree turn plus an extension of at least four bar diameters, but not less than $2^1/_2$ inches (63 mm) at the free end of the bar.

2. A 135-degree turn plus an extension of at least six bar diameters at the free end of the bar.

3. A 90-degree turn plus an extension of at least 12 bar diameters at the free end of the bar.

MSJC Table 1.12.6.1, Minimum diameters of bend

Bar size and type	Minimum diameter
No. 3 through No. 7 (M #10 through # 22) Grade 40 (Grade 300)	5 bar diameters
No. 3 through No. 8 (M #10 through #25) Grade 50 or 60 (Grade 350 or 420)	6 bar diameters
No. 9, No. 110, and No. 11 (M #29, #32, and #36) Grade 50 or 60 (Grade 350 or 420)	8 bar diameters

IBC Table 2108.9.2.9, Minimum diameters of bend

BAR SIZE	GRADE	MINIMUM BEND
No. 3 thru No. 7	40	5 bar diameter
No.3 thru No. 8	50 or 60	6 bar diameter
No. 9	50 or 60	8 bar diameter

UBC Table 21-G-Minimum diameters of bend

BAR SIZE	MINIMUM DIAMETER
No. 3 through No. 8	6 bar diameters
No. 9 through No. 11	8 bar diameters

Table 5-I *Standard Hook and Bend*   (*UBC*)

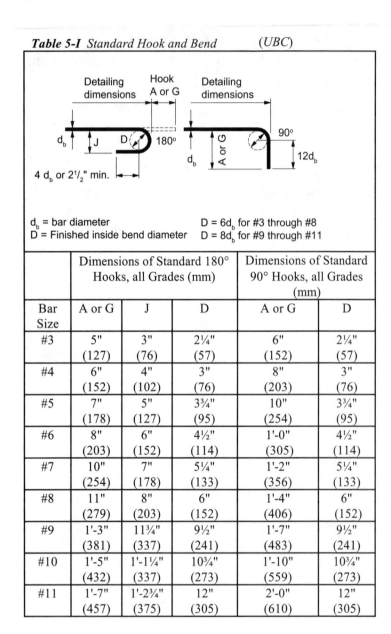

d_b = bar diameter   D = 6d_b for #3 through #8
D = Finished inside bend diameter   D = 8d_b for #9 through #11

Bar Size	Dimensions of Standard 180° Hooks, all Grades (mm)			Dimensions of Standard 90° Hooks, all Grades (mm)	
	A or G	J	D	A or G	D
#3	5" (127)	3" (76)	2¼" (57)	6" (152)	2¼" (57)
#4	6" (152)	4" (102)	3" (76)	8" (203)	3" (76)
#5	7" (178)	5" (127)	3¾" (95)	10" (254)	3¾" (95)
#6	8" (203)	6" (152)	4½" (114)	1'-0" (305)	4½" (114)
#7	10" (254)	7" (178)	5¼" (133)	1'-2" (356)	5¼" (133)
#8	11" (279)	8" (203)	6" (152)	1'-4" (406)	6" (152)
#9	1'-3" (381)	11¾" (337)	9½" (241)	1'-7" (483)	9½" (241)
#10	1'-5" (432)	1'-1¼" (337)	10¾" (273)	1'-10" (559)	10¾" (273)
#11	1'-7" (457)	1'-2¾" (375)	12" (305)	2'-0" (610)	12" (305)

5.10   ANCHORAGE OF SHEAR REINFORCING STEEL

Reinforcing steel to resist shear loads must be anchored according to the model building codes. Refer to Figure 5.15.

MSJC Code Section 1.13.6.4 (Seismic Category D)
Shear reinforcement shall be anchored around vertical reinforcing bars with a standard hook.

IBC Code Section 2106.5.3.1 (Seismic Category D)
2106.5.3.1 Shear wall reinforcement requirements. Shear walls shall be reinforced in accordance with Section 2106.5.2 and the maximum spacing of vertical and horizontal reinforcement shall be the smaller of one-third the length of the shear wall, one-third the height of the shear wall, or 48 inches (1219 mm). The minimum cross-sectional area of vertical reinforcement shall be one-third of the required shear reinforcement. Shear reinforcement shall be anchored around vertical reinforcing bars with a standard hook.

UBC Section 2106.1.12.4.2.1 (Seismic Zones 3 & 4)
Reinforcement required to resist in-plane shear shall be terminated with a standard hook as defined in Section 2107.2.2.5 or with an extension of proper embedment length beyond the reinforcement at the end of the wall section. The hook or extension may be turned up, down or horizontally. Provisions shall be made not to obstruct grout placement. Wall reinforcement terminating in columns or beams shall be fully anchored into these elements.

UBC Section 2106.3.5

2106.3.5 Anchorage of shear reinforcement. Single, separate bars used as shear reinforcement shall be anchored at each end by one of the following methods:

1. Hooking tightly around the longitudinal reinforcement through 180 degrees.

2. Embedment above or below the mid-depth of the beam on the compression side a distance sufficient to develop the stress in the bar for plain or deformed bars.

3. By a standard hook, as defined in Section 2107.2.2.5, considered as developing 7,500 psi (52 MPa), plus embedment sufficient to develop the remainder of the stress to which the bar is subjected. The effective embedment length shall not be assumed to exceed the distance between the mid-depth of the beam and the tangent of the hook.

The ends of bars forming a single U or multiple U stirrup shall be anchored by one of the methods set forth in Items 1 through 3 above or shall be bent through an angle of at least 90 degrees tightly around a longitudinal reinforcing bar not less in diameter than the stirrup bar, and shall project beyond the bend at least 12 stirrup diameters.

The loops or closed ends of simple U or multiple U stirrups shall be anchored by bending around the longitudinal reinforcement through an angle of at least 90 degrees and project beyond the end of the bend at least 12 stirrup diameters.

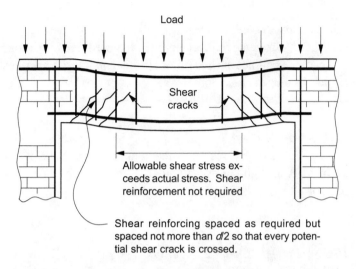

Load

Shear cracks

Allowable shear stress exceeds actual stress. Shear reinforcement not required

Shear reinforcing spaced as required but spaced not more than $d/2$ so that every potential shear crack is crossed.

Figure 5.15 Example of shear reinforcement in beams, and possible crack patterns from excessive loads.

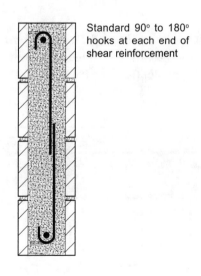

Standard 90° to 180° hooks at each end of shear reinforcement

Figure 5.16 Shear steel for beams.

191

IBC Section 2108.9.3.6 (Strength Design)
1. Where transverse reinforcement is required, the maximum spacing shall not exceed one-half the depth of the member nor 48 inches (1219 mm).

UBC Section 2108.2.3.7 (Strength Design)
1. Where transverse reinforcement is required, the maximum spacing shall not exceed one half the depth of the member nor 48 inches (1219 mm).

IBC Section 2108.9.3.9.2 (Strength Design)
2108.9.3.9.2 Longitudinal reinforcement. The variation in the longitudinal reinforcing bars shall not be greater than one bar size. Not more than two bars sizes shall be used in a beam.

UBC Section 2108.2.3.10.2 (Strength Design)
1. The variation in the longitudinal reinforcing bars shall not be greater than one bar size. Not more than two bars sizes shall be used in a beam.

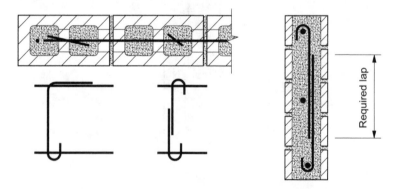

Figure 5.17 Details of beam shear reinforcement.

IBC Section 2106.5.2 (Seismic Category D)

2106.5.2 Minimum reinforcement requirements for masonry walls. Masonry walls other than those covered by Section 2106.4.1 shall be reinforced in both the vertical and horizontal direction. The sum of the cross-sectional area of horizontal and vertical reinforcement shall be at least 0.002 times the gross cross-sectional area of the wall, and the minimum cross-sectional area in each direction shall be not less than 0.0007 times the gross cross-sectional area of the wall. Reinforcement shall be uniformly distributed. The maximum spacing of reinforcement shall be 48 inches (1219 mm) except for stack bond masonry. Wythes of stack bond masonry shall be constructed of fully grouted hollow open-end units, fully grouted hollow units laid with full head joints or solid units. Maximum spacing of reinforcement for walls with stack bond masonry shall be 24 inches (610 mm).

MSJC Code Section 1.13.6.3 (Seismic Category D)

1.13.6.3 *Minimum reinforcement requirements for masonry walls* - Masonry walls other than those covered by Section 1.13.5.2.3 shall be reinforced in both the vertical and horizontal direction. The sum of the cross-sectional area of horizontal and vertical reinforcement shall be at least 0.002 times the gross cross-sectional area of the wall, and the minimum cross-sectional area in each direction shall be not less than 0.0007 times the gross cross-sectional area of the wall, using specified dimensions. Reinforcement shall be uniformly distributed. The maximum spacing of reinforcement shall be 48 in. (1219 mm) except for stack bond masonry. Wythes of stack bond masonry shall be constructed of fully grouted hollow open-end units, fully grouted hollow units laid with full head joints or solid units. Maximum spacing of reinforcement for wall with stack bond masonry shall be 24 in. (610 mm).

> **UBC Section 2106.1.12.4.2.1 (Seismic Zones 3 & 4)**
> 2.1 **Reinforcement.** The portion of the reinforcement required to resist shear shall be uniformly distributed and shall be joint reinforcement, deformed bars or a combination thereof. The spacing of reinforcement in each direction shall not exceed one half the length of the element, nor one half the height of the element, nor 48 inches (1219 mm).

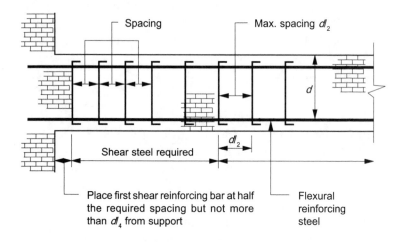

Figure 5.18 Vertical web or shear reinforcing steel arrangement for beams.

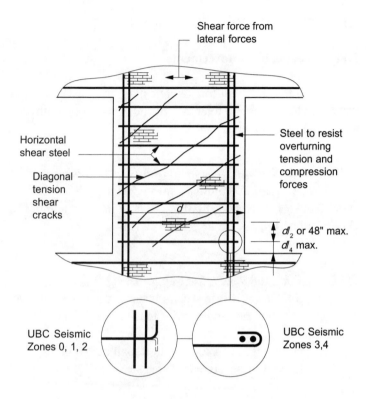

Figure 5.19 Shear wall reinforced with horizontal steel to resist lateral shear forces induced by wind or seismic forces.

5.11   COLUMN REINFORCEMENT

5.11.1   Vertical Reinforcement

Steel reinforcement for concrete masonry must conform to the same clearances and tolerances as other masonry, with some additional requirements.

MSJC Code Section 2.1.4.4 (Working Stress Design)
2.1.4.4 Vertical column reinforcement shall not be less than $0.0025A_n$ nor exceed $0.04A_n$. The minimum number of bars shall be four.

IBC Section 2108.9.3.11.2 (Strength Design)
2108.9.3.11.2 Longitudinal reinforcement. Longitudinal reinforcement shall be minimum of four bars, one in each corner of the column.
 1. Maximum reinforcement area shall be $0.03A_e$.
 2. Minimum reinforcement area shall be $0.005A_e$.

UBC Section 2107.2.13.1 (Working Stress Design)
2107.2.13.1   Vertical reinforcement. The area of vertical reinforcement shall not be less than $0.005A_e$ and not more than $0.04A_e$. At least four No. 3 bars shall be provided. The minimum clear distance between parallel bars in columns shall be two and one half times the bar diameter.

UBC Section 2108.2.3.12.2 (Strength Design)
2108.2.3.12.2   Longitudinal reinforcement. Longitudinal reinforcement shall be a minimum of four bars, one in each corner of the column.
 1. Maximum reinforcement area shall be $0.03A_e$.
 2. Minimum reinforcement area shall be $0.005A_e$.

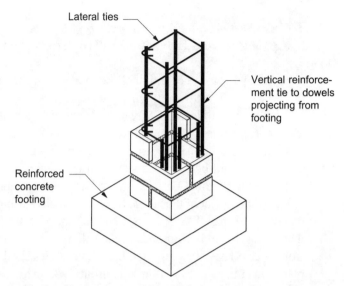

Figure 5.20 Construction of reinforced concrete masonry column.

5.11.2 Reinforcing Tie Details

A. Lateral Tie Details are shown in Figure 5.21.

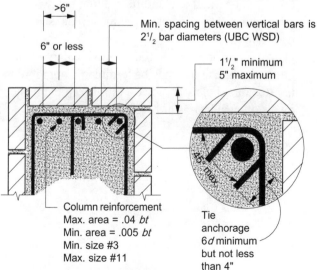

Figure 5.21 Tie details (UBC).

MSJC Code, Section 2.1.4.6 (Working Stress Design)

2.1.4.6 *Lateral ties* - Lateral ties shall conform to the following:

(a) Longitudinal reinforcement shall be enclosed by lateral ties at least $^1/_4$ in. (6.4 mm) in diameter.

(b) Vertical spacing of lateral ties shall not exceed 16 longitudinal bar diameters, 48 lateral tie bar or wire diameters, or least cross-sectional dimension of the member.

(c) Lateral ties shall be arranged such that every corner and alternate longitudinal bar shall have lateral support provided by the corner of the lateral tie with an included angle of not more than 135 degrees. No bar shall be farther than 6 in. (152 mm) clear on each side along the lateral tie from such a laterally supported bar. Lateral ties shall be placed in either a mortar joint or in grout. Where longitudinal bars are located around the perimeter of a circle, a complete circular tie is permitted. Lap length for circular ties shall be 48 tie diameters.

(d) Lateral ties shall be located vertically not more than one-half lateral tie spacing above the top of footing or slab in any story, and shall be spaced as provided herein to not more than one-half a lateral tie spacing below the lowest horizontal reinforcement in beam, girder, slab, or drop panel above.

(e) Where beams or brackets frame into a column from four directions, lateral ties may be terminated not more than 3 in. (76.2 mm) below the lowest reinforcement in the shallowest of such beams or brackets.

UBC Section 2106.3.6

2106.3.6 Lateral ties. All longitudinal bars for columns shall be enclosed by lateral ties. Lateral support shall be provided to the longitudinal bars by the corner of a complete tie having an included angle of not more tha 135 degrees or by a standard hook at the end of a tie. The corner bars shall have such support provided by a complete tie enclosing the longitudinal bars. Alternate longitudinal bars shall have such lateral support provided by ties and no bar shall be farther than 6 inches (152 mm) from such laterally supported bar.

Lateral ties and longitudinal bars shall be placed not less than $1^1/_2$ inches (38 mm) and not more than 5 inches (127 mm) from the surface of the column. Lateral ties may be placed against the longitudinal bars or placed in the horizontal bed joints where the requirements of Section 2106.1.8 are met. Spacing of ties shall not exceed 16 longitudinal bar diameters, 48 tie diameters or the least dimension of the column but no more than 18 inches (457 mm).

Ties shall be at least $1/_4$ inch (6.4 mm) in diameter for No. 7 or smaller longitudinal bars and at least No. 3 for longitudinal bars larger than No. 7. Ties smaller than No. 3 may be used for longitudinal bars larger than No. 7, provided the total cross-sectional area of such smaller ties crossing a longitudinal plane is equal to that of the larger ties at their required spacing.

UBC Section 2107.2.13.1 (Working Stress Design)

2107.2.13.1 Vertical reinforcement. The area of vertical reinforcement shall not be less than $0.005 A_e$ and not more than $0.04 A_e$. At least four No. 3 bars shall be provided. The minimum clear distance between parallel bars in columns shall be two and one half times the bar diameter.

UBC Section 2108.2.2.2 (Strength Design)

In columns and piers, the clear distance between vertical reinforcing bars shall not be less than one and one-half times the nominal bar diameter, nor less than $1^1/_2$ inches (38 mm).

IBC Section 2108.9.2.4 (Strength Design)

2108.9.2.4 Clear distance between vertical bars in columns and piers. In columns and piers, the clear distance between vertical reinforcing bars shall not be less than one and one-half times the nominal bar diameter, nor less than $1^1/_2$ inches (38 mm).

MSJC Code, Section 1.13.6.7 (Seismic Category D)

1.13.6.7 *Lateral tie anchorage* - Standard hooks for lateral tie anchorage shall be either a 135 degree standard hook or a 180 degree standard hook.

IBC Section 2106.5.6 (Seismic Category D)

2106.5.6 Lateral tie anchorage. Standard hooks for lateral tie anchorage shall be either a 135-degree (2.36 rad) standard hook or a 180-degree (3.14 rad) standard hook).

UBC Section 2106.1.12.4.1 (Seismic Zones 3 & 4)

Column ties shall terminate with a minimum 135-degree hook with extensions not less than six bar diameters or 4 inches (102 mm). Such extensions shall engage the longitudinal column reinforcement and project into the interior of the column. Hooks shall comply with Section 2107.2.2.5, Item 3.

> **EXCEPTION:** Where ties are placed in horizontal bed joints, hooks shall consist of a 90-degree bend having an inside radius of not less than four tie diameters plus an extension of 32 tie diameters.

Table 5-J *Tie Spacing - 16 Bar Diameters*

Compression Steel Bar No.	Maximum Tie Spacing
#3	6" (152 mm)
#4	8" (203 mm)
#5	10" (254 mm)
#6	12" (305 mm)
#7	14" (356 mm)
#8	16" (406 mm)
#9	18" (457 mm)
#10	20" (508 mm)
#11	22" (559 mm)

Maximum tie spacing may not exceed 16 bar diameters, 48 tie diameters nor the least dimension column. Coordinate this table with Table 5-I. UBC contains an additional limitation of 18 inches (457 mm).

Table 5-K *Tie Spacing - 48 Tie Diameters[1]*

Tie Steel Size	Maximum Tie Spacing
$^1/_4$"	12" (305 mm)
#3	18" (457 mm)
#4	24" (610 mm)
#5	30" (762 mm)

[1] Maximum tie spacing may not exceed 16 longitudinal bar diameters, 48 tie diameters, or the least column dimensions. Coordinate this with Table 5-H. UBC contains an additional limitation of 18 inches (457 mm).

NOTE: #2 ($^1/_4$") (6 mm) ties at 8" (203 mm) spacing is equivalent to #3 ($^3/_8$") (10 mm) ties at 16" (406 mm) spacing.

In addition to the column tie spacing requirements set forth above, there are more stringent spacing requirements for columns in moderate to high seismic exposure areas.

IBC Section 2106.5.4 (Seismic Category D)
2106.5.4 Minimum reinforcement for masonry columns.
Lateral ties in masonry columns shall be spaced not more than 8 inches (203 mm) on center and shall be at least $^3/_8$ inch (9.5 mm) diameter. Lateral ties shall be embedded in grout.

MSJC Code Section 1.13.6.5 (Seismic Category D)
1.13.6.5 *Minimum reinforcement for masonry columns* - Lateral ties in masonry columns shall be spaced not more than 8 in. (203 mm) on center and shall be at least $^3/_8$ in. (9.5 mm) diameter. Lateral ties shall be embedded in grout.

UBC Section 2106.1.12.4.1 (Seismic Zones 3 & 4)
1. Column reinforcement ties. In columns that are stressed by tensile or compressive axial overturning forces from seismic loading, the spacing of column ties shall not exceed 8 inches (203 mm) for the full height of such columns. In all other columns, ties shall be spaced a maximum of 8 inches (203 mm) in the tops and bottoms of the columns for a distance of one sixth of the clear column height, 18 inches (457 mm), or the maximum column cross-sectional dimension, whichever is greater. Tie spacing for the remaining column height shall not exceed the lessor of 16 bar diameters, 48 tie diameters, the least column cross-sectional dimension, or 18 inches (457 mm).

Model building codes are also clear on the issue of grouting columns.

IBC Section 2107.2.2.4 (Working Stress Design)
4. Columns shall be grouted solid.

IBC Section 2108.9.3.11.4 (Strength Design)
2108.9.3.11.4 Construction. Columns shall be solid grouted.

MSJC Specification Section 3.4.C.1
1. Completely embed reinforcing bars in grout in accordance with Article 3.5.

UBC Section 2104.6.1
All cells and spaces containing reinforcement shall be filled with grout.

B.   Lateral Tie Spacing, SDC A, B, C; SZ 0, 1, 2.

Lateral column ties around vertical bars for columns in Seismic Design Categories A, B, and C and in Seismic Zone 0, 1 and 2 are illustrated in Figure 5.22.

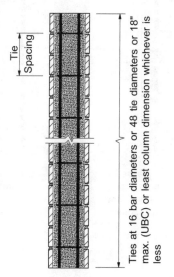

Column not stressed by overturning forces
Figure 5.22 Tie spacing for columns in Seismic Design Categories A, B, and C, and in Seismic Zones 0, 1 and 2.

C.   Lateral Tie Spacing, SDC D & E, SZ 3 & 4.

The Model Building Codes specify additional requirements for moderate to high seismic exposure as shown in Figure 5.23.

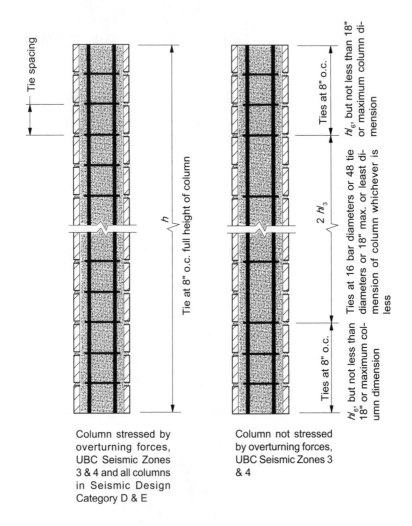

Column stressed by overturning forces, UBC Seismic Zones 3 & 4 and all columns in Seismic Design Category D & E

Column not stressed by overturning forces, UBC Seismic Zones 3 & 4

Figure 5.23 Tie spacing in columns with moderate to high seismic exposure.

D. **Layout of Ties** in concrete masonry columns is shown in Figure 5.24. Unexposed webs and face shells should be removed for additional grout continuity.

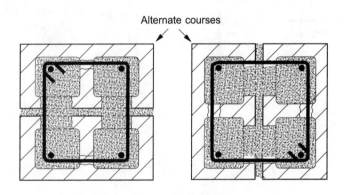

Built with standard two
core masonry units

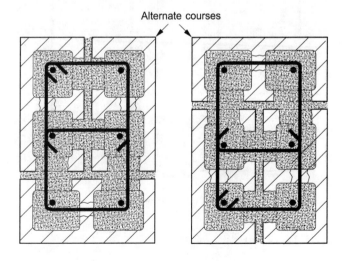

Figure 5.24 Layout of concrete masonry units for column with tie details.

Alternate courses

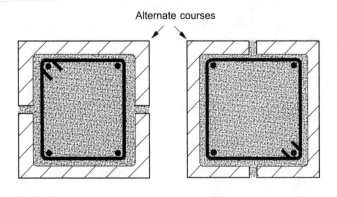

Alternate courses

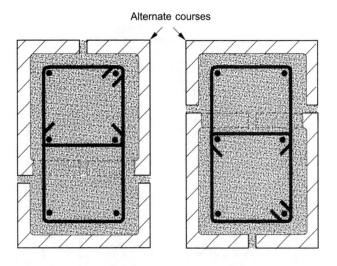

Built with pilaster units

Figure 5.24 (Cont'd).

5.11.3 Projecting Wall Columns or Pilasters

Girders framing into a wall that are heavily loaded may require substantial base plates and columns to carry the load. Columns may be built projecting out from the wall to provide a convenient seat or surface to support the girders.

Projecting pilasters also serve to stiffen the wall and are supported at the top and bottom. The wall between the pilasters can be designed to span horizontally. By this technique, very high walls can be built using nominal thicknesses. See Figure 5.25 and 5.26.

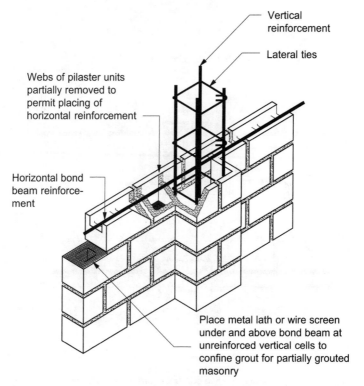

Figure 5.25 Construction of reinforced concrete masonry pilaster with continuous bond beam.

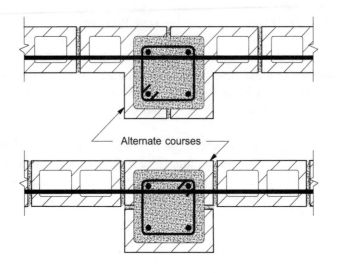

Built with pilaster units

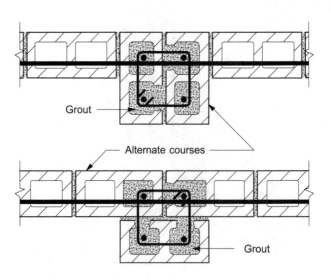

Built with two core standard masonry units

Figure 5.26 Projecting wall column masonry unit details.

5.11.4   Flush Wall Columns, Pilasters and Compression Steel at End of Walls

If engineering design permits, it is to the economic benefit of the owner and to the construction benefit of the contractor to build columns that are contained within the wall and are flush with the wall. The wall contained columns permit faster construction, cause no projections from the wall, and do not require special units. The reinforcing steel must be tied in accordance with the code requirements (refer to Figure 5.27).

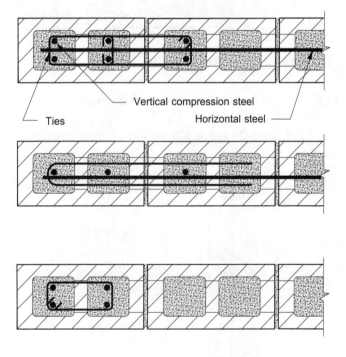

Figure 5.27 Ties around column bars and compression bars at end of wall.

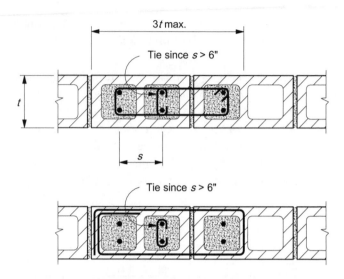

Figure 5.28 Flush wall concrete masonry wall.

5.11.5   Ties on Compression Steel in Beams

See Figure 5.29 for an illustration of ties for compression steel in beams.

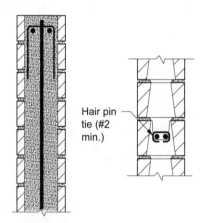

Figure 5.29 Ties for compression steel in beams.

5.11.6 Anchor Bolts

5.11.6.1 Anchor Bolt Clearance. It is necessary to have clearance around anchor bolts so that the grout can fully surround the bolt. Certain Code provisions require 1 inch (25 mm) of grout between anchor bolts and the masonry. It should be noted that this requirement ensures adequate grout around the bolt and the exposed face shell of the masonry unit and that it was not intended to apply behind the bolt head. Instead at least $\frac{1}{4}$ inch (6 mm) minimum clearance, $\frac{1}{2}$ inch (13 mm) preferred, should be provided between the bolt and masonry units behind. See Figure 5-32.

IBC Section 2108.6 (Strength Design)

2108.6 Headed and bent-bar anchor bolts. Embedded bolts shall be grouted in place with at least 1 inch (25 mm) of grout between the bolt and the masonry, except that $\frac{1}{4}$ inch (6.4 mm) bolts are permitted be placed in bed joints which are at least $\frac{1}{2}$ inch (12.7 mm) in thickness.

UBC Section 2106.2.14.1

The effective embedment depth l_b for plate or headed anchor bolts shall be the length of embedment measured perpendicular from the surface of the masonry to the bearing surface of the plate or head of the anchorage, and l_b for bent bar anchors shall be the length of embedment measured perpendicular from the surface of the masonry to the bearing surface of the bent end minus one anchor bolt diameter. All bolts shall be grouted in place with at least 1 inch (25 mm) of grout between the bolt and the masonry, except that $\frac{1}{4}$-inch-diameter (6.4 mm) bolts may be placed in bed joints which are least $\frac{1}{2}$ inch (12.7 mm) in thickness.

5.11.6.2 Anchor Bolt Ties. In order that lateral forces on anchor bolts be transferred to vertical steel, ties may be required around the anchor bolts and steel.

Certain IBC and UBC provisions allow smaller ($^1/_4$ inch) anchor bolts to be placed in mortar joints at least $^1/_2$ inch thickness.

IBC Section 2106.4.2.2 (Seismic Category C)

2106.4.2.2 Connections to masonry columns. Connectors shall be provided to transfer forces between masonry columns and horizontal elements in accordance with the requirements of ACI 530/ASCE 5/TMS 402, Section 2.1.6. Where anchor bolts are used to connect horizontal elements to the tops of columns, anchor bolts shall be placed within lateral ties. Lateral ties shall enclose both the vertical bars in the column and the anchor bolts. There shall be a minimum of two No. 4 lateral ties provided in the top 5 inches (127 mm) of the column.

MSJC Code Section 1.13.5.3.2 (Seismic Category C)

1.13.5.3.2 *Connections to masonry columns* - Connectors shall be provided to transfer forces between masonry columns and horizontal elements in accordance with the requirements of Section 2.1.6. Where anchor bolts are used to connect horizontal elements to the tops of columns, anchor bolts shall be placed within lateral ties. Lateral ties shall enclose both the vertical bars in the column and the anchor bolts. There shall be a minimum of two No. 4 (M #13) lateral ties provided in the top 5 in. (127 mm) of the column.

UBC Section 2106.3.7

2106.3.7 Column anchor bolt ties. Additional ties shall be provided around anchor bolts which are set in the top of columns. Such ties engage at least four bolts or, alternately, at least four vertical column bars or a combination of bolts and bars totaling at least four. Such ties shall be located within the top 5 inches (127 mm) of the column and shall provide a total of 0.4 square inch (260 mm²) or more in cross-sectional area. The uppermost tie shall be within 2 inches (51 mm) of the top of the column.

5.11.6.3 Anchor Bolts in Walls. Anchor bolts must be placed with adequate edge distance and spacing to ensure adequate performance. Refer to Table 5-L and Figure 5.31.

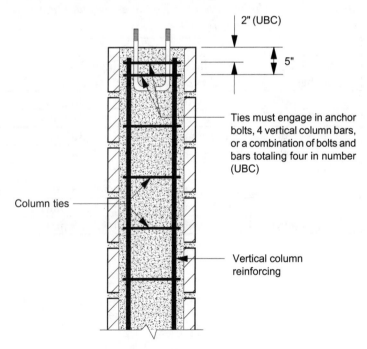

Figure 5.30 Ties of anchor bars on top of columns.

UBC Section 2106.2.14.2

2106.2.14.2 Minimum edge distance. The minimum anchor bolt edge distance l_{be} measured from the edge of the masonry parallel with the anchor bolt to the surface of the anchor bolt shall be $1^1/_2$ inches (38 mm).

UBC Section 2106.2.14.4

2106.2.14.4 Minimum spacing between bolts. The minimum center-to-center distance between anchor bolts shall be four bolt diameters

Table 5-L   *Minimum Anchor Bolt Spacing and Edge Distance (UBC)*

Bolt Dia. (inches)	Minimum	
	Spacing (inches)	Edge Distance (inches)
$^1/_4$" (6 mm)	1" (25 mm)	$1^1/_2$" (38 mm)
$^3/_8$" (10 mm)	$1^1/_2$" (38 mm)	$1^1/_2$" (38 mm)
$^1/_2$" (13 mm)	2" (51 mm)	$1^1/_2$" (38 mm)
$^5/_8$" (16 mm)	$2^1/_2$" (64 mm)	$1^1/_2$" (38 mm)
$^3/_4$" (19 mm)	3" (76 mm)	$1^1/_2$" (38 mm)
$^7/_8$" (22 mm)	$3^1/_2$" (89 mm)	$1^1/_2$" (38 mm)
1" (25 mm)	4" (102 mm)	$1^1/_2$" (38 mm)
$1^1/_8$" (29 mm)	$4^1/_2$" (114 mm)	$1^1/_2$" (38 mm)

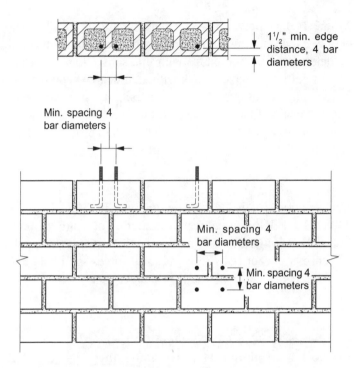

Figure 5.31 Anchor bolt spacing and edge distance (UBC).

5.11.6.4 Embedment of Anchor Bolts.

MSJC Specification Section 3.2E

3.2E. *Reinforcement* - Place reinforcement and ties in grout spaces prior to grouting.

UBC Section 2104.6.2

2104.6.2 Construction requirements. Reinforcement shall be placed prior to grouting. Bolts shall be accurately set with templates or by approved equivalent means and held in place to prevent dislocation during grouting

UBC Section 2106.2.14.1

2106.2.14.1 General. Placement requirements for plate anchor bolts, headed anchor bolts and bent bar anchor bolts shall be determined in accordance with this subsection. Bent bar anchor bolts shall have a hook with a 90-degree bend with an inside diameter of three bolt diameters, plus an extension of one and one half bolt diameters at the free end. Plate anchor bolts shall have a plate welded to the shank to provide anchorage equivalent to headed anchor bolts.

IBC Section 2108.6.2.2.1 (Strength Design)

2108.6.2.2.1 Minimum effective embedment length of bent-bar anchor bolts. The minimum effective embedment length of bent-bar anchor bolts resisting axial forces shall be 4 bolt diameters or 2 inches (51 mm), whichever is greater.

IBC Section 2108.6.3.2 (Strength Design)

2108.6.3.2 Minimum effective embedment length. The minimum effective embedment length of headed or bent-bar anchor bolts resisting shear forces shall be 4 bolt diameters or 2 inches (51 mm), whichever is greater.

MSJC Code Section 2.1.2.2.1 (Working Stress Design)

2.1.2.2.1 The minimum effective embedment length shall be 4 bolt diameters, but not less than 2 in. (50.8 mm)

UBC Section 2106.2.14.3

2106.2.14.3 Minimum embedment depth. The minimum embedment depth of anchor bolts l_b shall be four bolt diameters but not less than 2 inches (51 mm).

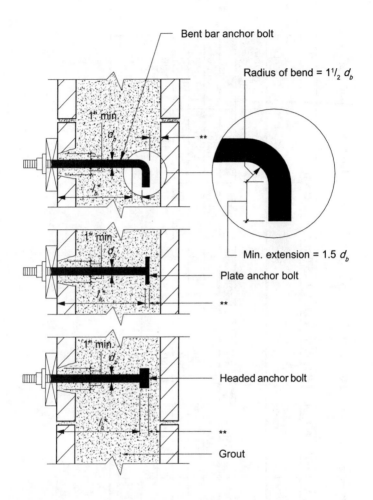

*Minimum embedment length l_b = 4d_b but l_b may not be less than 2" (51 mm).

* $1/_4$" for fine grout
* $1/_2$" for coarse (pea gravel) grout

Figure 5.32 Embedment of plate or headed anchor bolts and bent bar anchor bolts.

217

Table 5-M *Allowable Tension, B_t for Embedded Anchor Bolts for Clay and Concrete Masonry, pounds[1, 2, 3, 4]*

f'_m (psi) x 6.89 for kPa	EMBEDMENT LENGTH, l_b, or EDGE DISTANCE, l_{be} (inches)						
	2	3	4	5	6	8	10
						x 25.4 for mm x 4.45 for N	
1,500	240	550	970	1,520	2,190	3,890	6,080
1,800	270	600	1,070	1,670	2,400	4,260	6,660
2,000	280	630	1,120	1,760	2,520	4,500	7,020
2,500	310	710	1,260	1,960	2,830	5,030	7,850
3,000	340	770	1,380	2,150	3,100	5,510	8,600
4,000	400	890	1,590	2,480	3,580	6,360	9,930
5,000	440	1,000	1,780	2,780	4,000	7,110	11,100
6,000	480	1,090	1,950	3,040	4,380	7,790	12,200

[1] The allowable tension values in Table M are based on compressive strength of masonry assemblages. Where yield strength of anchor bolt steel governs, the allowable tension in pounds is given in Table N.
[2] Values are for bolts of a least A 307 quality. Bolts shall be those specified in ASTM A 307.
[3] Values shown are for work with or without special inspection.
[4] UBC Table 21-E-1.

Table 5-N *Allowable Tension B₁ for Embedded Anchor Bolts for Clay and Concrete Masonry, pounds* [1,2,3]

BENT BAR ANCHOR BOLT DIAMETER (inches) x 25.4 for mm							
$^1/_4$	$^3/_8$	$^1/_2$	$^5/_8$	$^3/_4$	$^7/_8$	1	$1^1/_8$
				x 4.45 for N			
350	790	1,410	2,210	3,180	4,330	5,650	7,160

[1] Values are for bolts of at least A 370 quality. Bolts shall be those specified in ASTM A 307.
[2] Values shown are for work with or without special inspection.
[3] UBC Table 21-E-2.

Table 5-O *Allowable Shear, B_v for Embedded Anchor Bolts for Clay and Concrete Masonry, pounds[1,2,3]*

$f'm$ (psi)	BENT BAR ANCHOR BOLT DIAMETER (inches) x 25.4 for mm						
	3/8	1/2	5/8	3/4	7/8	1	1 1/8
			x 4.45 for N				
1,500	480	850	1,330	1,780	1,920	2,050	2,170
1,800	480	850	1,330	1,860	2,010	2,150	2,280
2,000	480	850	1,330	1,900	2,060	2,200	2,340
2,500	480	850	1,330	1,900	2,180	2,330	2,470
3,000	480	850	1,330	1,900	2,280	2,440	2,590
4,000	480	850	1,330	1,900	2,450	2,620	2,780
5,000	480	850	1,330	1,900	2,590	2,770	2,940
6,000	480	850	1,330	1,900	2,600	2,900	3,080

[1] Values are for bolts of at least A 307 quality. Bolts shall be those specified in ASTM A 307.
[2] Vlaues shown are for work with or without special inspection.
[3] UBC Table 21-E-3.

Grouting of Concrete Masonry Walls

6.1   GENERAL

Model building codes state the allowable grouting height limitations as contained in Tables.

The most important function of masonry grout is to tie the system together to act as a single structural element. This is emphasized in the UBC language below.

MSJC Specification Section 3.5 B
3.5 B. *Confinement* - Confine grout to the areas indicated on the Project Drawings. Use material to confine grout that permits bond between masonry units and mortar.

UBC Section 2104.6.1
2104.6.1 General conditions. Grouted masonry shall be constructed in such a manner that all elements of the masonry act together as a structural element.

All cells and spaces containing reinforcement shall be filled with grout.

6.2　　MORTAR PROTRUSIONS

Mortar projections should not obstruct the placement and consolidation of grout. Take reasonable care either to prevent mortar projections as the masonry units are placed or the projections must be removed while the mortar is plastic or broken off when hard and removed through the cleanout openings.

> **MSJC Specification Section 3.3 B. 1. c**
>
> c. Remove masonry protrusions extending $^1/_2$ in. (12.7 mm) or more into cells or cavities to be grouted.

> **UBC Section 2104.6.1**
>
> Prior to grouting, the grout space shall be clean so that all spaces to be filled with grout do not contain mortar projections greater than $^1/_2$ inch (12.7 mm), mortar droppings or other foreign material. Grout shall be placed so that all spaces designated to be grouted shall be filled with grout and the grout shall be confined to those specific spaces.

Clean means reasonably clean, not surgically clean. A demonstration for the California Division of the State Architect showed that a small amount of mortar droppings had virtually no detrimental structural impact on the masonry system.

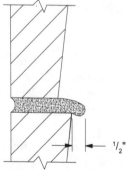

Figure 6.1　Mortar projection into grout space.

6.3   GROUT SLUMP

Grout must be plastic with a slump fluidity of 8 inches (178 mm) to 11 inches (279 mm) when tested in accordance with ASTM C 143 and be cohesive to avoid segregation of materials, particularly pea gravel. See Figure 6.2.

MSJC Specification 2.6 B.

2.6 B. *Grout*
1. Unless otherwise required, proportion and mix grout in accordance with the requirements os ASTM C 476.
2. Unless otherwise required, mix grout to a consistency that has a slump between 8 and 11 in. (203 and 279 mm). When Tests are required, test grout slump in accordance with ASTM C 143.

UBC Section 2104.6.1

Grout materials and water content shall be controlled to provide adequate fluidity for placement without segregation to the constituents, and shall be mixed thoroughly.

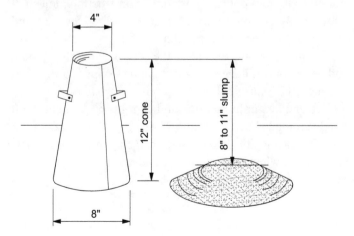

Figure 6.2 Slump of grout 8" (203 mm) to 11" (279 mm).

6.4   GROUTING LIMITATIONS

MSJC Specification Section 3.5

3.5 - Grout placement

3.5 A. *Placing time* - Place grout within $1\frac{1}{2}$ hr from introducing water in the mixture and prior to initial set.

3.5 B. *Confinement* - Confine grout to the areas indicated on the Project Drawings. Use material to confine grout that permits bond between masonry units and mortar.

3.5 C. *Grout pour height* - Do not exceed the maximum grout pour height given in Table 7.

3.5 D. *Grout lift height* - Place grout in lifts not exceeding 5 ft (1.52 m).

UBC Section 2104.6.1

The grouting of any section of wall shall be completed in one day with no interruptions greater than one hour.

Between grout pours, a horizontal construction joint shall be formed by stopping all wythes at the same elevation and with the grout stopping a minimum of $1\frac{1}{2}$ inches (38 mm) below a mortar joint, except at the top of the wall. Where bond beams occur, the grout pour shall be stopped a minimum of $\frac{1}{2}$ inch (12.7 mm) below the top of the masonry.

Size and height limitations of the grout space or cell shall not be less than shown in Table 21-C. Higher grout pours or smaller cavity widths or cell size than shown in Table 21-C may be used when approved, if it is demonstrated that grout spaces will be properly filled.

UBC Section 2104.2.7

7. Mortar or grout mixed at the jobsite shall be mixed for a period of time not less than three minutes or more than 10 minutes in a mechanical mixer with the amount of water required to provide the desired workability. Hand mixing of small amounts of mortar is permitted. Mortar may be retempered. Mortar or grout which has hardened or stiffened due to hydration of the cement shall not be used. In no case shall mortar be used two and one-half hours, nor grout used one and one-half hours after the initial mixing water has been added to the dry ingredients at the jobsite.

EXCEPTION: Dry mixes for mortar and grout which are blended in the factory and mixed at the jobsite shall be mixed in mechanical mixers until workable, but not to exceed 10 minutes.

The Uniform Building Code Commentary explains the application of the one and one-half hour time limitation for masonry grout. Specifically, the UBC Code language is not intended to apply time limitations to ready mix grout. This approach is consistent with time limitations set forth for concrete in ASTM C 94 *Standard Specification for Ready-Mixed Concrete*, Section 11.7, which permits placing time greater than $1^1/_2$ hours, providing the slump of the concrete is within tolerance.

TABLE 6-1A - UBC GROUTING LIMITATIONS[5]

Grout Type[1]	Grout Pour Maximum Height (Feet)[1]	Minimum Dimensions of the Total Clear Areas Within Grout Spaces and Cells[2,3,4] (in)	
		x 25.4 for mm	
	x 304.8 for mm	Multiwythe Masonry	Hollow-unit Masonry
Fine	1	$^3/_4$	$1^1/_2$ x 2
Fine	5	$1^1/_2$	$1^1/_2$ x 2
Fine	8	$1^1/_2$	$1^1/_2$ x 3
Fine	12	$1^1/_2$	$1^3/_4$ x 3
Fine	24	2	3 x 3
Coarse	1	$1^1/_2$	$1^1/_2$ x 3
Coarse	5	2	$2^1/_2$ x 3
Coarse	8	2	3 x 3
Coarse	12	$2^1/_2$	3 x 3
Coarse	24	3	3 x 4

[1] Fine and coarse grout are defined in ASTM C 476. Grout shall attain a minimum compressive strength of 2000 psi (13.79 MPa) at 28 days.

[2] The actual grout space or grout cell dimension must be larger than the sum of the following items: (1) The required minimum dimensions of total clear areas in Table 1; (2) The width of any mortar projections within the space; and (3) The horizontal projections of the diameters of the horizontal reinforcing bars within a cross section of the grout space or cell.

[3] The minimum dimensions of the total clear areas shall be made up of one or more open areas, with at least one area being $^3/_4$ inch (19 mm) or greater in width.

[4] Area of vertical reinforcement shall not exceed 6 percent of the area of the grout space.

[5] UBC Table 21-C.

TABLE 6-1B - MSJC Grout Space Requirements[5]

Grout type[1]	Maximum grout pour height, ft (m)	Minimum width of grout space,[2,3] in. (mm)	Minimum grout space dimensions for grouting cells of hollow units,[3,4] in. x in. (mm x mm)
Fine	1 (0.30)	$^3/_4$ (19.1)	$1^1/_2$ x 2 (38.1 x 50.8)
Fine	5 (1.52)	2 (50.8)	2 x 3 (50.8 x 76.2)
Fine	12 (3.66)	$2^1/_2$ (63.5)	$2^1/_2$ x 3 (63.5 x 76.2)
Fine	24 (7.32)	3 (76.2)	3 x 3 (76.2 x 76.2)
Coarse	1 (0.30)	$1^1/_2$ (38.1)	$1^1/_2$ x 3 (38.1 x 76.2)
Coarse	5 (1.52)	2 (50.8)	$2^1/_2$ x 3 (63.5 x 76.2)
Coarse	12 (3.66)	$2^1/_2$ (63.5)	3 x 3 (76.2 x 76.2)
Coarse	24 (7.32)	3 (76.2)	3 x 4 (76.2 x 102)

[1] Fine and coarse grouts are defined in ASTM C 476. Grout shall attain a minimum compressive strength of 2000 psi (13.79 MPa) at 28 days.

[2] For grouting between masonry wythes.

[3] Grout space dimension is the clear dimension between any masonry protrusion and shall be increased by the diameters of the horizontal bars within the cross section of the grout space.

[4] Area of vertical reinforcement shall not exceed 6 percent of the area of the grout space.

[5] MSJC Code Table 1.15.2, MSJC Specification Table 7.

Section 2.11.2 of this handbook explains the types of grout, fine and coarse.

6.5.   LOW LIFT GROUTING

The grouting method commonly known as low lift grouting is performed in grout pours of five feet (1.5 m) or less in height.

The wall is constructed in five feet (1.5 m) increments. Prior to grouting, horizontal and vertical reinforcement, bolts and other embedded items are positioned. It is important that sufficient time is allowed for the mortar joints to set and be able to withstand the grout pressure. For hollow-unit concrete masonry it is common and successful practice to lay the masonry units one day and grout the wall the following morning.

Grout is poured into all reinforced cells and other designated cells, if required, to a height even or slightly above the last bed joint (mortared or top of wall increment). The water loss and consolidation will allow the grout to settle approximately $1^1/_2$ inches (38 mm) below the mortar joint forming a key between the grout and masonry units. For bond-beam units containing horizontal reinforcement, this key should be controlled to $^1/_2$ inch (13 mm) to allow for adequate coverage of the horizontal reinforcement. The top lift is poured so that the settled grout will be even with the top of the wall.

Vertical cells to be filled must align vertically to maintain a continuous unobstructed cell area not less than $1^1/_2$ inches x 2 inches (38 mm x 51 mm), or as dimensionally required by Table 6-1A or 6-1B. Horizontal beams to be grouted should be isolated horizontally with metal lath or special concrete block units to prevent the grout from flowing into cells that should be void. Paper should not be used for this purpose.

The principal advantage of the low-lift grouting method is that cleanouts or inspection openings are not required. The inspector can visually check the cells for proper alignment, check that the bottom of the cells are reasonably clean and free of excessive mortar protrusions and verify the reinforcing steel location, all before grouting the wall.

Between grout pours, a horizontal construction joint is formed by stopping all wythes at the same elevation and with the grout stopping a minimum of $1^1/_2$ inches (38 mm) below a mortar joint, except at the top of a wall. (Refer to Figure 6.3). Where bond beams occur, stop the grout pour a minimum of $^1/_2$ inch (13 mm) below the top of the masonry.

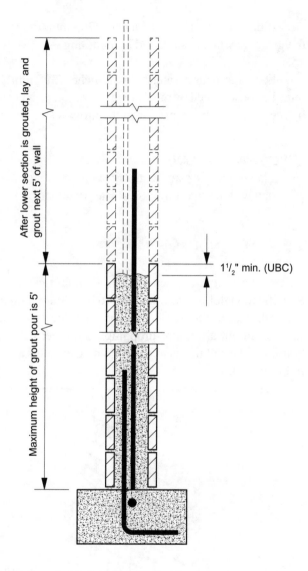

Delay approximately 3 to 5 minutes allowing the water to be absorbed by the masonry units, then consolidate the grout by mechanically vibrating.

Figure 6.3 Grouting without cleanouts, commonly called low-lift grouting.

If the grout pours are 12 inches (305 mm) or less in height, the grout may be consolidated by puddling.

For grout pour greater than 12 inches (305 mm), the grout must be consolidated by mechanical vibration and reconsolidated by mechanical vibration prior to the grout losing its plasticity.

UBC Section 2104.6.1
The grouting of any section of wall shall be completed in one day with no interruptions greater than one hour.

6.6 CLEANOUTS

A cleanout is an opening or hole of sufficient size (MSJC Specification defined as 3 inches [76 mm] minimum dimension either direction) through the face of the block used to successfully clean out all mortar droppings and other debris from the bottom of the cell that is to be grouted. Cleanouts are illustrated in Figure 6.4.

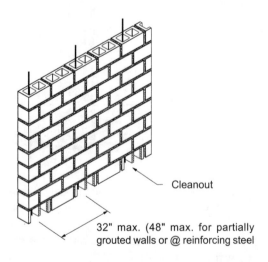

Cleanout

32" max. (48" max. for partially grouted walls or @ reinforcing steel

Figure 6.4 Cleanouts in wall for solid grout pours higher than five feet (1.5 m).

MSJC Specification 3.2 F

3.2 F. *Cleanouts* - Provide cleanouts in the bottom course of masonry for each grout pour, when the grout pour height exceeds 5 ft (1.52 m).

1. Where required, construct cleanouts adjacent to each vertical bar. In solid grouted masonry, space cleanouts horizontally a maximum of 32 in. (813 mm) on center.
2. Construct cleanouts with an opening of sufficient size to permit removal of debris. The minimum opening dimension shall be 3 in. (76.2 mm).
3. After cleaning, close cleanouts with closures braced to resist grout pressure.

UBC Section 2104.6.1

Cleanouts shall be provided for all grout pours over 5 feet (1524 mm) in height.

Where required, cleanouts shall be provided in the bottom course at every vertical bar but shall not be spaced more than 32 inches (813 mm) on center for solidly grouted masonry. When cleanouts are required, they shall be sealed after inspection and before grouting.

Where cleanouts are provided, special provisions must be made to keep the bottom and sides of the grout spaces, as well as the minimum total clear as required by Table 21-C, clean and clear prior to grouting.

6.7   HIGH-LIFT GROUTING

When grout pours exceed five feet (1.5 m), cleanouts must be provided and the method commonly known as high-lift grouting is used.

In high-lift grouting, illustrated in Figure 6.5, the walls are built to their full height before grouting, up to a maximum of 24 feet (7.3 m). Cleanout holes are required at the bottom of all vertical cells containing vertical reinforcing steel, but not more than 32 inches (813 mm) apart for solid grouted masonry. Partially grouted masonry should have cleanouts at the cells containing vertical reinforcement, with cleanout spacing not exceeding 48 inches (1.2 m). It is recommended for walls that are solid grouted, the first course be an inverted bond beam unit to allow for cleaning mortar droppings or debris from the foundation and between cleanouts, which may be as much as 32 inches (813 mm) on center. This also improves the flow of grout at the foundation and provides maximum shear interface between the grout and the foundation.

> **UBC Section 2104.6.1**
> Units may be laid to the full height of the grout pour and grout shall be placed in a continuous pour in grout lifts not exceeding 6 feet (1830 mm). When approved, grout lifts may be greater than 6 feet (1830 mm) if it can be demonstrated the grout spaces can be properly filled.

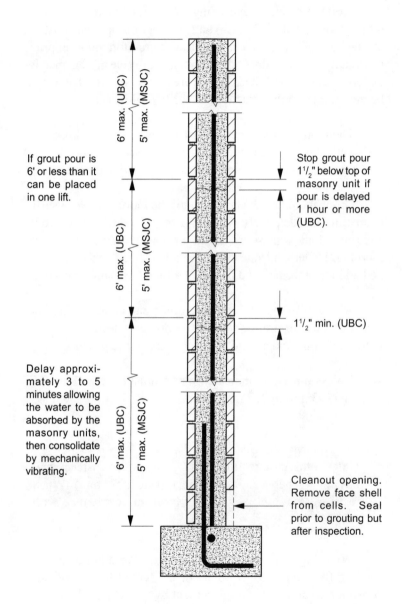

Figure 6.5 High-lift method of grouting block.

Mortar projections exceeding the vertical height of the mortar joint, or $^1/_2$ inches (13 mm) and all mortar droppings must be cleaned out of the grout cells and off the reinforcing steel prior to grouting. "Clean" does not mean "surgically clean", but merely no loose deleterious material in the areas to be grouted that would be detrimental to the structural integrity of the masonry.

There are various methods of cleaning mortar droppings and overhangs which include using compressed air, a rod, a stick, or a high-pressure jet stream of water to dislodge the material.

Grout should not be poured until the mortar has set a sufficient time to adequately withstand the pressure of the grout. Typically, hollow masonry is laid one day and grouted the next morning. Under moderate to ideal weather conditions, units could be laid in the morning and be safely grouted the same afternoon.

All reinforcing steel, bolts, other embedded items and cleanout closures are required to be properly secured in place before grouting and should be inspected prior to grouting.

Unless otherwise indicated, grout must have an 8 inch to 11 inch (203 mm to 279 mm) slump.

MSJC Specification Section 2.6 B.2
2. Unless otherwise required, mix grout to a consistency that has a slump between 8 and 11 in. (203 and 279 mm). When tests are required, test grout slump in accordance with ASTM C 143.

When high-lift grouting, the grout is placed in lifts not exceeding five feet (1.5 m) MSJC or six feet (1.8 m) UBC and consolidated at the time of placement by a mechanical vibrator. After each lift is placed, wait for absorption of water into the block, approximately 5 to 10 minutes, and then reconsolidate the grout before it loses its plasticity. The next lift should be placed immediately, or as soon as reasonable. The full height of any section of wall should be completed in one day, with no interruption between lifts greater than one hour. After the last lift at the top of the wall is consolidated, the grout space is filled to the top.

6.8   CONSOLIDATION OF GROUT

Grout is required to be consolidated by means of a mechanical vibrator if the lift is more than 12 inches (305 mm). The vibrator, shown in Figure 6.6, is usually on a flexible cable with the head from $^3/_4$ inch to $1^1/_2$ inches (19 mm to 38 mm) in width. While the vibrator is on, it need only be lowered into the grout and slowly removed. Excessive vibration can cause segregation of grout. If cells are congested with steel, adjacent grouted cells can be consolidated by vibration.

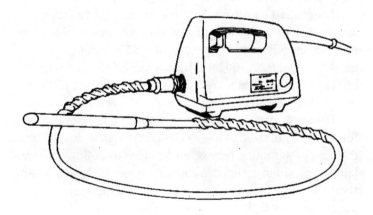

Figure 6.6 Grout vibrator.

MSJC Specification 3.5 E

3.5 E. *Consolidation* - Consolidate grout at the time of placement.
1. Consolidate grout pours 12 in. (305 mm) or less in height by mechanical vibration or by puddling.
2. Consolidate pours exceeding 12 in. (305 mm) in height by mechanical vibration and reconsolidate by mechanical vibration after initial water loss and settlement has occurred.

UBC Section 2104.6.2

2104.6.2 Construction requirements. Reinforcement shall be placed prior to grouting. Bolts shall be accurately set with templates or by approved equivalent means and held in place to prevent dislocation during grouting.

Segregation of the grout materials and damage to the masonry shall be avoided during the grouting process.

Grout shall be consolidated by mechanical vibration during placement before loss of plasticity in a manner to fill the grout space. Grout pours greater than 12 inches (300 mm) in height shall be reconsolidated by mechanical vibration to minimize voids due to water loss. Grout pours 12 inches (300 mm) or less in height shall be mechanically vibrated or puddled.

In one-story buildings having wood-frame exterior walls, foundations not over 24 inches (600 mm) high measured from the top of the footing may be constructed of hollow-masonry units laid in running bond without mortared head joints. Any standard shape unit may be used, provided the masonry units permit horizontal flow of grout to adjacent units. Grout shall be solidly poured to the full height in one lift and shall be puddled or mechanically vibrated.

Reconsolidation of grout is necessary after excess water is absorbed into the masonry. A film of water between the masonry shell and the grout can form and consolidating the grout closes up this space causing the grout to have intimate contact with the shell and thus achieve bond.

6.9   FLUID MORTAR FOR GROUT

UBC Section 2104.6.2

In nonstructural elements which do not exceed 8 feet (2440 mm) in height above the highest point of lateral support, including fireplaces and residential chimneys, mortar of pouring consistency may be substituted for grout when the masonry is constructed and grouted in pours of 12 inches (300 mm) or less in height.

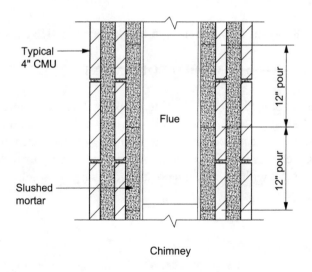

Chimney

Figure 6.7 Mortar slushed into non-structural element.

6.10   GROUT BARRIERS

UBC Section 2104.6.2
In multiwythe grouted masonry, vertical barriers of masonry shall be built across the grout space the entire height of the grout pour and spaced not more than 30 feet (9144 mm) horizontally. The grouting of any section of wall between barriers shall be completed in one day with no interruption longer than one hour.

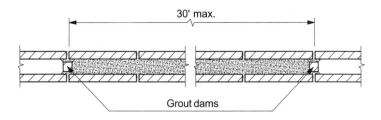

Figure 6.8 Grout flow barriers in block masonry (UBC).

6.11   USE OF ALUMINUM EQUIPMENT

Grout pumped through aluminum pipes will cause an abrasion of the interior of the pipe This abrasion will cause aluminum particles to be mixed with the grout and may reduce strength and cause expansion of the grout. Aluminum powder or particles can react with cement and create hydrogen gas, which expands.

UBC Section 2104.7
2104.7 Aluminum Equipment. Grout shall not be handled nor pumped utilizing aluminum equipment unless it can be demonstrated with the materials and equipment to be used that there will be no deleterious effect on the strength of the grout.

6.12   PUMPING GROUT

Grout is commonly placed into masonry walls using a grout pump. The grout is loaded into a grout pump directly from a transit mix truck and then pumped into the masonry cells through a long hose.

Lime or fly ash can be used to aid pumping. The use of fly ash can save on cement.

Grout pumps are specifically made to pump high slump pea gravel, grout and do not handle concrete, which is stiffer with larger aggregate. Figure 6.9 shows a typical masonry grout pump.

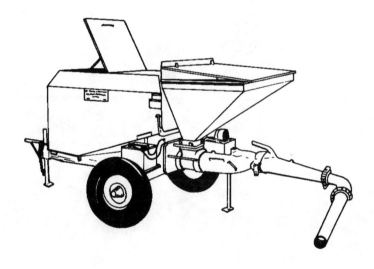

Figure 6.9 Typical masonry grout pump.

Special Provisions for Seismic Design and Construction

7.1   GENERAL

Earthquakes are a recognized threat to life, safety and buildings. To help prevent loss of life and reduce damage to structures, special detailing requirements are imposed by the Building Codes. These requirements are based on the seismic exposure in which the building is located.

This Chapter presents the seismic requirements of the Uniform Building Code and the International Building Code (which references the MSJC Code) individually, since each has a unique approach in considering seismic exposure.

The Uniform Building Code takes into account the geographic location when determining seismic risk and divides the United States into Seismic Zones as depicted in UBC Figure 16.2 (Page 246). The designer applies a building importance factor after establishing the Seismic Zone to refine the design requirements. For example, a hospital is designed to a higher standard than a small shopping center based on the application of an importance factor.

The International Building Code uses Seismic Design Categories instead of Seismic Zones. The Seismic Design Category is defined as a classification assigned to a structure based on its Seismic Use Group and the severity of the design earthquake ground motion at the site. In other words, the importance factor is considered before the Seismic Design Category (SDC) is determined. Another important item considered before establishing the Seismic Design Category is the site soil condition. It is therefore conceivable that one project would be assigned SDC D and a nearby project would be assigned SDC C due solely to soil conditions.

7.2   UBC SEISMIC ZONES

Section 2106.1.12 of the Uniform Building Code contains applicable seismic requirements relating to masonry.

UBC Section 2106.1.12

2106.1.12 Special provisions in areas of seismic risk.

2106.1.12.1 General. Masonry structures constructed in the seismic zones shown in Figure 16-2 shall be designed in accordance with the design requirements of this chapter and the special provisions for each seismic zone given in this section.

There are also some significant provisions in Chapter 16 of the UBC that relate to masonry.

UBC Section 1633.2.8 and 1633.2.9.5

1633.2.8 Anchorage of concrete or masonry walls. Concrete or masonry walls shall be anchored to all floors and roofs that provide out-of-plane lateral support of; the wall. The anchorage shall provide a positive direct connection between the wall and floor or roof construction capable of resisting the larger of the horizontal forces specified in this section and Sections 1611.4 and 1632. In addition, in Seismic Zones 3 and 4, diaphragm to wall anchorage using embedded straps shall have the straps attached to or hooked around the reinforcing steel or otherwise terminating to effectively transfer forces to the reinforcing steel. Requirements for developing anchorage forces in diaphragms are given in Section 1633.2.9. Diaphragm deformation shall be considered in the design of the supported walls.

1633.2.9.5 Diaphragms

5. Where wood diaphragms are used to laterally support concrete or masonry walls, the anchorage shall conform to Section 1633.2.8. In Seismic Zones 2, 3 and 4 anchorage shall not be accomplished by use of toenails or nails subject to withdrawal, wood ledgers or framing not be used in cross-grain bending or cross-grain tension, and the continuous ties required by Item 4 shall be in addition to the diaphragm sheathing.

7.2.1   Seismic Zones Nos. 0 and 1

Since there is little to no seismic exposure in Zones 0 and 1, the UBC appropriately addresses the issue.

UBC Section. 2106.1.12.2

2106.1.12.2 Special provisions for Seismic Zones 0 and 1. There are no special design and construction provisions in this section for structures built in Seismic Zones 0 and 1.

Notwithstanding the absence of seismic requirements, it is suggested that horizontal reinforcement be placed in the top of footings, on all sides of wall openings, at roof and floor levels and at the top of parapet walls. Horizontal reinforcement in a wall is generally for temperature and shrinkage, and the exact positioning is not critical. Steel must be in place or laid on top of the cross webs in concrete masonry prior to grouting. The horizontal steel should be placed with enough clearance between bars to allow the grout to flow through and completely surround the bar. This will help insure the development of good bond.

7.2.2   Seismic Zone No. 2

As seismic exposure increases, so do the requirements affecting masonry construction. The exposure associated with Seismic Zone 2 is considered low to moderate, therefore, minimum requirements of reinforcing steel and material restrictions appear.

UBC Section. 2106.1.12.3
    2106.1.12.3   Special provisions for Seismic Zone 2. Masonry structures in Seismic Zone 2 shall comply with the following special provisions:

    1. Columns shall be reinforced as specified in Sections 2106.3.6, 2106.3.7 and 2107.2.13.

2. Vertical wall reinforcement of at least 0.20 square inches (130 mm²) in cross-sectional area shall be provided continuously from support to support at each corner, at each side of each opening, at the ends of walls and at maximum spacing of 4 feet (1219 mm) apart horizontally throughout walls.

3. Horizontal wall reinforcement not less than 0.2 square inch (130 mm²) in cross-sectional area shall be provided (1) at the bottom and top of wall openings and shall extend not less than 24 inches (610 mm) or less than 40 bar diameters past the opening, (2) continuously at structurally connected roof and floor levels and at the top of walls, (3) at the bottom of walls or in the top of foundations when doweled in walls, and (4) at maximum spacing of 10 feet (3048 mm) unless uniformly distributed joint reinforcement is provided. Reinforcement at the top and bottom of openings when continuous in walls may be used in determining the maximum spacing specified in Item 1 of this paragraph.

4. Where stack bond is used, the minimum horizontal reinforcement ratio shall be $0.0007bt$. This ratio shall be satisfied by uniformly distributed joint reinforcement or by horizontal reinforcement space not over 4 feet (1219 mm) and fully embedded in grout or mortar.

5. The following materials shall not be used as part of the vertical or lateral load-resisting systems: Type O mortar, masonry cement, plastic cement, nonloadbearing masonry units and glass block.

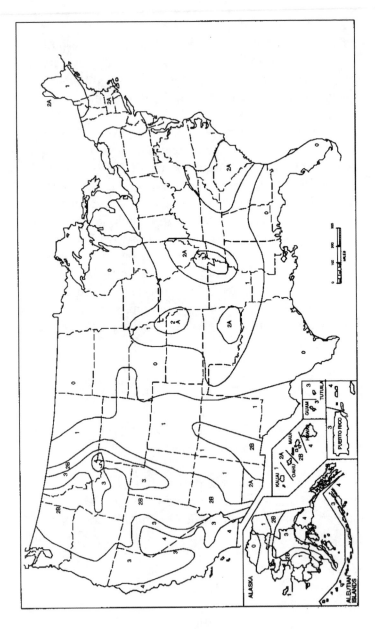

UBC Figure No. 16-2, Seismic Zone Map of the United States.

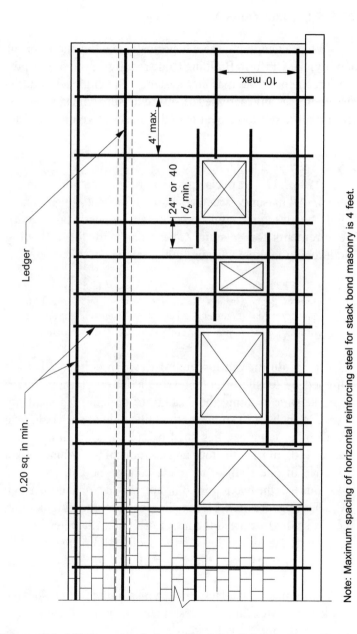

Figure 7.1 Minimum reinforcement for Seismic Zone No. 2.

7.2.3   Seismic Zones Nos. 3 And 4

When a geographic area historically exhibits more seismic activity, the Uniform Building Code requires more prescriptive reinforcement in the masonry system. The engineered design also addresses any increased seismic exposure which may easily require more reinforcement than the prescriptive minimums.

UBC Section. 2106.1.12.4

2106.1.12.4   Special provisions for Seismic Zones 3 and 4. All masonry structures built in Seismic Zones 3 and 4 shall be designed and constructed in accordance with requirements for Seismic Zone 2 and with the following additional requirements and limitations:

EXCEPTION: One- and two-story masonry buildings of Group R. Division 3 and Group U Occupancies in Seismic Zone 3 having masonry wall h'/t ratios not greater than 27 and using running bond construction when provisions of Section 2106.1.12.3 are met.

1.   Column reinforcement ties. In columns that are stressed by tensile or compressive axial overturning forces from seismic loading, the spacing of column ties shall not exceed 8 inches (203 mm) for the full height of such columns. In all other columns, ties shall be spaced a maximum of 8 inches (203 mm) in the tops and bottoms of the columns for a distance of one sixth of the clear column height, 18 inches (457 mm), or the maximum column cross-sectional dimension, whichever is greater. Tie spacing for the remaining column height shall not exceed the lesser of 16 bar diameters, 48 tie diameters, the least column cross-sectional dimension, or 18 inches (457 mm). **[See Figures 5.20 and 5.23].**

Column ties shall terminate with a minimum 135-degree hook with extensions not less than six-bar diameters, or 4 inches (102 mm). Such extensions shall engages the longitudinal column reinforcement and projects into the interior of the column. Hooks shall comply with Section 2107.2.2.5, Item 3. **[See Table 5-G].**

> **EXCEPTION:** Where the ties are placed in the horizontal bed joints, hooks shall consist of a 90-degree bend having an inside radius of not less than four tie diameters plus an extension of 32 tie diameters.

There are also seismic provisions addressing the interface of masonry walls and concrete surfaces.

UBC Section. 2106.1.12.4

4. **Concrete abutting structural masonry.** Concrete abutting structural masonry, such as at starter courses or at wall intersections not designed as true separation joints, shall be roughened to a full amplitude of $^1/_{16}$ inch (1.6 mm) and shall be bonded to the masonry in accordance with the requirements of this chapter as if it were masonry. Unless keys or proper reinforcement is provided, vertical joints as specified in Section 2106.1.4 shall be considered to be stack bond and the reinforcement as required for stack bond shall extend through the joint and be anchored into the concrete.

Although UBC contains most of the masonry seismic provisions in Section 2106.1.12, there are certain provisions exclusive to Working Stress Design for seismic zones 3 and 4.

UBC Section. 2107.1.3 [Working Stress Design]

2107.1.3 Minimum dimensions for masonry structures located in Seismic Zones 3 and 4. Elements of masonry structures located in Seismic Zones 3 and 4 shall be in accordance with this section.

2107.1.3.1 Bearing Walls. The nominal thickness of reinforced masonry bearing walls shall not be less than 6 inches (152 mm) except that nominal 4-inch-thick (102 mm) load-bearing reinforced hollow-clay unit masonry walls may be used, provided net area unit strength exceeds 8,000 psi (55 MPa), units are laid in running bond, bar sizes do not exceed ½ inch (12.7 mm) with no more than two bars or one splice in a cell, and joints are flush cut, concave or a protruding V section.

2107.1.3.2 Columns. The least nominal dimension of a reinforced masonry column shall be 12 inches (305 mm) except that, for working stress design, if the allowable stresses are reduced by one half, the minimum nominal dimension shall be 8 inches (203 mm).

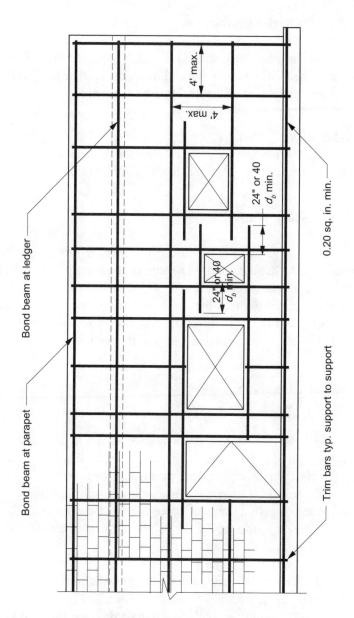

Figure 7.2 Minimum reinforcing bar locations in UBC Seismic Zones 3 and 4.

7.2.3.1 Material Restrictions

In addition to the material restrictions contained in Seismic Zone 2, the UBC contains one additional material restriction for masonry that is part of the load resisting system.

UBC Section. 2106.1.12.4
3. **Type N mortar.** Type N mortar shall not be used as part of the vertical- or lateral-load-resisting system.

7.2.3.2 Shear Walls

Seismic Zones 3 and 4 also require that reinforcement be continuous around corners. The sum of the areas of horizontal and vertical reinforcement shall be at least 0.002 times the gross cross-sectional area of the wall, and the minimum area of reinforcement in either direction shall not be less than 0.0007 times the gross cross-sectional area of the wall.

UBC Section. 2106.1.12.4
2. **Shear walls.**

> 2.1 **Reinforcement.** The portion of the reinforcement required to resist shear shall be uniformly distributed and shall be joint reinforcement, deformed bars or a combination thereof. The spacing of reinforcement in each direction shall not exceed one half the length of the element, nor one half the height of the element, nor 48 inches (1219 mm).
>
> Joint reinforcement used in exterior walls and considered in the determination of the shear strength of the member shall be hot-dipped galvanized in accordance with U.B.C. Standard 21-10.

Reinforcement required to resist in-plane shear shall be terminated with a standard hook as defined in Section 2107.2.2.5 or with an extension of proper embedment length beyond the reinforcement at the end of the wall section. The hook or extension may be turned up, down or horizontally. Provisions shall be made not to obstruct grout placement. Wall reinforcement terminating in columns or beams shall be fully anchored into these elements.

2.2 Bond. Multiwythe grouted masonry shear walls shall be designed with consideration of the adhesion bond strength between the grout and masonry units. When bond strengths are not known from previous tests, the bond strength shall be determined by tests.

2.3 Wall reinforcement. All walls shall be reinforced with both vertical and horizontal reinforcement. The sum of the areas of horizontal and vertical reinforcement shall be at least 0.002 times the gross cross-sectional area of the wall, and the minimum area of reinforcement in either direction shall not be less than 0.0007 times the gross cross-sectional area of the wall. The minimum steel requirements for Seismic Zone 2 in Section 2106.1.12.3 Items 2 and 3, may be included in the sum. The spacing of reinforcement shall not exceed 4 feet (1219 mm). The diameter of reinforcement shall not be less than $^3/_8$ inch (9.5 mm) except that joint reinforcement may be considered as a part or all of the requirement for minimum reinforcement. Reinforcement shall be continuous around wall corners and through intersections. Only reinforcement which is continuous in the wall or element shall be considered in computing the minimum area of reinforcement. Reinforcement with splices conforming to Section 2107.2.2.6 shall be considered as continuous reinforcement.

2.4 **Stack Bond.** Where stack bond is used, the minimum horizontal reinforcement ratio shall be 0.0015bt. Where open-end units are used and grouted solid, the minimum horizontal reinforcement ratio shall be 0.0007bt.

Reinforced hollow-unit stacked bond construction which is part of the seismic-resisting system shall use open-end units so that all head joints are made solid, shall use bond beam units to facilitate the flow of grout and shall be grouted solid.

7.3 IBC SEISMIC DESIGN CATEGORIES

Section 2106 of the International Building Code contains applicable seismic requirements. This Section should be coordinated with the referenced MSJC Code, Section 1.13.

IBC Section 2106.1

2106.1 Seismic design requirements for masonry. Masonry structures and components shall comply with the requirements in Sections 2106.1.1, 2106.2, 2106.3, 2106.4, 2106.5 or 2106.6 depending on the structure's seismic design category as defined in Section 1613.1, except that masonry structures designed by the working stress design method shall be permitted to comply with Section 2106.1.2.

There are also some significant provisions in Chapter 16 of the IBC that relate to masonry.

IBC Section 1613.1

1613.1 Definitions
SEISMIC DESIGN CATEGORY. A classification assigned to a structure based on its Seismic Use Group and the severity of the design earthquake ground motion at the site.

IBC Section 1604.8.2

1604.8.2 Concrete and masonry walls. Concrete and masonry walls shall be anchored to floors, roofs and other structural elements that provide lateral support for the wall. Such anchorage shall provide a positive direct connection capable of resisting the horizontal forces specified in this chapter but not less than a minimum horizontal force of 200 pounds per linear foot (2.92 kN/m) of wall, substituted for "*E*.*" Walls shall be designed to resist bending between anchors where the anchor spacing exceeds 4 feet (1219 mm). Required anchors in masonry walls of hollow units or cavity walls shall be embedded in a reinforced grouted structural element of the wall. See Sections 1609.6.5 and 1620 for wind and earthquake design requirements.

*Defined as the combined effect of horizontal and vertical earthquake induced forces.

There is also a Section in IBC Chapter 16 that addresses the importance of connections between floor and roof members and masonry walls.

IBC Section 1620.2.1

1620.2.1 Anchorage of concrete or masonry walls. Concrete or masonry walls shall be anchored to floors and roofs and members that provide out-of-plane lateral support for the wall or that are supported by the wall. The anchorage shall provide a positive direct connection between the wall and floor or roof capable of resisting the horizontal forces specified in Equation 16-64 for structures with flexible diaphragms or in Section 1621.1.4 for structures with diaphragms that are not flexible.

The MSJC Code contains an additional seismic provision relating to all masonry except glass unit masonry and masonry veneers. Although the provision is not something the inspector can observe, it is helpful for the masonry inspector to understand the implications of the quality of construction.

> **MSJC Section 1.13.2**
> **1.13.2** *General*
> **1.13.2.2** *Drift limits*—The calculated story drift of masonry structures due to the combination of seismic forces and gravity loads shall not exceed 0.007 times the story height.

7.3.1   Seismic Design Category A

The IBC requires that masonry structures constructed in Seismic Design Category A (SDC) meet the minimum requirements for: Working Stress Design contained in the MSJC Code, or Strength Design contained in either Section 2108.9 or 2108.10 of the IBC, or Empirical Design in accordance with Section 2109 of the IBC. Additionally, there is one other seismic requirement relating to anchorage of masonry walls in SDC A.

> **IBC Section 2106.2.1**
> **2106.2.1 Anchorage of masonry walls.** Masonry walls shall be anchored to the roof and floors that provide lateral support for the wall in accordance with Section 1616.4.3.

The MSJC Code contains a similar provision for Seismic Category A.

> **MSJC Section 1.13.3**
> **1.13.3** *Seismic Performance Category A*
> **1.13.3.2** *Anchorage of masonry* walls—Masonry walls shall be anchored to the roof and all floors that provide lateral support for the wall. The anchorage shall provide a direct connection between the walls and the floor or roof construction. The connections shall be capable of resisting the greater of a

seismic lateral force induced by the wall or 1000 times the effective peak velocity-related acceleration, lb per lineal ft of wall (14 593 times N per lineal m of wall).

Notwithstanding the absence of seismic requirements, it is suggested that horizontal reinforcement be placed in the top of footings, on all sides of wall openings, at roof and floor levels and at the top of parapet walls. Horizontal reinforcement in a wall is generally for temperature and shrinkage, and the exact positioning is not critical. Steel must be in place or laid on top of the cross webs in concrete masonry prior to grouting. The horizontal steel should be placed with enough clearance between bars to allow the grout to flow through and completely surround the bar. This will help ensure the development of good bond.

7.3.2 Seismic Design Category B

The designer must consider lateral seismic forces in accordance with Code requirements. These requirements are in addition to those stated in SDC A.

IBC Section 2106.3
2106.3 Seismic Design Category B. Structures assigned to Seismic Design Category B shall conform to the requirements for Seismic Design Category A.
2106.3.1 Masonry shear walls. Masonry shear walls shall comply with the requirements of ordinary plain masonry shear walls or ordinary reinforced masonry shear walls.

IBC Figure No. 1615(1), Seismic Map of the United States, 02 Sec Spectral Response Acceleration.

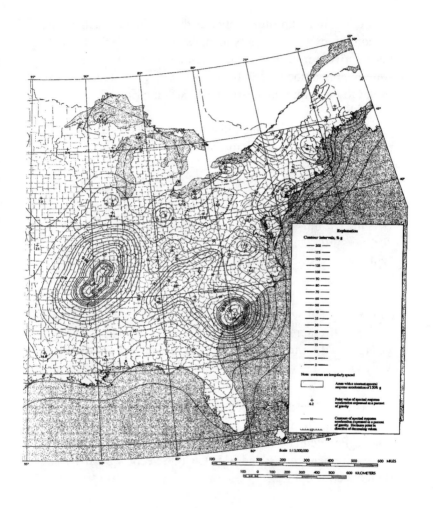

IBC Figure No. 1615(1), Seismic Map of the United States, 02
Sec Spectral Response Acceleration (Continued).

7.3.3   Seismic Design Category C

As seismic exposure increases due to factors such as site soil conditions and proximity to known earthquake faults, so do the requirements affecting masonry construction. The requirements associated with Seismic Design Category C are similar to the requirements for UBC Seismic Zone 2.

Naturally, the IBC and MSJC incorporate the requirements from Categories A and B into Category C.

> *IBC Section 2106.4*
>
> **2106.4 Seismic Design Category C.** Structures assigned to Seismic Design Category C shall conform to the requirements for Seismic Design Category B and to the additional requirements of this section.

> *MSJC Section 1.13.5*
>
> **1.13.5.1** Structures in Seismic Performance Category C shall comply with the requirements of Seismic Performance Category B and to the additional requirements of this section.

The IBC and MSJC contain separate requirements for elements that are part of, or not part of, the lateral load resisting system. For elements not part of the lateral load resisting system, the requirements are stated in IBC Code Section 2106.4.1 and MSJC Section 1.13.5.2.

> *IBC Section 2106.4.1*
>
> **2106.4.1 Design of elements that are not part of the lateral-force-resisting system.**
>
> **2106.4.1.2 Masonry partition walls.** Masonry partition walls, masonry screen walls and other masonry elements that are

not designed to resist vertical or lateral loads, other than those induced by their own mass, shall be isolated from the structure so that vertical and lateral forces are not imparted to these elements. Isolation joints and connectors between these elements and the structure shall be designed to accommodate the design story drift.

IBC Section 2106.4.1.3

2106.4.1.3 Reinforcement requirements for masonry elements. Masonry elements listed in Section 2106.4.1.3 shall be reinforced in either the horizontal or vertical direction dependent upon the location of the lateral supporting elements in accordance with the following:

1. Horizontal joint reinforcement shall consist of at least two longitudinal W1.7 wires spaced not more than 16 inches (406 mm) for walls greater than 4 inches (102 mm) in width and at least one longitudinal W1.7 wire spaced not more than 16 inches (406 mm) for walls not exceeding 4 inches (102 mm) in width; or at least one No. 4 bar spaced not more than 48 inches (1219 mm). Where two longitudinal wires of joint reinforcement are used, the space between these wires shall be the widest that the mortar joint will accommodate. Horizontal reinforcement shall be provided within 16 inches (406 mm) of the top and bottom of these masonry elements.

2. Vertical reinforcement shall consist of at least one No. 4 bar spaced not more than 48 inches (1219 mm). Vertical reinforcement shall be located within 16 inches (406 mm) of the ends of masonry walls.

MSJC Section 1.13.5.2

1.13.5.2 *Design of elements that are not part of the lateral-force-resisting system.*

1.13.5.2.2 Masonry partition walls, masonry screen walls and other masonry elements that are not designed to resist vertical or lateral loads, other than those induced by their own mass, shall be isolated from the structure so that vertical and lateral forces are not imparted to these elements. Isolation joints and connectors between these elements and the structure shall be designed to accommodate the design story drift.

1.13.5.2.3 *Reinforcement requirements*—Masonry elements listed in Section 1.13.5.2.2 shall be reinforced in either the horizontal or vertical direction in accordance with the following:

(a) *Horizontal reinforcement*—Horizontal joint reinforcement shall consist of at least two longitudinal W1.7 (MW11) wires spaced not more than 16 in. (406 mm) for walls greater than 4 in. (102 mm) in width and at least one longitudinal W1.7 (MW11) wire spaced not more than 16 in. (406 mm) for walls not exceeding 4 inches (102 mm) in width; or at least one No. 4 (M #13) bar spaced not more than 48 in. (1219 mm). Where two longitudinal wires of joint reinforcement are used, the space between these wires shall be the widest that the mortar joint will accommodate. Horizontal reinforcement shall be provided within 16 in. (406 mm) of the top and bottom of these masonry walls.

(b) *Vertical reinforcement*—Vertical reinforcement shall consist of at least one No. 4 (M #13) bar spaced not more than 48 in. (1219 mm). Vertical reinforcement shall be located within 16 in. (406 mm) of the ends of masonry walls.

Masonry walls that resist seismic forces, or elements that are part of the lateral-force-resisting system, are commonly known as shear walls. The IBC and MSJC make special provisions for these types of walls.

IBC Section 2106.4.2

2106.4.2 Design of elements that are part of the lateral-force-resisting system.

2106.4.2.1 Connections to masonry shear walls. Connectors shall be provided to transfer forces between masonry walls and horizontal elements in accordance with the requirements of ACI 530/ASCE 5/TMS 402, Section 2.1.6. Connectors shall be designed to transfer horizontal design forces acting either perpendicular or parallel to the wall, but not less than 200 pounds per lineal foot (2919 N/m) of wall. The maximum spacing between connectors shall be 4 feet (1219 mm).

2106.4.2.2 Connections to masonry columns. Connectors shall be provided to transfer forces between masonry columns and horizontal elements in accordance with the requirements of ACI 530/ASCE 5/TMS 402, Section 2.1.6. Where anchor bolts are used to connect horizontal elements to the tops of columns, anchor bolts shall be placed within lateral ties. Lateral ties shall enclose both the vertical bars in the column and the anchor bolts. There shall be a minimum of two No. 4 lateral ties provided in the top 5 inches (127 mm) of the column.

2106.4.2.3 Masonry shear walls. Masonry shear walls shall comply with the requirements for ordinary reinforced masonry shear walls or intermediate reinforced masonry shear walls.

2106.4.2.3.1 Minimum reinforcement requirements for masonry shear walls. Vertical reinforcement of at least 0.20 square inch (129 mm^2) in cross-sectional area shall be provided at corners, within 16 inches (406 mm) of each side of openings, within 8 inches (203 mm) of each side of movement joints, within 8 inches (203 mm) of the ends of walls, and at a maximum spacing of 10 feet (3048 mm).

Horizontal joint reinforcement shall consist of at least two wires of W1.7 spaced not more than 16 inches (406 mm); or bond beam reinforcement shall be provided of at least 0.2 square inch (129 mm^2) in cross-sectional area spaced not more than 10 feet (3048 mm). Horizontal reinforcement shall also be provided at the bottom and top of wall openings and shall extend not less than 24 inches (610 mm) nor less than 40 bar diameters past the opening; continuously at structurally connected roof and floor levels; and within 16 inches (406 mm) of the top of walls.

2106.4.2.4 Discontinuous members. Columns and pilasters supporting reactions from discontinuous stiff members such as walls shall be provided with transverse reinforcement spaced at no more than one-fourth of the least nominal dimension of the column or pilaster. The minimum transverse reinforcement ratio shall be 0.0015. Beams supporting reactions from discontinuous walls or frames shall be provided with transverse reinforcement spaced at no more than one-half of the nominal depth of the beam. The minimum transverse reinforcement ratio shall be 0.0015.

MSJC Section 1.13.5.3

1.13.5.3 *Design of elements that are part of the lateral-force-resisting system*

1.13.5.3.1 *Connections to masonry shear walls*—Connectors shall be provided to transfer forces between masonry walls and horizontal elements in accordance with the requirements of Section 2.1.6. Connectors shall be designed to transfer horizontal design forces acting either perpendicular or parallel to the wall, but not less than 200 lb per lineal ft (2919 N per lineal m) of wall. The maximum spacing between connectors shall be 4 feet (1.22 m).

1.13.5.3.2 *Connections to masonry columns*—Connectors shall be provided to transfer forces between masonry columns and horizontal elements in accordance with the requirements of Section 2.1.6. Where anchor bolts are used to connect horizontal elements to the tops of columns, anchor bolts shall be placed within lateral ties. Lateral ties shall enclose both the vertical bars in the column and the anchor bolts. There shall be a minimum of two No. 4 lateral ties provided in the top 5 in. (127 mm) of the column.

Masonry shear walls shall comply with the requirements for ordinary reinforced masonry shear walls or intermediate reinforced masonry shear walls.

1.13.5.3.3 *Minimum reinforcement requirements for masonry shear walls*—Vertical reinforcement of at least 0.2 in.^{2} (129 mm^2) in cross-sectional area shall be provided at corners, within 16 in. (406 mm) of each side of openings, within 8 in. (203 mm) of each side of movement joints, within 8 in. (203 mm) of the ends of walls, and at a maximum spacing of 10 ft (3.05 m).

Horizontal joint reinforcement shall consist of at least two wires of W1.7 (MW11) spaced not more than 16 in. (406 mm); or bond beam reinforcement shall be provided of at least 0.2 in.^{2} (129 mm^2) in cross-sectional area spaced not more than 10 ft (3.05 m). Horizontal reinforcement shall also be provided at the bottom and top of wall openings and shall extend not less than 24 in. (610 mm) nor less than 40 bar diameters past the opening; continuously at structurally connected roof and floor levels; and within 16 in. (406 mm) of the top of walls.

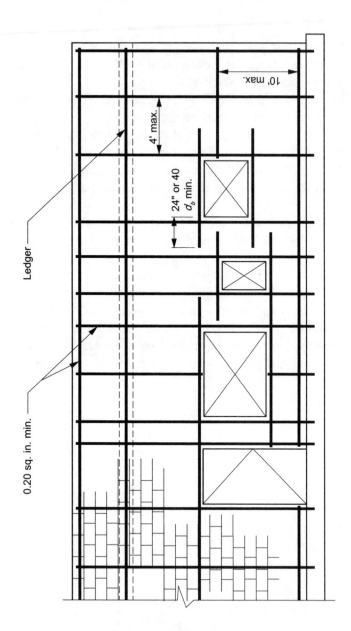

Figure 7.3 Minimum reinforcement for lateral load resisting system in Seismic Category C.

7.3.4 Seismic Design Category D

Seismic exposure increases design and construction requirements. As one would expect, the requirements for Seismic Categories A, B and C also apply to Seismic Category D.

IBC Section 2106.5

2106.5 Seismic Design Category D. Structures assigned to Seismic Design Category D shall conform to all of the requirements for Seismic Design Category C and the additional requirements of this section.

MSJC Section 1.13.6.1

1.13.6.1 Structures in Seismic Performance Category D shall comply with the requirements of Seismic Performance Category C and the additional requirements of this section.

There are general design requirements for masonry structures in Seismic Category D.

IBC Section 2106.5

2106.5.2 Minimum reinforcement requirements for masonry walls. Masonry walls other than those covered by Section 2106.4.1 shall be reinforced in both the vertical and horizontal direction. The sum of the cross-sectional area of horizontal and vertical reinforcement shall be at least 0.002 times the gross cross-sectional area of the wall, and the minimum cross-sectional area in each direction shall be not less than 0.0007 times the gross cross-sectional area of the wall. Reinforcement shall be uniformly distributed. The maximum spacing of reinforcement shall be 48 inches (1219 mm) except for stack bond masonry. Wythes of stack bond masonry shall be constructed of fully grouted hollow open-end units, fully grouted hollow units laid with full head joints or solid units. Maximum spacing of reinforcement for walls with stack bond masonry shall be 24 inches (610 mm).

2106.5.4 Minimum reinforcement for masonry columns. Lateral ties in masonry columns shall be spaced not more than 8 inches (203 mm) on center and shall be at least $^3/_8$ inch (9.5 mm) diameter. Lateral ties shall be embedded in grout.

2106.5.6 Lateral tie anchorage. Standard hooks for lateral tie anchorage shall be either a 135-degree (2.36 rad) standard hook or a 180-degree (3.14 rad) standard hook.

Similar provisions are contained in the MSJC.

MSJC Section 1.13.6

1.13.6.3 *Minimum reinforcement requirements for masonry walls*—Masonry walls other than those covered by Section 1.13.5.2.3 shall be reinforced in both the vertical and horizontal direction. The sum of the cross-sectional area of horizontal and vertical reinforcement shall be at least 0.002 times the gross cross-sectional area of the wall, and the minimum cross-sectional area in each direction shall be not less than 0.0007 times the gross cross-sectional area of the wall, using specified dimensions. Reinforcement shall be uniformly distributed. The maximum spacing of reinforcement shall be 48 in. (1219 mm) except for stack bond masonry. Wythes of stack bond masonry shall be constructed of fully grouted hollow open-end units, fully grouted hollow units laid with full head joints or solid units. Maximum spacing of reinforcement for walls with stack bond masonry shall be 24 in. (610 mm).

1.13.6.5 *Minimum reinforcement for masonry columns—*
Lateral ties in masonry columns shall be spaced not more than
8 in. (203 mm) on center and shall be at least $^3/_8$ inch (9.5 mm)
diameter. Lateral ties shall be embedded in grout.

1.13.6.7 *Lateral tie anchorage—*Standard hooks for lateral tie
anchorage shall be either a 135-degree standard hook or a 180-
degree standard hook.

7.3.4.1 Material Restrictions

Seismic Category C imposes restrictions on use of certain
materials for the lateral-load-resisting system. Since Type N
mortar is not permitted, it is safe to assume that Type O is also
restricted. Similarly, plastic cement, a product used primarily
in stucco application is restricted by UBC, and since it is not
recognized in the masonry section of the IBC and MSJC, it is
also precluded from use in masonry construction.

IBC Section 2106.5.5

2106.5.5 Material requirements. Neither Type N mortar nor
masonry cement shall be used as part of the lateral-force-
resisting system.

MSJC Section 1.13.6.6

1.13.6.6 *Material requirements—*Neither Type N mortar nor masonry cement shall be used as part of the lateral-
force-resisting system.

7.3.4.2 Shear Walls

Similar to Seismic Category C, specific and more stringent
prescriptive reinforcement requirements apply to shear walls.

IBC Section 2106.5.3

2106.5.3 Masonry shear walls. Masonry shear walls shall comply with the requirements for special reinforced masonry shear walls.

2106.5.3.1 Shear wall reinforcement requirements. Shear walls shall be reinforced in accordance with Section 2106.5.2 and the maximum spacing of vertical and horizontal reinforcement shall be the smaller of one-third the length of the shear wall, one-third the height of the shear wall, or 48 inches (1219 mm). The minimum cross-sectional area of vertical reinforcement shall be one-third of the required shear reinforcement. Shear reinforcement shall be anchored around vertical-reinforcing bars with a standard hook.

MSJC Section 1.13.6.4

1.13.6.4 *Shear wall reinforcement requirement*—The maximum spacing of vertical and horizontal reinforcement shall be the smallest of: one-third the length of the shear wall, one-third the height of the shear wall, or 48 in. (1219 mm). The minimum cross-sectional area of vertical reinforcement shall be one-third of the required shear reinforcement.

Shear reinforcement shall be anchored around vertical-reinforcing bars with a standard hook.

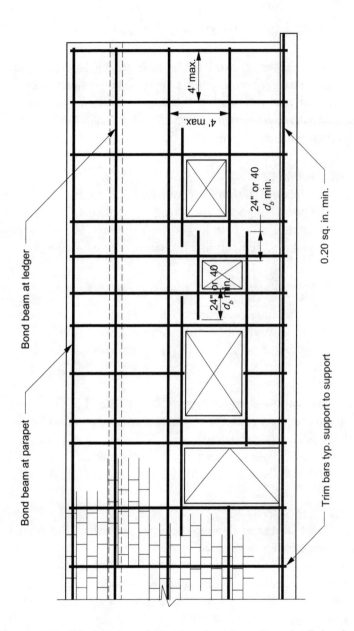

Figure 7.4 Minimum reinforcing bar locations in Seismic Category D.

7.3.5   Seismic Design Categories E and F

For masonry constructed in the highest seismic exposure, the most stringent requirements apply. The greatest concern is structural performance of stack bond masonry, hence, the additional reinforcement. As with other Seismic Categories, the requirements accumulate.

IBC Section 2106.6

2106.6 Seismic Design Category E or F. Structures assigned to Seismic Design Category E or F shall conform to the requirements of Seismic Design Category D and to the additional requirements and limitations of this section.

MSJC Section 1.13.7.1

1.13.7.1 Structures assigned to Seismic Performance Category E shall comply with the requirements of Seismic Performance Category D and to the additional requirements and limitations of this section.

As with Seismic Category C, the IBC and MSJC contain separate requirements for elements that are part of, or not part of, the lateral load resisting system. For elements not part of the lateral load resisting system, the requirements are stated in IBC Code Section 2106.6.1 and MSJC Section 1.13.7.2.

IBC Section 2106.6.1

2106.6.1 Design of elements that are not part of the lateral-force-resisting system. Stack bond masonry that is not part of the lateral-force-resisting system shall have a horizontal cross-sectional area of reinforcement of at least 0.0015 times the gross cross-sectional area of masonry. The maximum spacing of horizontal reinforcement shall be 24 inches (610 mm). These elements shall be solidly grouted and shall be constructed of hollow open-end units or two wythes of solid units.

MSJC Section 1.13.7.2

1.13.7.2 *Design of elements that are not part of the lateral-force-resisting system*—Stack bond masonry that is not part of the lateral-force-resisting system shall have a horizontal cross-sectional area of reinforcement of at least 0.0015 times the gross cross-sectional area of masonry. The maximum spacing of horizontal reinforcement shall be 24 in. (610 mm). These elements shall be solidly grouted and shall be constructed of hollow open-end units or two wythes of solid units.

For stack bond masonry walls that are part of the lateral-load-resisting system, the requirements are more stringent.

IBC Section 2106.6.2

2106.6.2 Design of elements that are part of the lateral-force-resisting system. Stack bond masonry that is part of the lateral-force-resisting system shall have a horizontal cross-sectional area of reinforcement of at least 0.0025 times the gross cross-sectional area of masonry. The maximum spacing of horizontal reinforcement shall be 16 inches (406 mm). These elements shall be solidly grouted and shall be constructed of hollow open-end units or two wythes of solid units.

MSJC Section 1.13.7.3

1.13.7.3 *Design of elements that are part of the lateral-force-resisting system*—Stack bond masonry that is part of the lateral force-resisting system shall have a horizontal cross-sectional area of reinforcement of at least 0.0025 times the gross cross-sectional area of masonry. The maximum spacing of horizontal reinforcement shall be 16 in. (406 mm). These elements shall be solidly grouted and shall be constructed of hollow open-end units or two wythes of solid units.

Wall Frames

8.1   GENERAL

Masonry walls are generally considered solid elements with few openings.

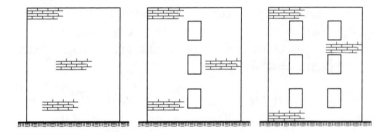

Figure 8.1   Shear walls with few small openings.

As the openings in the walls are increased in size, a system of vertical load carrying elements (columns) and horizontal spandrel elements (beams) is created. As the proportions of the piers and connecting elements are changed, the system approaches the concept of a building wall frame.

Piers are vertical members meeting dimension criteria of the Code and are capable of resisting lateral forces.

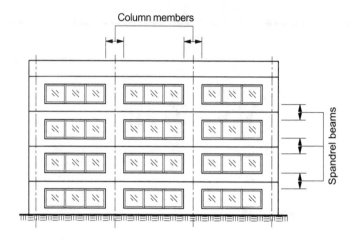

Figure 8.2   Elevation of a four story wall frame building.

The masonry wall frame system must be under-reinforced based on strength design requirements, and the concept of strong columns and weak beam is used. This is to insure a ductile mechanism forming in the beam and maintaining a strong column to support the vertical load.

The masonry frame must be solid grouted using open-end concrete or clay units. This insures the continuity of the grout within the wall. Special inspection is required.

(Note: Engineering criteria of the Code is not included. For Code in it's entirety, refer to the ICBO publication of the Uniform Building Code or ICC publication of the International Building Code.)

UBC Section 2108.2.6

2108.2.6 Design of moment-resisting wall frames.

2108.2.6.1 General requirements.

2108.2.6.1.1 Scope. The requirements of this section are for the design of fully grouted moment-resisting wall frames constructed of reinforced open-end concrete of hollow-unit clay masonry.

2108.2.6.1.2 Dimensional limits. Dimensions shall be in accordance with the following.

Beams. Clear span for the beam shall not be less than two times its depth.

The nominal depth of the beam shall not be less than two units or 16 inches (406 mm), whichever is greater. The nominal beam depth to nominal beam width ratio shall not exceed 6.

The nominal width of the beam shall be the greater of 8 inches (203 mm) or $\frac{1}{26}$ of the clear span between pier faces.

Piers. The nominal depth of piers shall not exceed 96 inches (2438 mm). Nominal depth shall not be less than two full units or 32 inches (813 mm), whichever is greater.

The nominal width of piers shall not be less than the nominal width of the beam, nor less than 8 inches (203 mm) or $\frac{1}{14}$ of the clear height between beam faces, whichever is greater.

The clear height-to-depth ratio of piers shall not exceed 5.

2108.2.6.2.3 Design Assumptions for nominal strength.

The value of f'_m shall not be less than 1,500 psi (10.3 MPa) or greater than 4,000 psi (27.6 MPa).

2106.2.6.2.4 Reinforcement

Lap splices shall be as defined in Section 2108.2.2.7.

The center of the lap splice shall be at the center of the member clear length.

2108.2.2.7 Splices. Reinforcement splices shall comply with one of the following:

1. The minimum length of lap for bars shall be 12 inches (305 mm) or the length determined by Formula (8-22).

$$l_d = l_{de}/\phi \qquad (8\text{-}22)$$

Bars spliced by noncontact lap splices shall be spaced transversely not farther apart than one fifth the required length of lap nor more than 8 inches (203 mm).

2. A welded splice shall have the bars butted and welded to develop in tension 125 percent of the yield strength of the bar, f_y.

3. Mechanical splices shall have the bars connected to develop in tension or compression, as required, at least 125 percent of the yield strength of the bar f_y.

2108.2.6.2.4 Reinforcement.

Welded splices and mechanical connections conforming to Section 1912.14.3, Items 1 through 4, may be used for splicing the reinforcement at any section provided not more than alternate longitudinal bars are spliced at a section, and the distance between splices of alternate bars is at least 24 inches (610 mm) along the longitudinal axis.

Reinforcement shall not have a specified yield strength greater than 60,000 psi (413 MPa). The actual yield strength based on mill tests shall not exceed the specified yield strength times 1.3.

2108.2.6.2.5 Flexural members (beams).

1. Longitudinal reinforcement. At any section of a beam, each masonry unit through the beam depth shall contain longitudinal reinforcement.

The variation in the longitudinal reinforcement area between units at any section shall not be greater than 50 percent, except multiple No. 4 bars shall not be greater than 100 percent of the minimum area of longitudinal reinforcement contained by any one unit, except where splices occur.

2. Transverse reinforcement. Transverse reinforcement shall be hooked around top and bottom longitudinal bars with a standard 180-degree hook, as defined in Section 2108.2.2.4, and shall be single pieces.

Within an end region extending one beam depth from pier faces and at any region at which beam flexural yielding may occur during seismic or wind loading, maximum spacing of transverse reinforcement shall not exceed one fourth the nominal depth of the beam.

The maximum spacing of transverse reinforcement shall not exceed one half the nominal depth of the beam.

The first transverse bar shall not be more than 4 inches (102 mm) from the face of the pier.

2108.2.6.2.6 Members subjected to axial force and flexure.
1. Longitudinal reinforcement. A minimum of four longitudinal bars shall be provided at all sections of every pier.

Flexural reinforcement shall be distributed across the member depth. Variation in reinforcement area between reinforced cells shall not exceed 50 percent.

Maximum bar diameter shall be one eighth nominal width of the pier.

2. Transverse reinforcement. Transverse reinforcement shall be hooked around the extreme longitudinal bars with standard 180-degree hook as defined in Section 2108.2.2.4.

Within an end region extending one pier depth from the end of the beam, and at any region at which flexural yielding may occur during seismic or wind loading, the maximum spacing of transverse reinforcement shall not exceed one fourth the nominal depth of the pier.

The maximum spacing of transverse reinforcement shall not exceed one half the nominal depth of the pier.

IBC Section 2106.1.1.6

2106.1.1.6 Masonry wall frames. Masonry wall frames shall comply with Section 2108.9.6.

As with the Uniform Building Code, only excerpts of the Section on Wall Frames are presented. The full text can be found in the 2000 International Building Code.

IBC Section 2108.9.6

2108.9.6 Special masonry moment frames (wall frames).

2108.9.6.2 Reinforcement.

2108.9.6.2.2 Lap splices. Lap splices are permitted only within the center half of the member length.

2108.9.6.2.3 Other splices. Welded splices and mechanical connections may be used for splicing the reinforcement at any section, provided not more than alternate longitudinal bars are spliced at a section, and the distance between splices on alternate bars is at least 24 inches (610 mm) along the longitudinal axis.

2108.9.6.2.4 Yield strength. Reinforcement shall have a specified yield strength of 60,000 psi (414 MPa). The actual yield strength shall not exceed 1.25 times the specified yield strength.

2108.9.6.3 Wall frame beams.

2108.9.6.3.3 Minimum clear span. Clear span for the beam shall not be less than two times its depth.

2108.9.6.3.4 Beam depth. Nominal depth of the beam shall not be less than two units or 16 inches (406 mm), whichever is greater. The nominal depth to nominal width ratio shall not exceed 6.

2108.9.6.3.5 Beam width. Nominal width of the beams shall equal or exceed the following criteria:

1. Eight inches (203 mm),

2. Width required by Section 2108.9.3.8, Item 1, and

[2108.9.3.8 Dimensional limits. Dimensions shall be in accordance with the following:
1. Beams.
1.1. The nominal width of a beam shall not be less than 6 inches (152 mm).
1.2. The clear distance between locations of lateral bracing of the compression side of the beam shall not exceed 32 times the least width of the compression area.
1.3. The nominal depth of a beam shall not be less than 8 inches (203 mm).]

3. 1/26 of the clear span between column faces.

2108.9.6.4 Longitudinal reinforcement for beams.

2108.9.6.4.1 Spacing. Longitudinal reinforcement shall not be spaced more than 8 inches (203 mm) on center.

2108.9.6.4.2 Distribution. Longitudinal reinforcement shall be uniformly distributed along the depth of the beam.

2108.9.6.4.4 Reinforcement for each masonry unit. At any section of a beam, each masonry unit through the beam depth shall contain longitudinal reinforcement.

2108.9.6.5 Transverse reinforcement for beams.

2108.9.6.5.2 Hooks. Transverse reinforcement shall be hooked around top and bottom longitudinal bars and shall be terminated with a standard 180-degree (3.14 rad) hook.

2108.9.6.5.3 End region spacing. Within an end region extending one beam depth from wall frame column faces and at any region at which beam plastic hinges may form during seismic or wind loading, maximum spacing of transverse reinforcement shall not exceed one-fourth the nominal depth of the beam.

2108.9.6.5.4 Other maximum spacing. The maximum spacing of transverse reinforcement shall not exceed one-half the nominal depth of the beam or that required for shear strength.

2108.9.6.5.6 First bar location. The first transverse bar shall not be more than 4 inches (102 mm) from the face of the column.

2108.9.6.6 Wall frame columns.

2108.9.6.6.2 Parallel column dimension. Nominal dimension of the column parallel to the plane of the wall frame shall not be less than two full units or 32 inches (813 mm), whichever is greater.

2108.9.6.6.3 Height-to-depth ratio. Nominal dimension of the column perpendicular to the plane of the wall frame shall not be less than 8 inches (203 mm) nor 1/14 of the clear height between beam faces.

2108.9.6.6.4 Height-to-depth ratio. The clear height-to-depth ratio of column members shall not exceed 5.

2108.9.6.7 Longitudinal reinforcement for columns.

2108.9.6.7.1 Minimum number. A minimum of four longitudinal bars shall be provided at all sections of every wall frame column member.

2108.9.6.7.2 Distribution. The flexural reinforcement shall be uniformly distributed across the member depth.

2108.9.6.8 Transverse reinforcement for columns.

2108.9.6.8.2 Hooks. Transverse reinforcement shall be hooked around the extreme longitudinal bars and shall be terminated with a standard 180-degree hook.
2108.9.6.8.3 Spacing. The spacing of transverse reinforcement shall not exceed one-fourth the nominal dimension of the column parallel to the plane of the wall frame.

2108.9.6.9 Wall frame beam-column intersection.

2108.9.6.9.2 Reinforcement details. Beam longitudinal reinforcement terminating in a wall frame column shall be extended to the far face of the column and shall be anchored by a standard hook bent back into the wall frame column.

Special horizontal shear reinforcement shall be anchored by a standard hook around the extreme wall frame column reinforcing bars.

8.2   PROPORTION REQUIREMENTS

The proportion and dimension requirements for the spandrel beam are shown in Figure 8.3, and for the vertical column/pier framing member are shown in Figure 8.4.

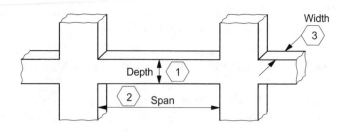

Figure 8.3 Horizontal spandrel beam framing.

⟨1.⟩ Depth of spandrel, horizontal beam between two columns not less than 16 inches (406 mm) or two masonry units, whichever is greater. The nominal depth to width ratio shall be 6 or less.

⟨2.⟩ The clear span of the beam shall be two times its depth, or more.

⟨3.⟩ The nominal width shall be 8 inches (203 mm) or $^{1}/_{26}$ of the clear span, whichever is greater.

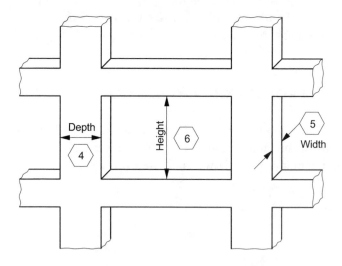

Figure 8.4 Vertical column/pier framing member.

⟨4.⟩ The nominal depth of the column shall not be more than 96 inches (2438 mm) nor less than the greater of two full units or 32 inches (813 mm).

⟨5.⟩ The nominal width of the column shall not be less than the nominal width of the beam and not less than 8 inches (203 mm) or $^1/_{14}$ the clean height between the beam faces, whichever is greatest.

⟨6.⟩ The clear height to depth ratio should not exceed 5.

8.3   REINFORCEMENT DETAILS

Lap splices are IBC defined in Section 2108.9.2.11 or UBC Section 2108.2.2.7. The center of the lap splice shall be at the center of the member clear length.

Welded splices and mechanical connections conforming to AWS D 1.4 (for IBC) or UBC Section 1912.15.3 may be used for splicing the reinforcement at any section provided not more than alternate longitudinal bars are spliced at a section, and the distance between splices on alternate bars is at least 24 inches along the longitudinal axis.

Reinforcement shall have a specified yield strength of 60 ksi. The actual yield strength based on mill tests shall not exceed 75 ksi for IBC or 78 ksi for UBC.

8.4   SPANDREL BEAMS

8.4.1   Longitudinal Reinforcement

At any section of a beam, each masonry unit through the beam depth shall contain longitudinal reinforcement.

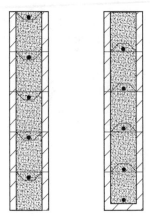

Figure 8.5 Uniform distribution of steel throughout the depth of the spandrel beam.

The variation in the longitudinal reinforcement area between units at any section shall not be greater than 50 percent, except multiple #4 bars shall not be greater than 100 percent, of the minimum area of longitudinal reinforcement contained by any one unit except where splices occur.

8.4.2 Transverse reinforcement

Transverse reinforcement shall be hooked around top and bottom longitudinal bars with standard 180-degree hooks and shall be single pieces.

Within an end region extending one beam depth from pier faces and at any region at which beam plastic hinges may form during seismic or wind loading, maximum spacing of transverse reinforcement shall not exceed one fourth the nominal depth of the beam.

The maximum spacing of transverse reinforcement shall not exceed one half the nominal depth of the beam.

The first transverse bar shall be not more than 4 inches (102 mm) from the face of the pier.

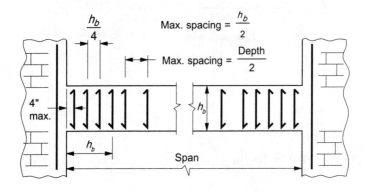

Figure 8.6 Maximum spacing of transverse shear reinforcement in spandrel beam.

8.5 PIERS SUBJECT TO AXIAL FORCE AND FLEXURE

8.5.1 Longitudinal reinforcement

A minimum of 4 longitudinal bars shall be provided at all sections of every pier.

Flexural reinforcement shall be essentially uniformly distributed across member depth.

Maximum bar diameter shall be $\frac{1}{8}$ nominal width of the pier.

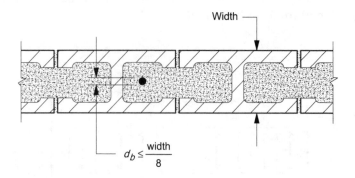

Figure 8.7 Maximum diameter of vertical reinforcing steel.

8.5.2 Transverse reinforcement

Transverse reinforcement shall be hooked around the extreme longitudinal bars with standard 180-degree hooks. This is usually constructed by installing individual pieces of reinforcement with end hooks and lapped in the middle of the masonry member.

Within an end region extending one pier depth from the end of the beam, and at any region at which plastic hinge may form during seismic or wind loading, the maximum spacing of transverse reinforcement shall not exceed one fourth of the nominal depth of the pier.

The maximum spacing of transverse reinforcement shall not exceed one half the nominal depth of the pier.

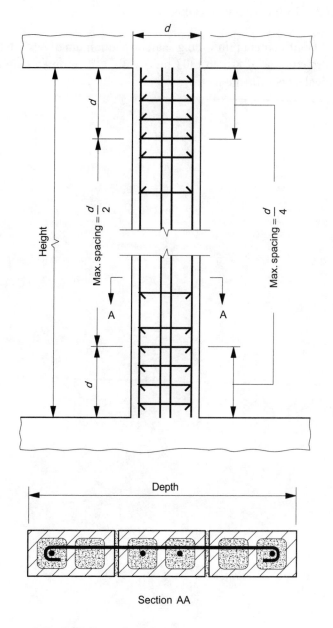

Figure 8.8 Spacing of transverse steel in pier.

8.5.3   Lateral reinforcement.

Confinement reinforcing shall be a minimum of No. 3 bars at a maximum of 8-inch (203 mm) within the grouted core or equivalent confinement.

SECTION 9

Post-Tensioned Masonry

9.1 GENERAL

Post-tensioned, prestressed masonry has been used in Europe for a number of years and is gaining in popularity in the United States. This type of masonry offers an alternative to conventional construction that can be advantageous to the owner, designer and contractor.

In order to understand prestressed masonry, it is helpful to review the definitions contained in the MSJC Specification.

MSJC Specification 1.2
1.2—Definitions
  E. *Bonded prestressing tendon*—Prestressing tendon that is encapsulated by prestressing grout in a corrugated duct that is bonded to the surrounding masonry through grouting.
  T. *Post-tensioning*—Method of prestressing in which prestressing tendons are tensioned after the masonry has been placed.
  U. *Prestressed masonry*—Masonry in which internal stresses have been introduced to counteract stresses in masonry resulting from applied loads.
  V. *Pretensioning*—Method of prestressing in which prestressing tendons are tensioned before the transfer of stress

into masonry.

W. *Prestressing grout*—A cementitious mixture used to encapsulate bonding prestressing tendons.

X. *Prestressing tendon*—Steel element such as wire, bar, or strand, or a bundle of such elements, used to impart prestress to masonry.

AK. *Unbonded prestressing tendon*—Prestressing tendon that is not permanently bonded to masonry.

By the definitions contained in the Specification, this type of masonry is constructed, then tensioned (post-tensioned) to a state where internal stresses are introduced prior to the service life of the masonry wall (prestressed).

Although MSJC Building Code Requirements Section 4.4 is directed toward the designer, the inspector should be aware of the important issues affecting prestressed masonry.

MSJC Section 4.4

4.4—Effective prestress

Computation of the effective prestress, f_{se}, shall include the effects of the following:

(a) anchorage seating loss,

(b) elastic shortening of masonry,

(c) creep of masonry,

(d) shrinkage of concrete masonry,

(e) relaxation of prestressing tendon stress,

(f) friction loss, and

(g) irreversible moisture expansion of clay masonry.

The inspector plays an important role in the quality control of the post-tensioned masonry system. Specifically, the inspector should be observant of the following:

a. Visual inspection of the layout, bond pattern and workmanship.
b. Verify placement and conformance of anchorage in footing.
c. Check that the tension rods are in compliance with the design criteria.
d. Verify threading of rods in accordance with manufacturers' requirements.
e. Verify proper rod tensions.

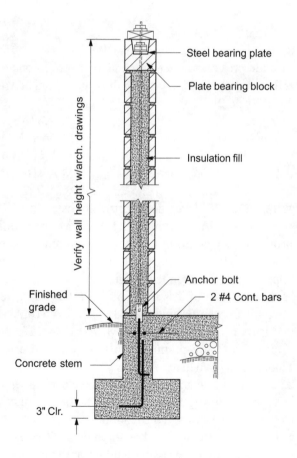

Figure 9.1 Post-tensioned masonry system.

9.2   MATERIALS

The inspector must be aware of the required materials for a prestressed masonry application. Manufacturers publish adequate information related to their particular prestressed masonry products and the designer must be clear in the project requirements. The information contained in the MSJC Specification relates to the minimum material requirements for the application of a prestressed masonry system.

MSJC Specification 2.4 B

2.4 B. *Prestressing tendons*

1. Provide prestressing tendons that conform to one of the following standards, except for those permitted in Articles 2.4 B.2 and 2.4 B.3:
   a. Wire...ASTM A 421
   b. Low-relaxation wire................................ASTM A 421
   c. Strand...ASTM A 416/A 416M
   d. Low-relaxation strand................ASTM A 416/A 416M
   e. Bar...ASTM A 722/A722M
2. Wire, strands and bars not specifically listed in ASTM A 416/A 416M, A 421, or A 722/A 722M are permitted, provided they conform to the minimum requirements in ASTM A 416/A 416M. A 421 or A 722/A 722M and are approved by the Architect/Engineer.
3. Bars and wires of less than 150 ksi (1034 MPa) tensile strength and conforming to ASTM A 82, A 510/A 510M, A 615/A 615M, A 616/A 616M, A 617/A 617M, or A 706/A 706M are permitted to be used as prestressed tendons provided that:
   a. The stress relaxation properties have been assessed by tests according to ASTM E 328 for the maximum permissible stress in the tendon.
   b. Other non-stress-related requirements of Code Chapter 4 addressing prestressing tendons are met.

Prior to installation, the inspector must verify that the materials meet the applicable ASTM requirements.

Additionally, the tendon materials must be protected to avoid any degradation of the tensile members. The masonry inspector should be aware of guidance provided to the designer.

MSJC Section 4.10.2

4.10.2 Corrosion protection of prestressing tendon shall not rely solely on masonry cover.

The masonry inspector also needs to be aware of the direction given to the contractor.

MSJC Specification 2.4 G

2.4 G. *Corrosion protection for tendons*—Protect tendons from corrosion when they are in exterior walls exposed to earth or weather or walls exposed to a mean relative humidity exceeding 75 percent (corrosive environment). Select corrosion protection methods for bonded and unbonded tendons from one of the following:

1. *Bonded tendons*—Encapsulate bonded tendons on corrosion resistant and watertight corrugated ducts complying with Article 2.4 G.1.a. Fill ducts with prestressing grout complying with Article 2.4 G.1b.
   a. Ducts—High-density polyethylene or polypropylene.
      1) Use ducts that are mortar-tight and non-reactive with masonry, tendons and grout.
      2) Provide ducts with an inside diameter at least 1/4 in. (6.4 mm) larger than the tendon diameter.
      3) Maintain ducts free of water if members to be grouted are exposed to temperatures below freezing prior to grouting.

---

4) Provide openings at both ends of ducts for grout injection.

b. Prestressing grout

1) Select proportions of materials for prestressing grout using either of the following methods as accepted by the Architect/Engineer.

a) Results of tests on fresh and hardened prestressing grout—prior to the beginning of grouting operations, or

b) Prior documented experience with similar materials and equipment and under comparable field conditions.

2) Use portland cement conforming to ASTM C 150, Type I, II, or III, that correspond to the type upon which the selection of the prestressing grout was based.

3) Use the minimum water content necessary for proper pumping of prestressing grout; however, limit the water-cement ratio to a maximum of 0.45 by weight.

4) Discard prestressing grout that has begun to set due to delayed use.

5) Do not use admixtures, unless acceptable to the Architect/Engineer.

6) Use water that is potable and free of materials known to be harmful to masonry materials and reinforcement.

7) Use sand that conforms to ASTM C 144.

Many items in traditional masonry construction and prestressed masonry construction are similar: testing prestressed grout for acceptability or using historic documentation to verify the adequacy of prestressed grout, the use of portland cement in grout, discarding cementitious materials that have hardened, limitations on admixtures, use of clean water and sand conforming to ASTM C 144 (which is the same requirement for sand used in mortar).

One should be aware of significant differences that exist. The water content in prestressed grout is carefully limited whereas traditional masonry grout requires a very high water content.

When the designer elects to use a prestressed system with unbonded tendons, then it is essential the inspector be knowledgeable of the applicable requirements.

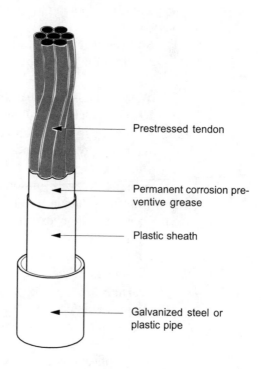

Prestressed tendon

Permanent corrosion preventive grease

Plastic sheath

Galvanized steel or plastic pipe

Figure 9.2 Corrosion protection system for an unbonded tendon.

MSJC Specification 2.4 G.2

2. *Unbonded tendons*—Coat unbonded tendons with a material complying with Article 2.4 G.2b and covered with a sheathing complying with Article 2.4 G.2a. Acceptable materials include a corrosion inhibiting coating material with a tendon covering (sheathing).

   a. Provide continuous tendon sheathing over the entire tendon length to prevent loss of coating materials during tendon installation and stressing procedures. Provide a sheathing of medium or high density polyethylene or polypropylene with the following properties:

      1) Sufficient strength to withstand damage during fabrication, transport, installation, and tensioning.

      2) Watertightness over the entire sheathing length.

      3) Chemical stability without embrittlement or softening over the anticipated exposure temperature range and service life of the structure.

      4) Nonreactive with masonry and the tendon corrosion-inhibiting coating.

      5) In normal (noncorrosive) environments, a sheathing thickness of not less than 0.025 in. (0.6 mm). In corrosive environments, a sheathing thickness of not less than 0.040 in. (1.0 mm).

      6) An inside diameter at least 0.010 in. (0.3 mm) greater than the maximum diameter of the tendon.

      7) For applications in corrosive environments, connect the sheathing to all intermediate and fixed anchorages in a watertight fashion, thus providing a complete encapsulation of the tendon.

b. Provide a corrosion-inhibiting coating material with the following properties:

1) Lubrication between the tendon and the sheathing.

2) Resist flow from the sheathing within the anticipated temperature range of exposure.

3) A continuous nonbrittle film at the lowest anticipated temperature of exposure.

4) Chemically stable and nonreactive with the tendon, sheathing material, and masonry.

5) An organic coating with appropriate polar-moisture displacing and corrosion-preventive additives.

6) A minimum weight not less than 2.5 lb of coating material per 100 ft (37.2 g of coating material per m) of 0.5 in. (12.7 mm) diameter tendon and 3.0 lb of coating material per 100 ft (44.6 g of coating material per m) of 0.6 in. (15.2 mm) diameter tendon. Use a sufficient amount of coating material to ensure filling of the annular space between tendon and sheathing.

7) Extend the coating over the entire tendon length.

8) Provide test results in accordance with Table 6 for the corrosion-inhibiting coating material.

One of the basic concepts of the Code is that alternate materials of equivalency are not restricted from use.

IBC Section 104.11

104.11 Alternative materials, design and methods of construction and equipment. The provisions of this code are not intended to prevent the installation of any material or to prohibit any design or method of construction not specifically prescribed by this code, provided that any such alternative has been approved. An alternative material, design or method of construction shall be approved where the building official finds that the proposed design is satisfactory and complies with the intent of the provisions of this code, and that the material, method or work offered is, for the purpose intended, at least the equivalent of that prescribed in this code in quality, strength, effectiveness, fire resistance, durability and safety.

The prestressed masonry section of the MSJC goes one step further in clarifying alternatives for corrosion protection.

MSJC Specification 2.4 G.3

3. Alternative methods of corrosion protection that provide a protection level equivalent to Articles 2.4 G.1 and 2.4 G.2 are permitted. Stainless steel prestressing tendons or tendons galvanized according to ASTM A 153, Class B, are acceptable alternative methods. If galvanized, further evidence must be provided that the coating will not produce hydrogen embrittlement of the steel.

Additionally, there are material requirements covering materials associated with anchoring the prestressed tendons.

MSJC Specification 2.4 H

2.4 H. *Prestressing anchorages, couplers, and end blocks*

1. Provide anchorages and couplers that develop at least 95 percent of the specified breaking strength of the tendons or prestressing steel when tested in an unbonded condition, without exceeding anticipated set.

2. Place couplers where accepted by Architect/Engineer. Enclose with housing that permits anticipated movements of the couplers during stressing.

3. Protect anchorages, couplers, and end fittings against corrosion.

4. Protect exposed anchorages, couplers, and end fittings to achieve the required mechanical protection and fire rating for the element as specified by local building codes.

9.3   CONSTRUCTION

Construction of prestressed masonry is somewhat more critical than with conventional masonry. This is apparent by the allowable tolerances contained in MSJC Specification Article 3.6 A. When the tendon is properly located, the stresses hold the masonry wall together, but if the tendon location is extreme to either face of the wall, the tendon could contribute in pulling the wall down.

Prior to construction, the inspector should be aware of certain design requirements affecting the layout of the tendons and tendon restraints.

MSJC Chapter 4
4.1.2 (b) The combined minimum number of bars and tendons shall be four.
4.9.3 Reinforcement shall be provided in masonry members near anchorages if tensile stresses created by bursting, splitting, and spalling forces induced by the prestressing tendon exceed the capacity of the masonry.

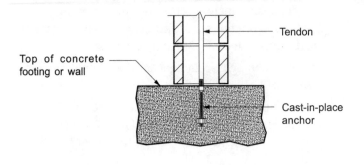

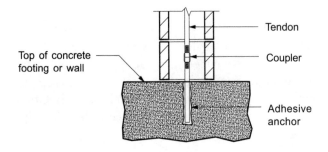

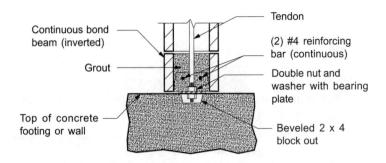

Figure 9.3 Typical bottom anchorage details.

MSJC Specification 3.6
3.6—Prestressing tendon installation and stressing procedure

3.6 A. *Site tolerances*

1. Tolerance for prestressing tendon placement in the out-of-plane direction in beams, columns, pilasters, and walls shall be $\pm \, ^1/_4$ in. (6.4 mm) for masonry cross-sectional dimensions less than nominal 8 in. (203 mm) and $\pm \, ^3/_8$ in. (9.5 mm) for masonry cross-sectional dimensions equal to or greater than nominal 8 in. (203 mm).

2. Tolerance for prestressing tendon placement in the in-plane direction of walls shall be $\pm \, 1$ in. (25.4 mm).

3. If prestressing tendons are moved more than one tendon diameter or a distance exceeding the tolerances stated in Articles 3.6 A.1 and 3.6 A.2 to avoid interference with other tendons, reinforcement, conduits, or embedded items, notify the Architect/Engineer for acceptance of the resulting arrangement of prestressing tendons.

3.6 B. *Application and measurement of prestressing force*

1. Determine the prestressing force by both of the following methods:

   a. Measure the prestressing tendon elongation and compare it with the required elongation based on average load-elongation curves for the prestressing tendons.

   b. Observe the jacking force on a calibrated gage or load cell or by use of a calibrated dynamometer. For prestressing tendons using bars of less than 150 ksi (1034 MPa) tensile strength, Direct Tension Indicator (DTI) washers complying with ASTM F 959 are acceptable.

2. Ascertain the cause of the difference in force determined by the two methods described in Article 3.6.B.1. When the difference exceeds 5 percent for

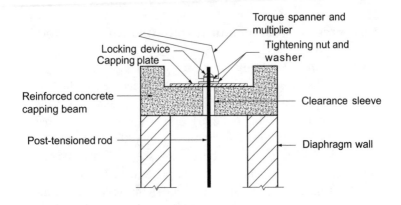

Figure 9.4   Torque anchorage.

Figure 9.5   Direct tension indicator (DTI) washer.

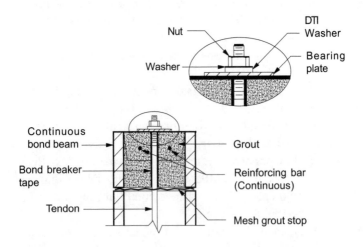

Figure 9.6   Top anchorage.

MSJC Specification 3.6 (Continued)

pre-tensioned elements or 7 percent for post-tensioned elements, and correct the cause of the difference.

3. When the total loss of prestress due to unreplaced broken prestressing tendons exceeds 2 percent of total prestress, notify the Architect/Engineer.

3.6 C. *Grouting bonded tendons*

1. Mix prestressing grout in equipment capable of continuous mechanical mixing and agitation so as to produce uniform distribution of materials, pass through screens, and pump in a manner that will completely fill tendon ducts.

2. Maintain temperature of masonry above 35°F (1.7°C) at time of grouting and until field-cured 2 in. (50.8 mm) cubes of prestressing grout reach a minimum compressive strength of 800 psi (5.52 MPa).

3. Keep prestressing grout temperatures below 90°F (32.2°C) during mixing and pumping.

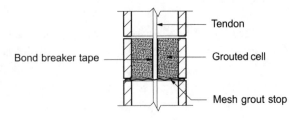

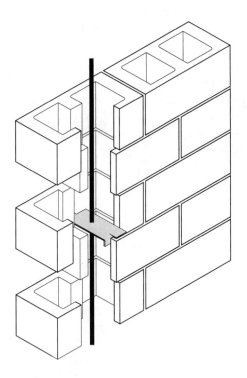

Figure 9.7 Typical lateral restraint.

When completing the prestressed masonry it is important to check for performance issues, such as fire protection of the members.

MSJC Section 4.10.3

4.10.3 Parts of prestressing tendons not embedded in masonry shall be provided with mechanical and fire protection equivalent to that of embedded parts of the tendon.

Accordingly, when finishing or removing excess tendon, it is necessary to see that such operations do not have an adverse affect on the permanent components.

MSJC Specification 3.6.D

3.6 D. *Burning and welding operations*—Carefully perform burning and welding operations in the vicinity of prestressing tendons so that tendons and sheathings, if used, are not subjected to excessive temperatures, welding sparks, or grounding currents.

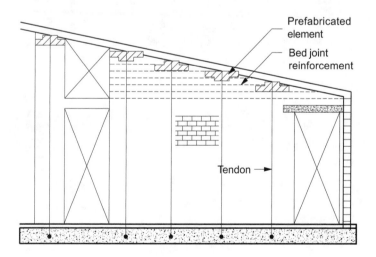

Figure 9.8 Typical prestressed masonry application.

307

Special Topics or Conditions

10.1 BRACING OF WALLS

Part of the construction process includes protection of the installed masonry work during construction. One of the issues associated with protection of work is bracing of the work during the construction process. Historically, this is a means-and-methods issue, not a code issue. It is, however, a potential life-safety issue during the construction process, which is everyone's responsibility.

It is recommended, and some jurisdictions require, that walls be braced during construction to prevent damage or collapse by wind or other forces.

The masonry industry publishes *Standard Practice for Bracing Masonry Walls Under Construction* which provides the guidelines and recommendations associated with bracing of masonry walls. The Standard addresses bracing of masonry walls against wind loads. It does not address bracing of masonry for seismic applications.

The Standard is developed to allow work to continue on a project during low speed wind conditions without bracing.

When wind reaches a critical velocity, the area near the wall is considered a restricted zone and the workers must leave. When work is finished for the day, or when a specified height of wall is reached, or work is interrupted, then that portion of wall must be braced.

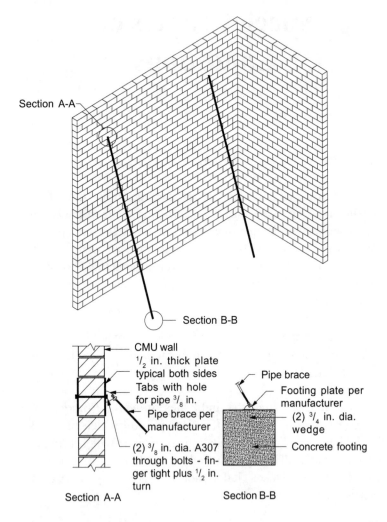

Figure 10.1 Typical wall bracing.

10.2   PIPES AND CONDUITS EMBEDDED IN MASONRY

Since masonry walls are solid, careful planning is necessary in coordinating other trades that interface with masonry. For example, if a mechanical penetration, such as an air shaft, is required to pass through a masonry wall, the plans should clearly show the manner in which the opening is structurally detailed.

MSJC Specification 3.3 E

3.3 E. *Embedded items and accessories*—Install embedded items and accessories as follows:

2. When required, place pipes and conduits passing horizontally through masonry beams or walls in steel sleeves or cored holes.
3. Install pipes and conduits passing horizontally through nonbearing masonry partitions.
4. Place pipes and conduits passing horizontally through piers, pilasters, or columns.
5. Place horizontal pipes and conduits in and parallel to plane of walls.

UBC Section 2106.1.9

2106.1.9 Pipes and conduits embedded in masonry. Pipes or conduit shall not be embedded in any masonry in a manner that will reduce the capacity of the masonry to less than that necessary for required strength or required fire protection.

Placement of pipes or conduits in unfilled cores of hollow-unit masonry shall not be considered as embedment.

> **EXCEPTIONS:** 1. Rigid electric conduits may be embedded in structural masonry when their locations have been detailed on the approved plan.

> 2. Any pipe or conduit may pass vertically or horizontally through any masonry by means of a sleeve at least large enough to pass any hub or coupling on the pipeline. Such sleeves shall not be placed closer than three diameters, center to center, nor shall they unduly impair the strength of construction.

The inspector should be aware that a large embedment (pipe) located in the wall in a horizontal orientation will have a significant structural impact on the performance of the wall.

10.3   ADJACENT WORK

Bolts, anchors and other inserts which attach adjoining construction to the walls should be embedded in mortar at the face shell and solidly grouted for the entire remaining embedment in the walls. Where possible, they should be wired to the reinforcing bars to keep them from dislodging during consolidation of the grout.

MSJC Specification 3.3 E
> 6. Install and secure connectors, flashing, weep holes, weep vents, nailing blocks, and other accessories.

Roof flashing should penetrate the mortar joints not more than one inch (25 mm). Metal door frames should be set and braced in-place before the masonry walls are erected. They should be anchored and solidly grouted in-place as the wall is constructed.

10.4   INTERSECTING STRUCTURAL ELEMENTS

10.4.1 Wall to Wall

It is often advantageous for a wall to be designed to work structurally with another intersecting wall or to a roof or floor. The intersecting structural elements must conform to the applicable code requirements.

MSJC Section 1.9.4

1.9.4   *Intersecting walls*

1.9.4.1 Wall intersections shall meet one of the following requirements:

(a) Design shall conform to the provisions of Section 1.9.4.2.

(b) Transfer of shear between walls shall be prevented.

1.9.4.2   *Design of wall intersection*

1.9.4.2.1 Masonry shall be in running bond.

1.9.4.2.2 Flanges shall be considered effective in resisting applied loads.

1.9.4.2.3 The width of flange considered effective on each side of the web shall be the lesser of 6 times the flange thickness or the actual flange on either side of the web wall.

1.9.4.2.4 Design for shear, including the transfer of shear at interfaces, shall conform to the requirements of Section 2.2.5 or 2.3.5.

1.9.4.2.5 The connection of intersecting walls shall conform to one of the following requirements:

(a) Fifty percent of the masonry units at the interface shall interlock.

(b) Walls shall be regularly toothed with 8 in. (203 mm) maximum offsets and anchored by steel connectors meeting the following requirements:

(1) Minimum size: $'/_4$ in. x 1'$/_2$ in. x 28 in. (6.4 mm x 38.1 mm x 711 mm) including 2 in. (50.8 mm) long 90 degree bend at each end to form a U or Z shape.

---

(2) Maximum spacing: 4 ft (1.22 m).

(c) Intersecting bond beams shall be provided in intersecting walls at a maximum spacing of 4 ft (1.22 m) on centers. Bond beams shall be reinforced and the area of reinforcement shall not be less than 0.1 in.^{2} per ft (211 mm^2/m) of wall. Reinforcement shall be developed on each side of the intersection.

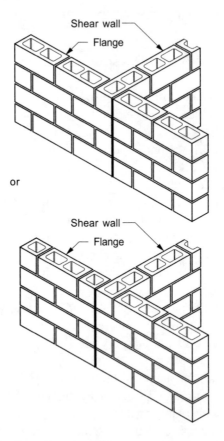

Figure 10.2 Running bond layout with interlocking intersecting wall.

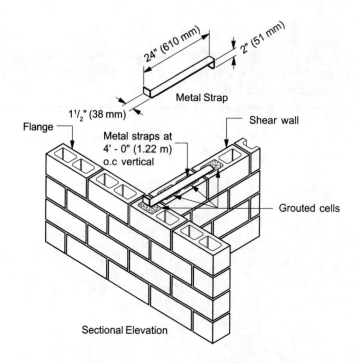

Figure 10.3   Metal strap anchorage at wall intersection.

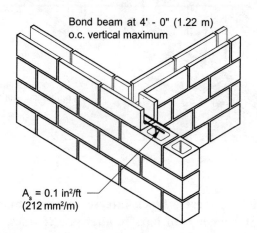

Figure 10.4   Grout and reinforcement bonding of intersecting walls.

Figure 10.5 shows a few traditional details that have been used to tie together corners or intersecting walls.

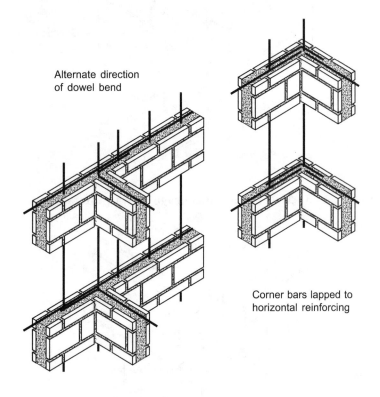

Alternate direction
of dowel bend

Corner bars lapped to
horizontal reinforcing

Figure 10.5 Concrete block intersecting wall and corner details. Stagger laps of bars in alternate courses. Lap all bars a minimum of 30 bar diameters or 24 inches (610 mm), whichever is greater (UBC).

316

10.4.2 Wall to Floor or Roof

In addition to the requirements of masonry construction, the masonry inspector must be aware of the interface of masonry with other building elements.

> ### *MSJC Section 1.15.4*
> **1.15.4** *Anchorage of masonry to structural members, frames and other construction.*
> Anchorage of masonry to structural members, frames, and other construction shall be detailed on the project drawings which shall show the type, size, and location of anchor bolts.

> ### *UBC Section 2106.2.11*
> **2106.2.11 Walls intersecting with floors and roofs.**
> Walls shall be anchored to all floors, roofs or other elements which provide lateral support for the wall. Where floors or roofs are designed to transmit horizontal forces to walls, the anchorage to such walls shall be designed to resist the horizontal force.

Precast floor planks can be used on an interior block wall. The planks change directions of span. A concrete topping is cast after the upper wall has been erected. Vertical reinforcing steel goes through the wall and is anchored in the topping concrete.

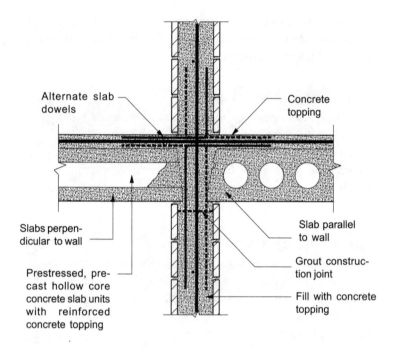

Figure 10.6 Floor to side wall connection details.

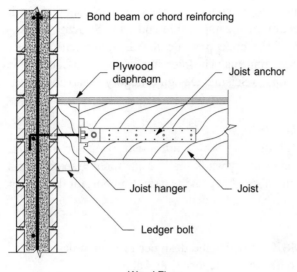

Bond beam or chord reinforcing

Plywood diaphragm

Joist anchor

Joist hanger

Joist

Ledger bolt

Wood Floor

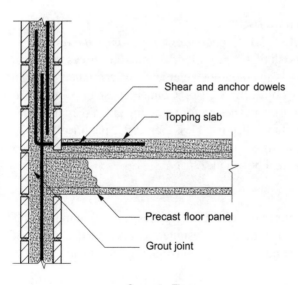

Shear and anchor dowels

Topping slab

Precast floor panel

Grout joint

Concrete Floor

Figure 10.7 Through floor and wall connection details.

In addition to the connection requirements contained in the masonry section of the applicable code, the Structural Design Provisions of the code provide the designer with specific connection requirements. The International Building Code applies these provisions to Seismic Design Category B and above.

> **IBC Section 1620.1.7**
>
> **1620.1.7 Bearing walls and shear walls.** In addition, concrete and masonry walls shall be anchored to the roof and floors and members that provide lateral support for the wall or that are supported by the wall.

The MSJC provides the designer minimum design levels that apply to Seismic Category C and above.

> **MSJC Section 1.13.5.3.1**
>
> **1.13.5.3.1** *Connections to masonry shear walls—* Connectors shall be provided to transfer forces between masonry walls and horizontal elements in accordance with the requirements of Section 2.1.6. Connectors shall be designed to transfer horizontal design forces acting either perpendicular or parallel to the wall, but not less than 200 lb per lineal ft (2929 N per lineal m) of wall. The maximum spacing between connectors shall be 4 ft (1.22m).

The Uniform Building Code applies higher minimum design levels for the benefit of the designer. Unlike the IBC, the UBC provisions are not sensitive to seismic regions or categories.

10.5   MULTIWYTHE WALLS

10.5.1 General

Masonry walls of two independent wythes (widths) must
be tied together in some manner according to the applicable code.
The MSJC provides the requirements for walls of composite and
noncomposite action.

UBC Section 2106.1.5

2106.1.5.1 General All wythes of multiwythe walls shall be bonded by grout or tied together by corrosion-resistant wall ties or joint reinforcement conforming to the requirements of Section 2102, and as set forth in this subsection. (See Figure 2.4 for an example).

Additionally, the Uniform Building Code requires grout barriers, or dams, in grouted multiwythe walls. Although this is not required in IBC or MSJC, it is a good practice to avoid long bell-shaped grout flow lines.

UBC Section 2104.6.1

In multiwythe grouted masonry, vertical barriers of masonry shall be built across the grout space the entire height of the grout pour and spaced not more than 30 feet (9144 mm) horizontally. The grouting of any section of wall between barriers shall be completed in one day with no interruption longer than one hour.

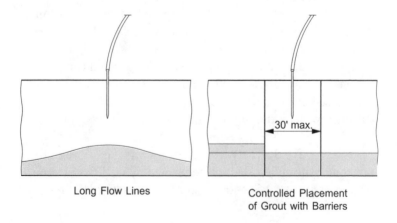

Long Flow Lines   Controlled Placement
                         of Grout with Barriers

Figure 10.8 Use of grout barriers.

10.5.2 Metal Ties for Cavity Wall Construction

In order to assure the performance of ties connecting wythes, the code provides mandatory guidelines for the material and installation of wall ties.

IBC Section 2104.1.3

2104.1.3 Installation of wall ties. The ends of wall ties shall be embedded in mortar joints. Wall tie ends shall engage outer face shells of hollow units by at least $1/_2$ inch (12.7 mm). Wire wall ties shall be embedded at least $1 \, 1/_2$ inch (38 mm) into the mortar bed of solid masonry units or solid-grouted hollow units. Wall ties shall not be bent after being embedded in grout or mortar.

MSJC Specification 3.4 D

3.4 D *Wall ties*

1. Embed the ends of wall ties in mortar joints. Embed wall tie ends at least $1/_2$ in. (13 mm) into the outer face shell of hollow units. Embed wire wall ties at least $1 1/_2$ in. (38.1 mm) into the mortar bed of solid masonry units or solid grouted hollow units.

2. Unless otherwise required, bond wythes not bonded by headers with wall ties as follows:

Wire size	*Minimum number of wall ties required*
W1.7 (MW I l)	One per 2.67 ft² (0.25 m²)
W2.8 (MW 18)	One per 4.50 ft² (0.42 m²)

The maximum spacing between ties is 36 in. (914 mm) horizontally and 24 in. (610 mm) vertically.

3. Unless accepted by the Architect/Engineer, do not bend wall ties after being embedded in grout or mortar.

4. Unless otherwise required, install adjustable ties in accordance with the following requirements:
   a. One tie for each 1.77 ft² (0.16 m²) of wall area
   b. Do not exceed 16 in. (406 mm) horizontal or vertical spacing.
   c. The maximum misalignment of bed joints from one wythe to the other is $1^1/_4$ in. (31.8 mm).
   d. The maximum clearance between connecting parts of the ties is $^1/_{16}$ in. (1.6 mm).
   e. When pintle legs are used, provide ties with at least two legs made of wire size W2.8 (MW 18).
5. Install wire ties perpendicular to a vertical line on the face of the wythe from which they protrude. Where one-piece ties or joint reinforcement are used, the bed joints of adjacent wythes shall align.

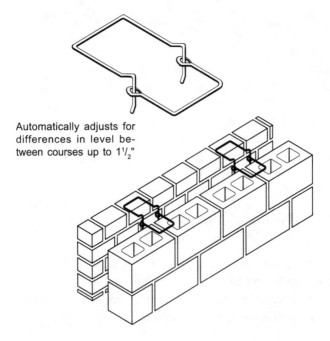

Automatically adjusts for differences in level between courses up to $1^1/_2$"

Figure 10.9 Adjustable wall tie (Pintel type).

6. Unless otherwise required, provide additional unit ties around all openings larger than 16 inches (406 mm) in either dimension. Space ties around perimeter of opening at a maximum of 3 ft (0.91 m) on center. Place ties within 12 in. (305 mm) of opening.

UBC Section 2106.1.5.2

2106.1.5.2 Wall ties in cavity wall construction. Wall ties shall be of sufficient length to engage all wythes. The portion of the wall ties within the wythe shall be completely embedded in mortar or grout. The ends of the wall ties shall be bent to 90-degree angles with an extension not less than 2 inches (51 mm) long. Wall ties not completely embedded in mortar or grout between wythes shall be a single piece with each end engaged in each wythe.

There shall be at least one $^3/_{16}$-inch-diameter (9.5 mm) wall tie for each $4^1/_2$ square feet (0.42 m^2) of wall area. For cavity walls in which the width of the cavity is greater than 3 inches (75 mm), but not more than $4^1/_2$ inches (115 mm), at least one $^3/_{16}$-inch-diameter (9.5 mm) wall tie for each 3 square feet (0.28 m^2) of wall area shall be provided.

Ties in alternate courses shall be staggered. The maximum vertical distance between ties shall not exceed 24 inches (610 mm) and the maximum horizontal distance between ties shall not exceed 36 inches (914 mm).

Additional ties spaced not more than 36 inches (914 mm) apart shall be provided around openings within a distance of 12 inches (305 mm) from the edge of the opening.

Adjustable wall ties shall meet the following requirements:

1. One tie shall be provided for each 1.77 square feet (0.16 m²) of wall area. Horizontal and vertical spacing shall not exceed 16 inches (406 mm). Maximum misalignment of bed joints from one wythe to the other shall be 1½ inches (32 mm).

2. Maximum clearance between the connecting parts of the tie shall be $^1/_{16}$ inch (1.6 mm). When used, pintle ties shall have at least two $^3/_{16}$-inch-diameter (4.8 mm) pintle legs.

Wall ties of different size and spacing that provide equivalent strength between wythes may be used.

10.5.3 Metal Ties for Grouted Multiwythe Construction

UBC Section 2106.1.5.3

2106.1.5.3 Wall ties for grouted multiwythe construction. Wythes of multiwythe walls shall be bonded together with at least $^3/_{16}$-inch-diameter (4.8 mm) steel wall tie for each 2 square feet (0.19 m²) of area. Wall ties of different size and spacing that provide equivalent strength between wythes may be used.

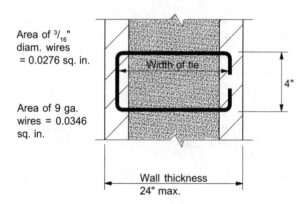

Area of $^3/_{16}$" diam. wires = 0.0276 sq. in.

Area of 9 ga. wires = 0.0346 sq. in.

Width of tie

4"

Wall thickness
24" max.

Figure 10.10 Typical positioning of grout tie.

Movement Joints and Crack Control

11.1   GENERAL

Cracking in concrete masonry can be caused by a number of factors and is usually aesthetic, not structural. It can, however, have structural implications. For example, if masonry cracks and moisture is allowed to freely migrate to the reinforcement, then the steel can degrade, which is not a desirable condition.

Historically, the building codes did not address the issue of control joints and expansion joints in walls, but the MSJC Code gives the designer some direction on considering the issue.

> **MSJC Section 1.7.4**
>
> **1.7.4** Consideration shall be given to the effects of forces and deformations due to prestressing, vibrations, impact, shrinkage, expansion, temperature changes, creep, unequal settlement of supports, and differential movement.

The subsequent MSJC Section (Section 1.8) provides the designer coefficient values to use in considering the effects on masonry.

11.2   JOINTING; CONTROL JOINTS AND EXPANSION JOINTS

11.2.1 Sources of Movement

All structures are subject to movement and it is vitally necessary to accommodate the possibilities of these movements. Movements can occur from a number of sources, such as:

a.   Temperature changes
b.   Material expansion and contraction
c.   Changes in moisture content or conditions
d.   Loading conditions
e.   Foundation movement
f.   Differential movement of various materials in the building
g.   Lateral deflections from wind loads
h.   Seismic activity

Masonry walls that move can develop cracking which may be due to the following:

11.2.2 Properties of Concrete Masonry Units

a.   Moisture content, e.g. green block at time of laying
b.   Shrinkage characteristics of the block
c.   Tensile strength
d.   Carbonation

11.2.3 Environmental Factors

a.   Temperature increases and decreases causing thermal expansion and contraction
b.   Moisture exposure, such as inclement weather

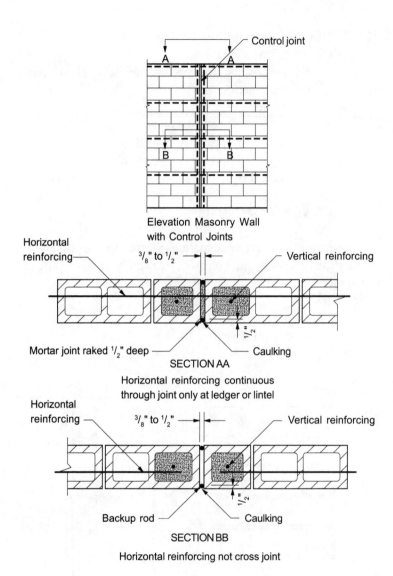

Elevation Masonry Wall
with Control Joints

SECTION AA

Horizontal reinforcing continuous
through joint only at ledger or lintel

SECTION BB

Horizontal reinforcing not cross joint

This detail as shown is intended to illustrate a general concept or method of construction. Not intended for use without review and approval of designer who shall be responsible for design and proper application.

Figure 11.1 Typical control joint layout.

11.2.4 Design/Construction Deficiencies

a. Excessive spacing of horizontal steel or joint reinforcement
b. Control joints
    i. None or too few
    ii. Improperly spaced
    iii. Improperly constructed
c. Embedded structural steel not properly isolated

11.3 CRACK CONTROL

There are three recommendations that reduce the possibility of unsightly cracks in concrete masonry walls. These recommendations are:

a. Proper jointing
b. Proper reinforcement
c. Moisture control

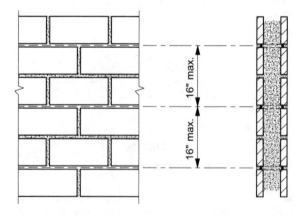

Figure 11.2 Joint reinforcement in alternate bed joints of CMU wall lay in running bond.

11.4   CONTROL JOINTS

Control joints are considered joints that will accommodate shortening, shrinkage and/or reduction in the length of the wall, while expansion joints will accommodate both expansion and contraction of the wall or increases and decreases in length.

Control joints are usually vertical and spaced at intervals so that when shortening occurs the resulting cracks will be at the location of the control joints. It is important to locate a sufficient number of control joints so that relative movement occurs at the control joint rather than through the blocks and mortar joints between the control joints.

Joints in the wall, whether they are control joints or expansion joints, should match any joints that are built into the roof system, the floor system, the spandrel beams, or other elements that are intended to accommodate movement of the building.

When horizontal reinforcing steel is used in the wall, either in bond beams or in the mortar bed with joint reinforcement, the spacing of the control joints to accommodate the shortening of the wall can be adjusted accordingly.

Historically, spacing of control joints was largely dependent on spacing of horizontal reinforcement and a variable ratio of panel length to height. This gave spacing recommendations of up to 60 feet between control joints. Current recommendations from the National Concrete Masonry Association (NCMA) are given in Table 11-A, however, based on engineering and aesthetic design, it is reasonable to maximize horizontal spacing of control joints at 25 to 30 feet.

Vertical control joints should be located in masonry walls at the following locations:

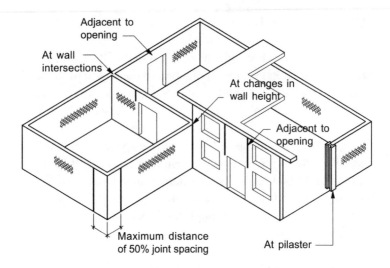

Figure 11.3 Typical control joint locations.

a. At determined intervals and spacing for the length of the wall
b. At major changes in the wall height
c. At changes in the wall thickness
d. At control joints in the foundation floor and roof
e. At wall openings
f. At wall intersections

Table 11-2—Recommended Control Joint Spacing for Above Grade Exposed Concrete Masonry Walls*
Distance between joints should not exceed the lesser of:

Length to height ratio	or feet (m)
$1\frac{1}{2}$	25 (7.62)

*Notes:
1. Table values based on the use of horizontal reinforcement having an equivalent area of not less than 0.025 in²/ft. (52.9 mm²/m) of height to keep unplanned cracks closed.
2. Criteria applies to all concrete masonry units.
3. This criteria is based on experience over a wide geographical area. Control joint spacing should be adjusted up or down where local experience justifies but no farther than 25 ft. (7.62 m).
4. NCMA TEK 10-2B, Table 1.

332

Control joints should be constructed with a vertical head joint, raking back the mortar at least one inch and interrupting the horizontal steel at least at every other bar or joint reinforcement. Control joints may also be mortarless head joints with flange as in Figure 11.5. To prevent the wall from displacing perpendicular to the plane of the wall, dowels may be used across the joint provided one end is encased in a plastic sleeve or pipe. Solid grouted walls crack at the control joint and provide aggregate interlock which prevents displacement and slip, dowels are not required. Primary structural reinforcing steel, such as perimeter chords beams and lintels, must not be cut. Caulk or sealant should fill the raked vertical head joints to keep the system weatherproof.

Typical caulking and sealant compounds can stretch best when the width of the joint is greater than the depth of the sealant, similar to a rubber band. Manufacturer's recommendations should always be followed. The usual practice is to place the caulking or sealant so the depth of sealant is only half the width. Sealant depth is controlled by using a compatible backup rod. See Figure 11.4.

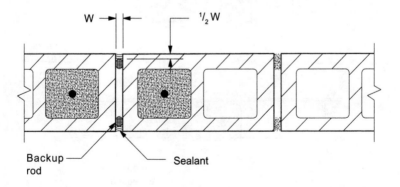

Figure 11.4 Control joint in a wall.

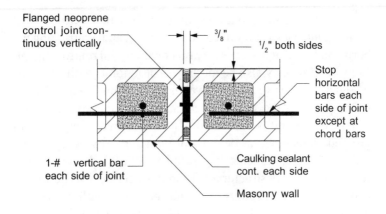

Figure 11.5 Wall control joint/flanged neoprene.

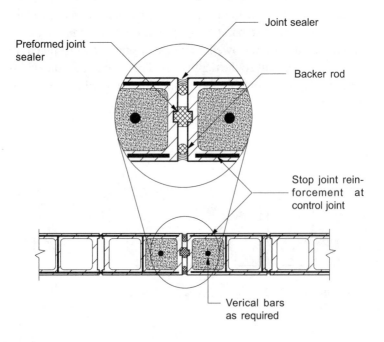

Figure 11.6 Preformed gasket.

11.5   EXPANSION JOINTS

Expansion joints can be used to accommodate increases in length in long runs of walls and where there are large temperature swings. When used, spacing of expansion joints should be between 150 and 200 feet (45.7 m and 61.0 m) and located with consideration to the shape and plan of the structure. Concern must be given to the expansion of the wall and the possibility of pushing out the adjoining perpendicular walls at the ends of walls, thus, the expansion joints should be near the ends of the building. Many conditions allow the expansion joints to be placed in the middle between ends of the walls, allowing movement of the walls both ways toward the center.

The expansion joint should be filled with a caulking or compressible sealant material that will both expand and compress and allow for total movement of the wall.

Expansion joints are similar to control joints in appearance, however, a control joint provides for movement of a wall in contraction and can have some solid masonry or grout in the joint. An expansion joint is used to provide for movement of a wall as it expands and must not contain any incompressible material.

11.6   SUMMARY

Crack control measures for concrete masonry walls are summarized as follows:

1. Use units in climatic balance. This means that the moisture condition of the concrete masonry units is in a state of equilibrium with the relative humidity of the project site.

2. Use joint reinforcement. This is effective when locating joint reinforcement in the bed joint mortar on the face shells.

3. Put in adequate, properly spaced and properly-constructed control joints and expansion joints.

The knowledge of the mason contractor and the masonry inspector can be used to alert the general contractor and the designer concerning potential problem areas for crack control. When potential problems are noted ahead of time, costly delays and disruptions are avoided.

11.7   CRACK REPAIR

If a crack does occur, the repair depends on location, how large the crack is, what kind of block is involved, and how important appearance is. Usually it is not possible to accomplish a repair with only paint or a clear sealer. Repeated movement will reopen cracks that have been bridged over. The crack must be opened up enough so that a bead of flexible caulking or sealant can be applied. The caulking or sealant should remain flexible even when dry. It can be painted with a compatible paint. Some caulks and sealants come in a range of colors and can be matched reasonably close to mortar colors when used on integral color block jobs.

Construction in Severe Weather Conditions

12.1   COLD WEATHER MASONRY CONSTRUCTION

12.1.1 General

The following cold weather provisions were initially prepared by the International Masonry Industry All Weather Council and are based on *Recommended Practice Guide Specification for Cold Weather Masonry, 1970*, applicable to UBC, BOCA and SBC. The publication has been updated by the Masonry Industry Council's *Hot & Cold Weather Masonry Construction, 1999*, which also applies to more recent IBC and MSJC Specification.

MSJC Specification 1.8B
    1.8B. *Masonry protection*—Cover top of unfinished masonry work to protect it from weather.

UBC Section 2104.3
2104.3   Cold-weather Construction.
    2104.3.1   General. All materials shall be delivered in a usable condition and stored to prevent wetting by capillary action, rain and snow.

The tops of all walls not enclosed or sheltered shall be covered with a strong weather-resistive material at the end of each day or shutdown.

Partially completed walls shall be covered at all times when work is not in progress. Covers shall be draped over the wall and extend a minimum of 2 feet (600 mm) down both sides and shall be securely held in place, except when additional protection is required in Section 2104.3.4.

12.1.2 Preparation

The IBC and MSJC contain preparation provisions within the construction requirements of the Code, whereas the UBC contains a specific section in Cold Weather Construction addressing preparation.

UBC Section 2104.3.2

2104.3.2 Preparation. If ice or snow has inadvertently formed on a masonry bed, it shall be thawed by application of heat carefully applied until top surface of the masonry is dry to the touch. A section of masonry deemed frozen and damaged shall be removed before continuing construction of that section.

12.1.3 Construction

All codes address cold weather construction with the same provisions.

IBC Section 2104.3

2104.3 Cold-weather construction. The following cold-weather procedures shall be implemented when either the ambient temperature falls below 40°F (4°C) or the temperature of masonry units is below 40°F (4°C):

1. Temperatures of masonry units shall not be less than 20°F (-7°C) when laid in the masonry. Visible ice on masonry units shall be removed before the unit is laid in the masonry.

2. Mortar sand or mixing water shall be heated to produce mortar temperatures between 40°F (4°C) and 120°F (49°C) at the time of mixing. Mortar shall be maintained above freezing until used in masonry.

3. Heat sources shall be used where ambient temperatures are between 20°F (-7°C) and 25°F (-4°C) on both sides of the masonry under construction and wind breaks shall be installed when wind velocity is in excess of 15 mph (24 km/hr).

4. Where ambient temperatures are below 20°F (-7°C), an enclosure for the masonry under construction shall be provided and heat sources shall be used in main temperatures above 32°F (0°C) within the enclosure.

5. Where mean daily temperatures are between 32°F (0°C) and 40°F (4°C), completed masonry shall be protected from rain or snow by covering with a weather-resistant membrane for 24 hours after construction.

6. Where mean daily temperatures are between 25°F (-4°C) and 32°F (0°C), completed masonry shall be completely covered with a weather-resistant membrane for 24 hours after construction.

7. Where mean daily temperatures are between 20°F (-7°C) and 25°F (-4°C), completed masonry shall be completely covered with insulating blankets or equal protection for 24 hours after construction.

8. Where mean daily temperatures are below 20°F (-7°C), masonry temperature shall be maintained above 32°F (0°C) for 24 hours after construction by enclosure with supplementary heat, by electric heating blankets, by infrared heat lamps or by other approved methods.

9. Glass unit masonry shall not be laid during cold periods as defined in this section. The temperature of glass unit masonry shall be maintained above 40°F (4°C) for the first 48 hours after construction.

MSJC Specification Section 1.8C

1.8C. *Cold weather construction*

    1. Implement the following requirements when:
       a. The ambient temperature falls below 40°F (4.4°C), or;
       b. The temperature of masonry units is below 40°F (4.4°C).

    2. Do not lay masonry units having a temperature below 20°F (-6.7°C). Remove visible ice on masonry units before the unit is laid in the masonry.

    3. Heat mortar sand or mixing water to produce mortar temperatures between 40°F (4.4°C) and 120°F (48.9°C) at the time of mixing. Maintain mortar above freezing until used in masonry.

    4. When ambient temperature is between 25°F (-3.9°C) and 20°F (-6.7°C) use heat sources on both sides of the masonry under construction and install wind breaks when wind velocity is in excess of 15 mph (24.1 km/h).

    5. When ambient temperature is below 20°F (-6.7°C), provide an enclosure for the masonry under construction and use heat sources to maintain temperatures above 32°F (0°C) within the enclosure.

    6. When mean daily temperature is between 40°F (4.4°C) and 32°F (0°C), protect completed masonry from rain or snow by covering with a weather-resistive membrane for 24 hr after construction.

    7. When mean daily air temperature is between 32°F (0°C) and 25°F (-3.9°C), completely cover completed masonry with a weather-resistive membrane for 24 hr after construction.

    8. When mean daily temperature is between 25°F (-3.9°C) and 20°F (-6.7°C), completely cover completed masonry with insulating blankets or equal protection for 24 hr after construction.

    9. When mean daily temperature is below 20°F (-6.7°C), maintain masonry temperature above 32°F (0°C) for 24 hr after

construction by enclosure with supplementary heat, by electric heating blankets, by infrared heat lamps, or by other acceptable methods.

10. Do not lay glass unit masonry during cold weather construction periods as defined in Article 1.8 C.1.a or 1.8 C.1.b. Maintain temperature of glass unit masonry above 40°F (4.4°C) for the first 48 hr after construction.

UBC Section 2104.3.3

2104.3.3 Construction. Masonry units shall be dry at the time of placement. Wet or frozen masonry units shall not be laid.

Special requirements for various temperature ranges are as follows:

1. Air temperature 40°F to 32°F (4.5°C to 0°C): Sand or mixing water shall be heated to produce mortar temperatures between 40°F and 120°F (4.5°C to 49°C).

2. Air temperature 32°F to 25°F (0°C to -4°C): Sand and mixing water shall be heated to produce mortar temperatures between 40°F and 120°F (4.5°C to 49°C). Maintain temperatures of mortar on boards above freezing.

3. Air temperature 25°F to 20°F (-4°C to -7°C): Sand and mixing water shall be heated to produce mortar temperatures between 40°F and 120°F (4.5°C to 49°C). Maintain mortar temperatures on board above freezing. Salamanders or other sources of heat shall be used on both sides of walls under construction. Windbreaks shall be employed when wind is in excess of 15 miles per hour (24 km/h).

4. Air temperature 20°F (-7°C) and below: Sand and mixing water shall be heated to produce mortar temperatures between 40°F and 120°F (4.5°C to 49°C). Enclosure and auxiliary heat shall be provided to maintain air temperature above freezing. Temperature of units when laid shall not be less that 20°F (-7°C).

In order to apply the above provisions, it is necessary to establish the mean daily temperature. The IBC defined the mean daily temperature as the average daily temperature of temperature extremes predicted by a local weather bureau for the subsequent 24 hour period.

12.1.4 Protection

IBC and MSJC incorporate protection provisions in the cold weather construction requirements, whereas the UBC provides for protection under a separate section.

UBC Section 2104.3.4

2104.3.4 Protection. When the mean daily air temperature is 40°F to 32°F (4.5°C to 0°C), masonry shall be protected from rain or snow for 24 hours by covering with a weather-resistive membrane.

When the mean daily air temperature is 32°F to 25°F (0°C to -4°C), masonry shall be completely covered with a weather-resistive membrane for 24 hours.

When the mean daily air temperature is 25°F to 20°F (4°C to -7°C), masonry shall be completely covered with insulating blankets or equally protected for 24 hours.

When the mean daily air temperature is 20°F (-7°C) or below, masonry temperature shall be maintained above freezing for 24 hours by enclosure and supplementary heat, by electric heating blankets, infrared heat lamps or other approved methods.

12.1.5 Placing Grout and Protection of Grouted Masonry

The UBC is also unique in grouting requirements for cold weather masonry construction.

UBC Section 2104.3.5

2104.3.5 Placing grout and protection of grouted masonry.

When air temperatures fall below 40°F (4.5°C), grout mixing water and aggregate shall be heated to produce grout temperatures between 40°F and 120°F (4.5°C and 49°C).

Masonry to be grouted shall be maintained above freezing during grout placement and for at least 24 hours after placement.

When atmospheric temperatures fall below 20°F (-7°C), enclosures shall be provided around the masonry during grout placement and for at least 24 hours after placement.

12.1.6 Summary of Recommended Cold Weather Practices

The following points are important factors in laying masonry work in cold weather.

- Schedule the work beforehand if masonry work is to be built in cold temperatures.
- Take advantage of warm days by working on the outside of the structure, saving the inside work for the colder days.
- Store all masonry units close to the structure. Be sure units are covered and off the ground to prevent moisture or frost from penetrating.
- Build a mortar mixing area covered with a roof. Keep the sand pile covered to prevent moisture, ice or snow from collecting on materials.

- Preheat sand and water before mixing mortar.
- If available, use Type III, high early strength portland cement or a non-chloride accelerator additive for a quicker set.
- Do not use antifreeze in the mortar. Calcium chloride is considered to be an accelerator not an antifreeze. Never use calcium chloride if there is metal in the mortar joints.
- Build protective shelters such as windbreaks and enclosures to protect the mason and masonry work.
- Observe good safety practices when building shelters to prevent them from collapsing or blowing over, causing damage and injury.
- Take protective measures at the end of the workday to protect the work and to ensure that work is started on time the next day. Some protective measures are covering the work and piles of materials, draining the hoses and cleaning out the mortar pans. Place a block of wood in the water barrel so the water does not freeze which also keeps the barrel from deforming.

The requirements for cold weather masonry construction are summarized in the following tables. The tables are based on the UBC with footnotes showing differences with IBC and MSJC. Additionally, the IBC and MSJC do not permit laying of glass block at temperatures below 40°F.

Laying the Units	*Temperature Range*			
ACTION	40° to 32°	32° to 25°	25° to 20°	20° & below
Heat sand *or* mixing water for mortar 40°F to 120°F	✔			
Heat sand *and* mixing water for mortar 40°F to 120°F[1]		✔	✔	✔
Maintain mortar above freezing[2]		✔	✔	
Use salamanders or equal			✔	
Windbreaks for excess of 15 mph			✔	
Provide enclosures & auxiliary heat to produce air temperature above 32° F				✔
Temperature of units to be at least 20°F[3]				✔

[1] IBC and MSJC do not require sand *and* mixing water (both) to be heated
[2] Applies to all construction below 40°F
[3] IBC and MSJC state this provision for all temperatures under 40°F

Protecting the Units	*Mean Daily Temperature*			
ACTION	40° to 32°	32° to 25°	25° to 20°	Below 20°
Protect for 24 hours with weather resistive membrane	✔	✔		
Protect for 24 hours with insulating blankets			✔	
Provide enclosure & auxiliary heat or equal to keep temperature above freezing for 24 hours				✔

Grouting the Units[1]	*Temperature Range*			
ACTION	40° to 32°	32° to 25°	25° to 20°	Below 20°
Heat aggregate *and* mixing water for grout 40°F to 120°F	✔	✔	✔	✔
Maintain wall above freezing for 24 hours	✔	✔	✔	✔
Enclosures for 24 hours				✔

[1] Cold weather grouting provisions not contained in IBC

12.2 HOT WEATHER MASONRY CONSTRUCTION

12.2.1 General

Building with masonry in hot weather of 90°F (32°C) and above can cause special problems. High temperatures can cause the materials to become very warm, affecting their performance. Rapid evaporation will also occur having an effect on hydration and curing. Special consideration must be given to the handling and selection of materials and to construction procedures during hot weather.

12.2.2 Performance

The physical properties of masonry will change with an increase in temperature.

1. Bond strength can decrease as units become hotter and drier, causing an increase in suction rate.
2. The compressive strength of the mortar and grout can also decrease if water quickly evaporates, leaving little for hydration.
3. Workability is affected, as more water is required in the mortar for constant consistency and in grout to make filling of spaces possible.
4. Heat will affect the amount of air entraining used, since more is required in hot weather.
5. The initial and final set of mortar will occur faster.
6. Water will evaporate quickly on a mortar joint's exterior surfaces, causing a decrease in strength and durability.
7. The initial water content of mortar will be higher, but the placing of mortar will be difficult and the time period for placing the mortar will be shortened.

12.2.3 Handling and Selection of Materials

When hot weather is expected, the materials should be stored in a shaded or cool place. Increasing the cement content will cause the mortar and grout to gain strength quickly but will also impose a demand on the available water in the mix. The amount of lime can be increased giving the mortar a higher water retentivity.

Covering the aggregate with a light color or clear plastic sheet will retard the evaporation of any moisture in the raw material. Adding extra water will help keep the aggregate cool since evaporation has a cooling effect.

The units used should be stored in the shade and covered. The use of cold water on the units, especially block, for cooling purposes is **not** recommended. The use of cold water or ice water as mixing water will lower the temperature of the mortar or grout. Ice can be used to cool the water only and should not directly contact the cement or aggregates.

12.2.4 Construction Procedure

When placing masonry units in hot weather, special consideration should be given to all equipment that comes in contact with the mortar. Flushing the mixers, tools and mortar board, occasionally with cold water helps keep temperature to a minimum.

Mortar should not be mixed too far ahead, and when mixed, should be stored in a cool, shady place. Avoid placing long mortar beds ahead of the units as bond is reduced.

When extremely high temperatures are expected, consideration should be given to stopping placement of masonry during the hottest times of day.

IBC Section 2104.4

2104.4 Hot weather construction. The following hot-weather procedures shall be implemented when the temperature or the temperature and wind-velocity limits of this section are exceeded.

2104.4.1 Preparation. The following requirements shall be met prior to conducting masonry work.

2104.4.1.1. Temperature. When the ambient temperature exceeds 100°F (38°C), or exceeds 90°F (32°C) with a wind velocity greater than 8 mph (13 km/h):

1. Necessary conditions and equipment shall be provided to produce mortar having a temperature below 120°F (49°C).

2. Sand piles shall be maintained in a damp, loose condition.

2104.4.1.2. Special conditions. When the ambient temperature exceeds 115°F (46°C), or 105°F (40°C) with a wind velocity greater than 8 mph (13 km/h), the requirements of Section 2104.4.1.1 shall be implemented, and materials and mixing equipment shall be shaded from direct sunlight.

2104.4.2 Construction. The following requirements shall be met while masonry work is in progress.

2104.4.2.1. Temperature. When the ambient temperature exceeds 100°F (38°C), or exceeds 90°F (32°C) with a wind velocity greater than 8 mph (13 km/h):

1. The temperature of mortar and grout shall be maintained below 120°F (49°C).

2. Mixers, mortar transport containers and mortar boards shall be flushed with cool water before they come into contact with mortar ingredients or mortar.

3. Mortar consistency shall be maintained by retempering with cool water.

4. Mortar shall be used within 2 hours of initial mixing.

2104.4.2.2. Special conditions. When the ambient temperature exceeds 115°F (46°C), or exceeds 105°F (40°C) with a wind velocity greater than 8 mph (13 km/h), the requirements of Section 2104.4.2.1 shall be implemented and cool mixing water shall be used for mortar and grout. The use of ice shall be permitted in the mixing water prior to use. Ice shall not be permitted in the mixing water when added to the other mortar or grout materials.

2104.4.3 Protection. When the mean daily temperature exceeds 100°F (38°C), or exceeds 90°F (32°C) with a wind velocity greater than 8 mph (13 km/h), newly constructed masonry shall be fog sprayed until damp at least three times a day until the masonry is three days old.

MSJC Specification 1.8D

1.8D *Hot weather construction*—Implement approved hot weather procedures and comply with the following provisions:

1. *Preparation*—Prior to conducting masonry work:

a. When the ambient air temperature exceeds 100°F (37.8°C), or exceeds 90°F (32.2°C) with a wind velocity greater than 8 mph (12.9 km/h):

1) Maintain sand piles in a damp, loose condition.

2) Provide necessary conditions and equipment to produce mortar having a temperature below 120°F (48.9°C).

b. When the ambient temperature exceeds 115°F (46.1°C), or 105°F (40.6°C) with a wind velocity greater than 8 mph (12.9 km/h), implement the requirements of Atricle 1.8 D.1.a and shade materials and mixing equipment shall be shaded from direct sunlight.

2. *Construction*—While masonry work is in progress.

a. When the ambient air temperature exceeds 100°F (37.8°C), or exceeds 90°F (32.2°C) with a wind velocity greater than 8 mph (12.9 km/h):

1) Maintain temperature of mortar and grout below 120°F (48.9°C).

2) Flush mixer, mortar transport container, and mortar boards with cool water before they come into contact with mortar ingredients or mortar.

3) Maintain mortar consistency by retempering with cool water.

4) Use mortar within 2 hours of initial mixing.

b. When the ambient temperature exceeds 115°F (46.1°C), or exceeds 105°F (40.6°C) with a wind velocity greater than 8 mph (12.9 km/h), implement the requirements of Article 1.8 D.2.a and use cool mixing water for mortar and grout. Ice is permitted in the mixing water prior to use. Do not permit ice in the mixing water when added to the other mortar or grout materials.

3. *Protection*—When the mean daily temperature exceeds 100°F (37.8°C), or exceeds 90°F (32.2°C) with a wind velocity greater than 8 mph (12.9 km/h), fog spray all newly constructed masonry until damp, at least three times a day until the masonry is three days old.

12.2.5 Summary of Recommended Hot Weather Practices

The following points are important factors in laying masonry work in hot weather.

- Schedule the work beforehand if masonry work is to be built in hot temperatures.
- Start and end workday earlier to avoid the hottest times of the day.
- Implement hot weather construction provisions consistent to those contained in the Code.
- Receive and store materials to minimize heat absorption and heat containment.
- Cover materials, both stock and installed, so that materials can maintain some moisture content.

12.3 WET WEATHER MASONRY CONSTRUCTION

12.3.1 General

Building with masonry in rainy weather is possible if some type of shelter or covering is provided.

12.3.2 Performance

Rain can cause excessive wetting of materials, affecting their performance. The change in unit moisture content can cause change in dimension. The amount will vary with the type of material used. Moisture will also reduce the absorptive quality of the units so that poor bond occurs between the units, the mortar and the grout. Water will evaporate more slowly so less mixing water need be added.

If it rains on a building before the mortar is set, the cementitious material may be washed out. The mortar could also be washed over the faces of the units causing a staining effect.

12.3.3 Construction Procedures

Building can be done in wet weather providing rain does not fall on the masonry materials or on the freshly laid walls. The cement, units and sand should be covered to keep them dry. They should also be stored off the ground so there is no migration of moisture from the ground to the materials particularly for the cement and lime.

A masonry wall, built in rainy conditions, should be built under or behind a shelter. This can be in the form of a roof or floor slab, or inside an enclosure similar to the type used in cold weather. Walls should be protected from rain 24 to 48 hours, depending on the temperature, so that the mortar is fully set and bond has occurred.

12.3.4 Protection of Masonry

Partially completed masonry walls that are exposed to rain may become so saturated with water that they require some time to dry out. This may cause efflorescence or water soaking into the framing.

While the masonry walls are being built, it is the responsibility of the mason to be sure that the walls are covered at all times (when not being worked on). The covering can be of plastic, canvas, or some other suitable material that not only covers the top of the wall but hangs over at least two feet (610 mm) on the face. It should also be weighted down to prevent the wind from getting under it and damaging the wall. The common practice of laying a heavy board on top of the wall at the end of the workday does not keep the work protected and can cause the masonry underneath to sag or bow out of position.

When work resumes after a period of rain, the question of how dry must the block units be in order to be laid is frequently asked. Although there is no guidance in the Code, some suggest that if water is splashed on the block and a color difference does not occur (from the water) then the block units are too wet to be placed into the wall.

Masonry Inspection Checklist

13.1 GENERAL

Any effective quality control program that includes inspection must include the necessary reporting to document the program. The following guidelines are given to assist the designer, contractor and inspector on items for consideration in the program.

Many items on this may not apply to a particular project, and there may be items on a project that are not included on this list. These should be considered in addition to this generic guide. Italics paragraphs following the items elaborate and clarify items on the list.

13.2 INSPECTOR'S CHECKLIST

PRE-CONSTRUCTION VERIFICATION

1. Check the following points against the plans:............❏

   (a) Approved plans..❏
   (b) Approved specifications................................ ❏

(c) Change Orders and Requests for Information...❏
(d) Are deviations allowed by the plan check
    engineer?..❏
(e) Is continuous inspection necessary?.................❏
(f) What are the project testing requirements?.......❏
(g) Names of Contractors and Suppliers................❏
(h) Review of submittals......................................❏

2. Are pre-construction prism specimens required?.......❏

3. Were pre-construction prism specimens made?.........❏

Prior to starting construction, the involved parties, including the masonry inspector, must become familiar with the project. This activity includes becoming familiar with the approved plans and the special conditions relating to the project. The inspector should be aware of any special material requirements, such as high strength masonry units and design mix of masonry grout.

START UP OBSERVATIONS

4. Check materials for:..❏

(a) Compliance with submittals............................❏
(b) Site storage to avoid contamination.................❏
(c) Protection from weather................................❏
(d) Consistency...❏

Knowing what materials are required and the proper handling methods will assist the mason and the inspector in the quality control associated with the project.

5. Check sample panels for:...................................... ❏

    (a) Material conformance.................................... ❏
    (b) Workmanship.. ❏
    (c) Conformance to plan details........................... ❏
    (d) Observation at proper distance for acceptance. ❏

The material standard associated with concrete block construction is ASTM C 90 which requires observation at a distance of 20 feet under diffused lighting. This acceptance requirement also applies to sample panels.

PRE PLACEMENT OBSERVATIONS

Materials

6. Check the type and quality of CMU used................. ❏

7. Check Concrete Masonry Units for:........................ ❏

    (a) Overall conformance to applicable material
        standard.. ❏
    (b) Correct size and type (ASTM C 90/UBC
        Standard 21-4)... ❏
    (c) Curing (ASTM C 90/UBC Standard 21-4,
        21-5)... ❏
    (d) Cleanliness.. ❏
    (e) Soundness (ASTM C 90/UBC Standard,
        21-5)... ❏

8. Check quality of the units by test specimens and
    determine:.. ❏

    (a) Is a laboratory test required?........................ ❏
    (b) Are any special inspection provisions required?. ❏

9. Check unit test requirement, if applicable (Unit Strength verification, f'_m).. ❏

10. Check structure compliance with plans and check:.. ❏

    (a) Strength of masonry....................................... ❏
    (b) Stress... ❏

Most concrete block manufacturers have very high internal quality control standards to assure that their product exceeds the requirements set forth in the applicable material standard, typically ASTM C 90. The inspector's observation should include verification of any special conditions, such as the requirement for high strength units. Another example of the material verification would be a visual check that the correct color and texture unit is supplied for the project.

Project Conditions

11. Check for separation between buildings................. ❏

12. Check thickness of walls...................................... ❏

13. Check the size of bond beams............................... ❏

14. Check reinforcing steel for:................................... ❏

    (a) Kind and grade.. ❏
    (b) Size.. ❏
    (c) Location and spacing...................................... ❏
    (d) Bracing.. ❏
    (e) Clearances.. ❏
    (f) Deformation.. ❏
    (g) Additional steel requirements around openings.. ❏
    (h) Placement within allowable tolerances............. ❏

Some might consider site conditions beyond the scope of the masonry inspector, however, if the inspector has the insight that coordination or construction issues with another trade can create a problem, then it is diligent for the inspector to open a dialogue to resolve the issue before it becomes a problem.

15. Check the following points for connections........... ❏

    (a) Size and location of joist anchors..................... ❏
    (b) Size, location and number of bolts.................. ❏
    (c) Size and location of dowels............................ ❏
    (d) Location of stirrups... ❏
    (e) Veneer ties (if applicable)............................... ❏

16. Check the placement of headers and lintels of material other than masonry............................... ❏

WORKMANSHIP

Mortar Mixing Observation

17. Check to see that clean water is used.................. ❏

18. Check mortar compliance by type and use............ ❏

19. Are the materials clean and covered?................... ❏

20. Are the manufacturers mixing specifications followed?... ❏

21 Check sand for:.. ❏

    (a) Cleanliness.. ❏
    (b) Quality and fineness.. ❏
    (c) Aggregate compliance (ASTM C 144)............. ❏

22. Verify that cement meets specified standard......... ❑

23. Verify proportions of the mortar mix and time of
    mixing... ❑

24. Is a container of known quantity being used
    instead of shovel measurement?.......................... ❑

25. Is the correct type of mixer being used?.............. ❑

26. Is mixer operating properly?................................ ❑

27. Is the same operator mixing every batch?............. ❑

28. Is batch or mortar used within correct time limits?. ❑

29. Check lime for conformance to applicable
    standard..❑

30. Check plasticizing agents for conformance to
    material standards... ❑

31. Verify that admixtures conform to the following
    requirements:.. ❑

    (a) Have been approved....................................❑
    (b) Are properly proportioned.............................❑
    (c) Are not used with plastic cement...................❑

32. Check the consistency of mortar......................... ❑

33. Verify that mortar is properly handled in mixing..... ❑

34. See that mortar is not excessively retempered....... ❑

35. Were samples taken for testing?.......................... ❏

36. Are mortar samples required?.............................❏

37. Were mortar samples taken, if required?...............❏

Mortar can be mixed from the components at the project site, or it can be factory blended and shipped to the project in sacks or silos. For factory-blended mortar, the manufacturers recommendations should be followed. Field mixed mortar is done in accordance with the time provisions in the code.

Mortar should be mixed in a paddle type mixer and kept workable for the mason. Occasionally, mortar samples are required for testing. Mortar samples should be spread over a masonry unit for a period of one minute to replicate initial hydration of the mortar before it is put into a cylinder. The standard for preparing mortar samples is very detailed in the test preparation procedure. When masonry prisms are constructed, the mortar is tested as part of the prism; therefore individual mortar samples are unnecessary.

Grout Observations

38. Check grout for:...❏

    (a) Design mix or proportions......................... ❏
    (b) Consistency (Slump)...............................❏
    (c) Compressive strength............................... ❏
    (d) Handling...❏
    (e) Non-Segregation... ❏
    (f) Is grout being placed in units as specified?..❏
    (g) Placement method, high lift or low lift........ ❏
    (h) Proper consolidation.................................... ❏

39. Are grout samples required?................................... ❏

40. Were grout samples taken, if required?................... ❏

Masonry grout is the bridge between the masonry unit and reinforcing steel that makes masonry work. It is important for the grout to completely fill the cells, which are usually restricted, therefore, an 8 to 11 inch slump is mandatory for proper flow. Immediately, the excess water bleeds of into the unit, thereby allowing the grout to hydrate in the normal manner. It is undesirable to place the grout too dry and allow the grout to become caught in the congested areas causing voids below. Proper moisture content, consolidation and reconsolidation all contribute to making the grout a full and homogeneous component in masonry.

In a sense, transit mixed grout mechanically pumped is somewhat self-checking. If the cement content of the masonry grout is less than 6.5 sack equivalent, the grout will frequently plug the hose. A 6.5 cement content far exceeds the minimum code required compressive strength of 2,000 psi.

Construction

41. Verify that all head, bed and wall joints are:........... ❏

   (a) Watertight (Holes filled)................................. ❏
   (b) Correct size... ❏
   (c) Properly filled with mortar............................. ❏
   (d) Buttered where required................................. ❏

42. Verify joint size and type of joints are as required.. ❏

43. Check head and bed joints for:...............................❏

    (a) Proper size...❏
    (b) Complete filling of head joints as required........❏
    (c) Filling of end joints with mortar........................❏

44. Check joints where fresh masonry is joined to set
    (previously laid) masonry.......................................❏

45. Check reinforced hollow unit masonry for:..............❏

    (a) Vertical alignment and continuity of cells.........❏
    (b) Lapping..❏
    (c) Leakage of grout...❏
    (d) Cleanout openings for pours over 5 feet...........❏
    (e) Overhanging mortar..❏
    (f) Sealing of cleanout openings...........................❏
    (g) Position/securing of reinforcement..................❏
    (h) Control joint location and reinforcement...........❏
    (i) Requirements when work is stopped for more
        than one our..❏

46. Are prism specimens required for verification
    of f'_m?...❏

47. Were prism specimens made for testing?................❏

48. Is masonry observed at proper distance for
    acceptance?..❏

Correct placement of reinforcement is essential for the proper performance of structural masonry. Since the reinforcement is fully encased in the grout it is essential that the inspector understand that the location of the reinforcement will determine structural performance and that the grout must completely surround the reinforcement for an effective masonry system.

In order to verify the structural integrity of the masonry, the code provides for verification of the compressive strength of masonry. One appropriate method is through construction of masonry wall assemblages, or prisms, with subsequent testing to determine the ultimate test compressive strength. Since the prism specimens are handled and physically transported to the lab, the Standards are very specific on handling, curing and testing procedures. Failure to follow the guidelines can negatively impact the test results.

CONSTRUCTION DETAILS

49. Does contractor use a string line?........................... ❏

50. Does contractor periodically check plumbness
   of units?.. ❏

51. Are industry standard tolerances implemented?....... ❏

52. Observe hot and cold weather construction and
   protection requirements.. ❏

53. Check unprotected steel supporting members for:..... ❏

   (a) Correct location of mechanical installation
      supports... ❏
   (b) Size and location of bolts and connections........ ❏
   (c) Size and spacing of bracing connections........... ❏
   (d) Size and alignment of connection holes............ ❏
   (e) Shims and drypacking...................................... ❏
   (f) Location and size of stiffeners.......................... ❏
   (g) Size and alignment of base plates..................... ❏

Although the Code does not address means and methods of construction, it is appropriate for the contractor to use the best methods available for quality installation. This includes laying the units to a string line and a periodic check of the masonry to be sure that the installed work is within industry tolerances.

54. Check the following points of inspection of
bearing on solid masonry... ❏

    (a) Suitability of bearing masonry......................... ❏
    (b) Size of bearing masonry................................. ❏
    (c) Size, length, placement and embedment of
        connectors in masonry..................................... ❏
    (d) Location of bolt ties....................................... ❏

55. Verify proper sill material and check for
anchorage of supporting members to footings......... ❏

56. Verify the following points in checking anchoring
of wood floor joists to supporting masonry members ❏

    (a) Required size of ledges.................................... ❏
    (b) Required size, spacing and length of bolts
        and joist anchors.. ❏

57. Where wood floor joists are parallel to wall,
check for:... ❏

    (a) Placement of required blocking...................... ❏
    (b) Type of anchors required............................... ❏
    (c) Use of proper connections to anchors............ ❏

58. Verify the following in inspecting floor joists tying to a masonry wall:... ❏

    (a) Required size, spacing and bearing of joints...... ❏
    (b) Required air space around joists..................... ❏
    (c) Required bridging and/or blocking.................. ❏
    (d) Connection to ledger....................................... ❏
    (e) Required connectors for anchors.................... ❏
    (f) Required anchors... ❏

59. Verify the following points in the inspection of a masonry building where fire-resistive floors are required:... ❏

    (a) Proper material for fire resistance.................. ❏
    (b) Required thickness of floor slab..................... ❏
    (c) Required supports.. ❏
    (d) Required reinforcement............................... ❏
    (e) Required time for supports and forms to remain in place for concrete floors................. ❏

Many of the above items relate to the interface of masonry with other trades. Consideration of these items is appropriate, however, it may be necessary for the masonry inspector to coordinate with others to verify the compatibility with other trades.

60. Contraction joints and control joints are located and provided as indicated or required........................... ❏

The issue of control joints is important to masonry construction. Concrete masonry, like any cementitious product shrinks, and subsequently cracks. Control joints are installed for the purpose of focusing cracks into a specific location where a caulk, or sealant, is applied. This enhances the overall performance of masonry. Control joints should be specified for type and location by the designer based on published industry standards.

61. Weepholes are provided, if required........................☐

Weepholes can be installed in drainage systems where there is a vertical void for the water to gravitate downward, and subsequently travel to the exterior of the masonry. Installation of weepholes permits the water to follow the path of least resistance.

62. Cover the following points in checking for the
    height of masonry building:.....................................☐

    (a) Approved materials...☐
    (b) Placement and spacing of reinforcement.........☐
    (c) Correct grouting procedure.............................☐

63. Verify the following when inspecting chases:...........☐

    (a) Location and spacing on approved plans........☐
    (b) Purpose...☐
    (c) Maximum permitted depth.............................☐
    (d) No reduction of the required strength and for
        resistance of the wall....................................☐

64. Check bearing walls for:...☐

    (a) End support...☐
    (b) Footings...☐
    (c) Thickness of walls...☐
    (d) Bond beams...☐
    (e) Materials used..☐
    (f) Joints..☐
    (g) Reinforcing steel...☐
    (h) Grout..☐
    (i) Shoring or bracing (if required).....................☐
    (j) Anchorage...☐

65. Inspect non-loadbearing walls for:........................ ❏

    (a) Location, height and thickness of walls........... ❏
    (b) Approved materials....................................... ❏
    (c) Type of units used... ❏
    (d) Proper placement of ties, anchors and bolts... ❏

66. Where there is a change in the thickness of non
    loadbearing walls, be sure to:............................... ❏

    (a) Locate the position on the approved plans...... ❏
    (b) Check for compliance of required top plates.. ❏
    (c) Verify location of ties, anchor bolts and
        blocking.. ❏

67. Check racking and toothing at wall intersections...... ❏

Racking and toothing are typically addressed in project specifications when it is a concern. Whenever masonry is toothed, care must be taken to see that the toothed masonry is properly constructed.

68. Check wall ties... ❏

69. Check corners and returns................................... ❏

70. Check masonry on concrete for:............................ ❏

    (a) Width and depth of footing excavations.......... ❏
    (b) Compliance of masonry units........................ ❏
    (c) Grouting and metal inserts............................ ❏
    (d) Anchorage around main steel........................ ❏
    (e) Embedment of ties or connection to main
        steel.. ❏
    (f) Type, spacing and material of ties................... ❏

71. Check corbelling for:.. ❑

    (a) Maximum projections.................................... ❑
    (b) Bonding and anchorage................................ ❑
    (c) Required temporary supports........................ ❑
    (d) Required reinforcing steel............................ ❑

72. Are walls secured once they are completed?.......... ❑

73. Check to see that the work is kept dry.................... ❑

74. Are walls protected from rain and inclement
    weather on a daily basis?.. ❑

Although it is desirable to keep newly constructed masonry protected, it is unusual to protect the masonry from inclement weather in the middle of summer. Reasonable precaution should be exercised. In most cases, rain will not damage masonry once it has started the curing process, however, protection of masonry during the rainy season will allow the mason to resume construction as soon as the rain stops, as opposed to waiting several days for the materials and constructed work to dry.

75. Was the superintendent or on-site representative
    notified of any discrepancies?................................❑

If there are noted discrepancies, the inspector has the responsibility to immediately notify the involved parties for correction. If the discrepancies are unresolved, then there are code directives to further notify the concerned parties, in writing. It is inappropriate for the inspector to hold corrosion notices and initially advise the contractor at project completion.

76. Pointing, replacement of defective units, and repair
    of other defects are properly performed..................❑

77. Methods of final cleaning are as required...............❏

78. Waterproofing of walls is performed as required..... ❏

Masonry Units

14.1   EVALUATION REPORTS

Historically, masonry inspection was prominent in the higher seismic regions of the Western United States. As a result, the ICBO Evaluation Reports listed in this section were significant to the inspector.

Part of the Code consolidation process includes uniting the Evaluation Services under the International Code Council Evaluation Services (ICC ES). ICC ES is working on making the transition as smooth and seamless as possible, More information can be obtained from the ICC ES website (*http://iccint.intlcode.org*).

14.2   TYPICAL CONCRETE MASONRY UNITS

14.2.1   Precision Units

Figures 14.1 through 14.8 illustrate typical concrete masonry units used in construction and manufactured in accordance with applicable Standards.

14.2.2   Slumped Blocks

Spanish adobe type slumped units are available in various sizes (Figure 14.9, Table 14-B) and colors. Mortar joints are typically larger than for precision units to allow for slump unit dimensional variations while maintaining bond.

Table 14-A *ICBO Evaluation Reports*			
Company	No.	Products	Date of Last Action
Allan Block Corp. Edina, MN Air Vol Block San Luis Obispo, CA Calstone Co. Sunnyvale, CA Orco Block Co. Stanton, CA	5087	Allen Block Retaining Wall System	05/01/00
American Colloid Co., Arlington Heights, IL	3759	Easy/Spred Plasticizer for Mortar	12/01/98
Anchor Wall Systems, Inc., Minnetonka, MN	4952	Diamond Block Wall System	02/01/96
Angelus Block Co. Orange, CA	5845	Angelus Block Masonry Fence Wall System	03/01/02
Erico Products, Inc. Solon, OH	3967	Reinforcing Steel Couplers and Splices	01/01/01
Gibco Industries, Inc. Tulsa, OK Hanson Permanente Pleasanton, CA Mitsubishi Cement Lucerne Valley, CA Patio Industries Ontario, CA	3213	Gibco MRF and PRF Liquid and Dry Admixture, Patio Premium Plastering Cement, Patio Premium Mortar Cement, Kaiser Premium Plastering Cement, Kaiser Premium Mortar Cement and Blok-Lok Mortar	07/01/94

Table 14-A	ICBO Evaluation Reports (Cont'd)		
Graystone Block Co. Modesto, CA	3606	Solar Stone™ Hollow Load-Bearing Concrete Masonry Units	05/01/00
Haener Block, San Diego, CA	2996	Haener Mortarless Blocks™	12/01/01
Hokanson Building Block Co., Sacramento, CA	4528	Earthstone S Retaining Wall System	12/01/01
Insulated Masonry Systems, Inc., Cincinnatti, OH Precision Foam Molders Phoenix, AZ	4997	IMSI®Insulated Reinforced Masonry Wall System	03/01/01
Keystone Retaining Wall Systems, Inc. Edina, MN	4599	Keystone Retaining Wall System	05/01/97
Orco Block Co. Stanton, CA Calstone Co. Sunnyvale, CA Crystalite Block Co. Galt, CA Valley Block Co. Indio, CA RCP Block & Brick Lemon Grove, CA	5020	Wedgelock Block Walls	03/01/96
Retaining Walls Company	4927	Criblock Retaining Walls	09/01/99
Richmond Screw Anchor Co., Fort Worth, TX	4028	Dowel Bar Splice Systems	10/01/97

Table 14-A   ICBO Evaluation Reports (Cont'd)

Rockwood Retaining Walls Rochester, MN	5406	Rockwood lassic Retaining Wall System	08/01/99
Simpson Strong Tie Pleasanton, CA	4945	Epoxy Anchoring Systems	12/01/98
Slope Block, Inc. Newbury Park, CA	5863	Slope Block Wall System	12/01/01
Soil Retention Systems, Inc. Oceanside, CA	4610	Loffelstein Retaining Wall System	11/01/00
Superlite Block Phoenix, AZ Adams Products Co., Morrisville, NC Amcor/Utah Block Bountiful, UT Betco Block Manassas, VA Jewell Concrete Products, Waco, TX Miller Materials Kansas City, MO	4845P	Integra Masonry Wall System Post-tension Masonry Walls	12/01/95
Terraforce, Ltd. Cape Town, South Africa	5448	Terraforce Block Retaining Wall System	02/01/02
Tensar Earth Tech. Atlanta, GA	5435	Mesa Retaining Block Wall System	05/01/02
Versa-Lok®Retaining Wall Systems Oakdale, MN	4625	VERSA-LOK® Retaining Wall System	04/01/02

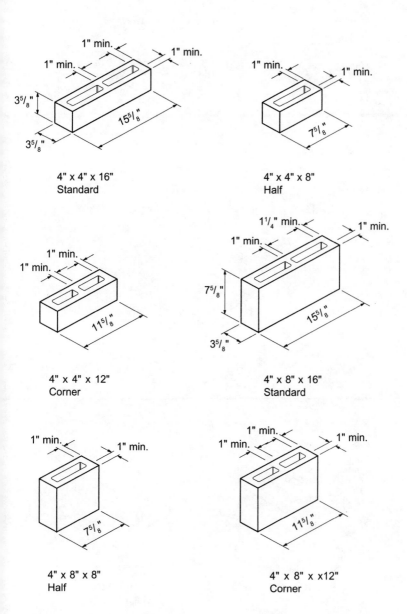

Figure 14.1 Four-inch-wide (102 mm) concrete masonry units.

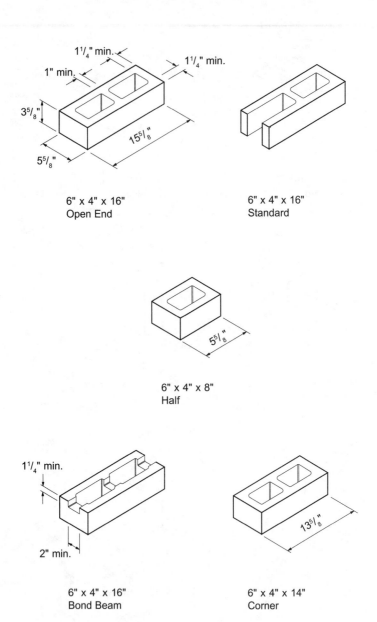

6" x 4" x 16"
Open End

6" x 4" x 16"
Standard

6" x 4" x 8"
Half

6" x 4" x 16"
Bond Beam

6" x 4" x 14"
Corner

Figure 14.2 Six-inch-wide (152 mm) concrete masonry units.

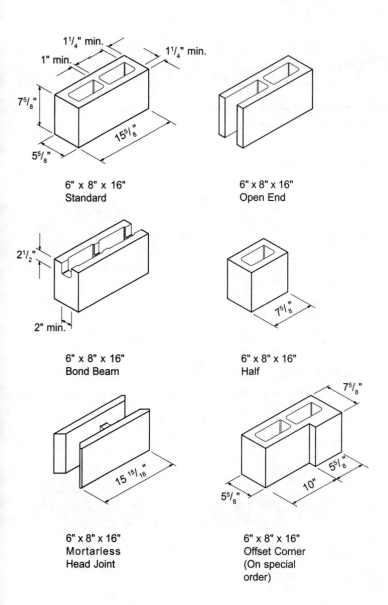

6" x 8" x 16"
Standard

6" x 8" x 16"
Open End

6" x 8" x 16"
Bond Beam

6" x 8" x 16"
Half

6" x 8" x 16"
Mortarless
Head Joint

6" x 8" x 16"
Offset Corner
(On special
order)

Figure 14.2 Six-inch-wide (152 mm) concrete masonry units (Continued).

377

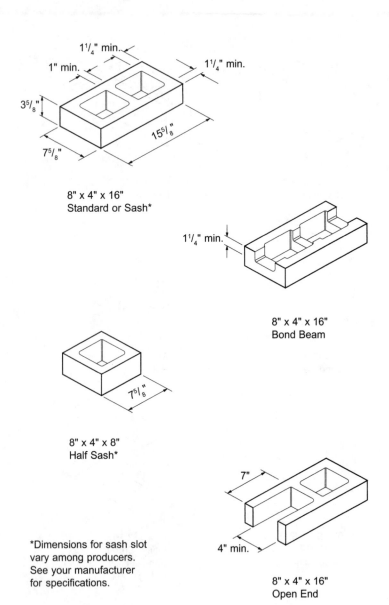

8" x 4" x 16"
Standard or Sash*

8" x 4" x 16"
Bond Beam

8" x 4" x 8"
Half Sash*

*Dimensions for sash slot
vary among producers.
See your manufacturer
for specifications.

8" x 4" x 16"
Open End

**Figure 14.3 Eight-inch-wide (203 mm) concrete masonry
units.**

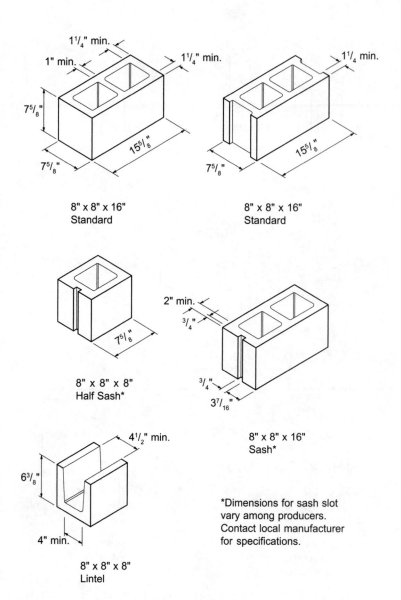

8" x 8" x 16"
Standard

8" x 8" x 16"
Standard

8" x 8" x 8"
Half Sash*

8" x 8" x 16"
Sash*

8" x 8" x 8"
Lintel

*Dimensions for sash slot
vary among producers.
Contact local manufacturer
for specifications.

**Figure 14.3 Eight-inch-wide (203 mm) concrete masonry
units (Continued).**

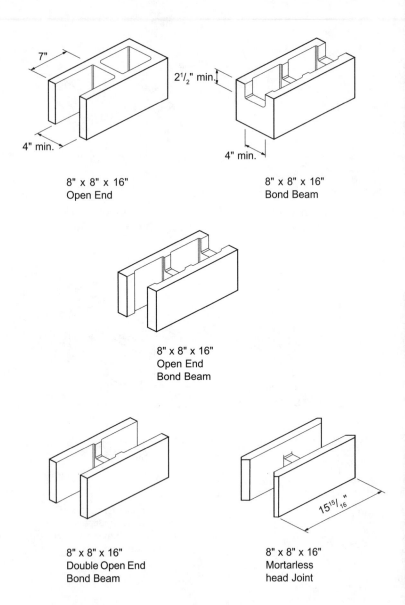

8" x 8" x 16"
Open End

8" x 8" x 16"
Bond Beam

8" x 8" x 16"
Open End
Bond Beam

8" x 8" x 16"
Double Open End
Bond Beam

8" x 8" x 16"
Mortarless
head Joint

Figure 14.3 Eight-inch-wide (203 mm) concrete masonry units (Continued).

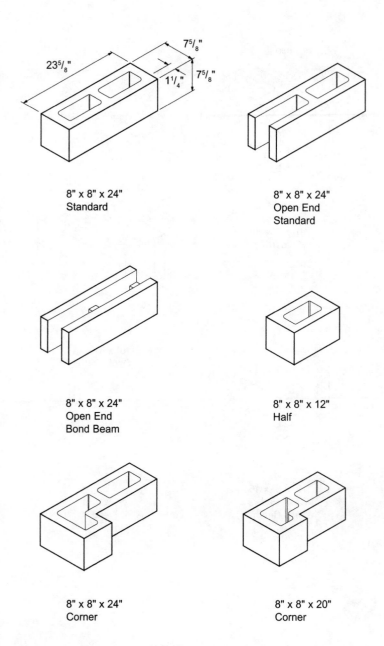

8" x 8" x 24"
Standard

8" x 8" x 24"
Open End
Standard

8" x 8" x 24"
Open End
Bond Beam

8" x 8" x 12"
Half

8" x 8" x 24"
Corner

8" x 8" x 20"
Corner

Figure 14.4 Eight-inch-wide by 24" long (203 mm x 610 mm) concrete masonry units.

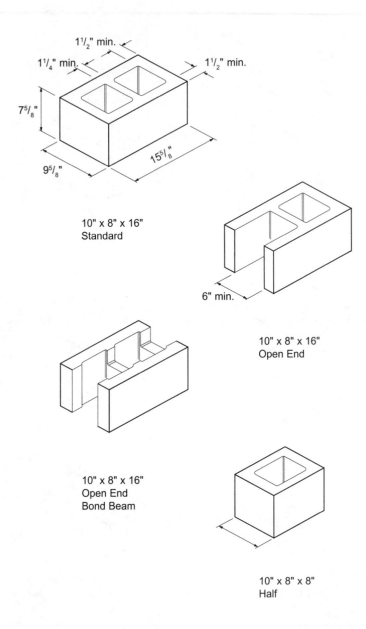

Figure 14.5 Ten-inch (254 mm) CMU.

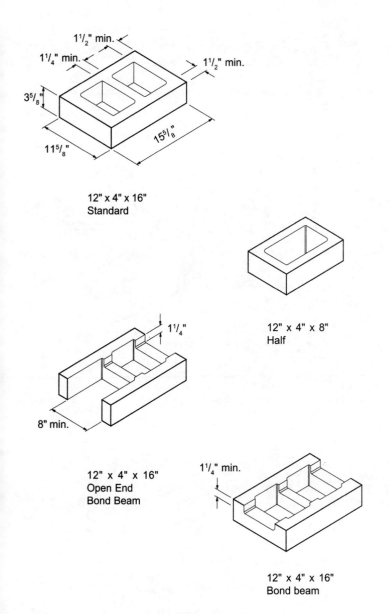

12" x 4" x 16"
Standard

12" x 4" x 8"
Half

12" x 4" x 16"
Open End
Bond Beam

12" x 4" x 16"
Bond beam

Figure 14.6 Twelve-inch (305 mm) CMU, four inches (102 mm) high.

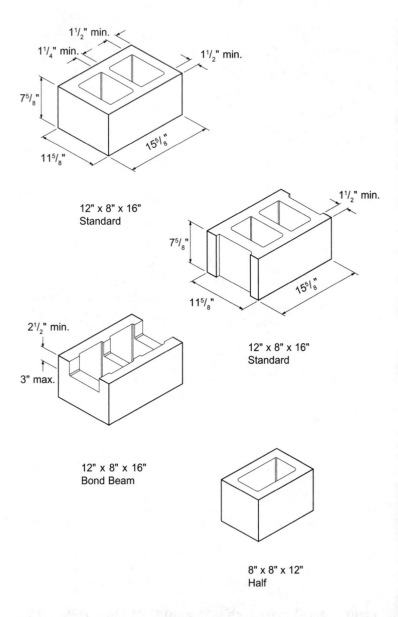

Figure 14.7 Twelve-inch (305 mm) CMU, eight inches (203 mm) high.

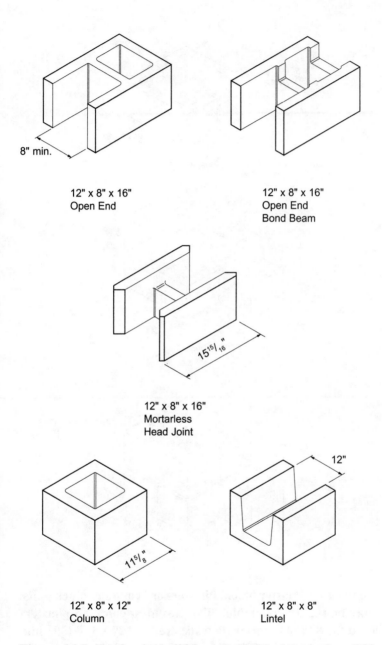

8" min.

12" x 8" x 16"
Open End

12" x 8" x 16"
Open End
Bond Beam

$15^{15}/_{16}$"

12" x 8" x 16"
Mortarless
Head Joint

$11^{5}/_{8}$"

12" x 8" x 12"
Column

12"

12" x 8" x 8"
Lintel

Figure 14.7 Twelve-inch (305 mm) CMU, eight inches (203 mm) high (Continued).

385

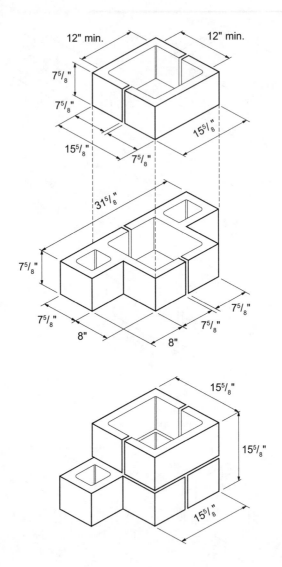

Figure 14.8 Pilaster block. Pilasters or "column" block units, may be readily available. The two most common pilasters used for 8" (203 mm) wide walls are the 12" x 16" (305 mm x 407 mm) and the 16" x 16" (407 mm x 407 mm).

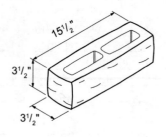

4" x 4" x 16"
Standard

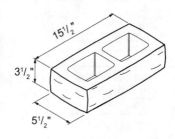

6" x 4" x 16"
Standard

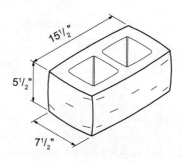

8" x 6" x 16"
Standard

Figure 14.9 Slumped block.

Table 14-B   Slumped block Nominal
Dimensions (width, height, length)
(For metric multiply inches by 25.4 mm)

Dimensions	Description
4 x 4 x 16	solid
4 x 4 x 12	solid corner
4 x 4 x 8	solid half
4 x 6 x 16	solid
6 x 4 x16	standard and bond beam
6 x 4 x 14	corner
6 x 4 x 12	three quarter
6 x 4 x 8	half
6 x 6 x 16	standard and bond beam
6 x 6 x 8	half
8 x 4 x 16	standard, bond beam, open end, and open end bond beam
8 x 4 x 8	half
8 x 6 x 16	standard, bond beam, open end and open end bond beam
8 x 6 x 8	half
12 x 4 x16	standard, bond beam, open end bond beam
12 x 4 x 12	corner/column
12 x 4 x 8	half
12 x 6 x 16	standard and bond beam
12 x 6 x 8	half
16 x 4 x 16	column
16 x 6 x 16	column
12 x 6 x 12	column
6 x 2 x 12	cap
8 x 2 x 16	cap
6 x 4 x 16	cap
8 x 4 x 16	cap

14.2.3 Custom Face Units

The custom face units shown in Figure 14.10 are a small sampling of the broad range of concrete masonry architectural units available from the industry on special order.

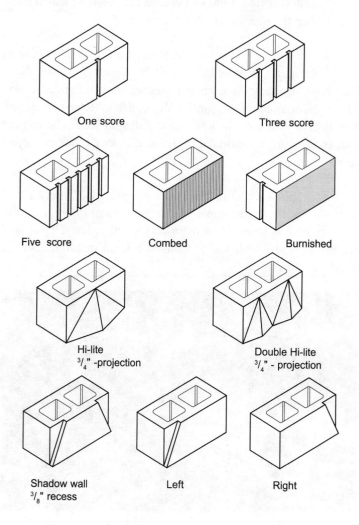

One score

Three score

Five score

Combed

Burnished

Hi-lite
$^3/_4$" -projection

Double Hi-lite
$^3/_4$" - projection

Shadow wall
$^3/_8$" recess

Left

Right

Figure 14.10 Custom face units.

14.2.4 Split Face Units

Split face block are manufactured as a single unit that is normally made double and is literally split apart on a splitter; a machine which resembles a guillotine. The splitter has blades at the top and bottom (and sometimes at the sides) which exert pressure on the blocks, breaking them apart.

Many factors determine the look of the split face, both as to size variances and the amount of aggregate exposure. Split face block is intended to have a rougher texture than precision block. Various configurations of block such as fluted and scored, will split in a different manner than a full split face. The vertical perpendicularity of scored and fluted split face block is subject to variation.

The split face units shown in Figure 14.12 are a small sampling of the broad range of concrete masonry architectural units available from the industry on special order. Depths and widths of scores will vary. Consult a local manufacturer for specific information.

Figure 14.11 Splitting process.

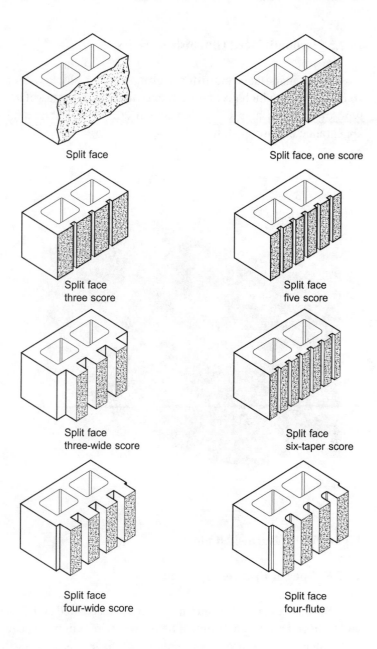

Split face

Split face, one score

Split face
three score

Split face
five score

Split face
three-wide score

Split face
six-taper score

Split face
four-wide score

Split face
four-flute

Figure 14.12 Split face units.

14.2.5   Ground Faced (Burnished) Units

Some manufacturers offer a ground faced block with a smooth texture which gives prominence to the aggregates. This type of unit can also be sealed which creates a texture and appearance of natural stone.

Figure 14.13 Burnished block.

14.2.6   Special Proprietary Units

Special concrete masonry units have been created and used when special requirements must be met. The requirements can be greater sound control, more energy efficiency, or increased ease of placement.

Sound blocks are made with slotted openings in one side of the face shells. This allows sound waves to enter the cell where the sound waves reflect back and forth. Desirable acoustical ratings are then achieved, especially in high noise areas such as large furnace rooms or gymnasiums (see Figure 2.3).

Energy efficiency can also be improved when special concrete masonry units are used that contain insulation inside the face shells, usually as part of the unit or as insets. The insulation helps reduce unwanted transfer of energy from one side of the wall to the other (see Figure 2.3).

Mortarless units have also been developed. These block are an attempt to reduce the cost of masonry construction. The block units either interlock without mortar or use thin high-bond mortars, or may have conventional mortared bed joints with beveled mortarless head joints. Mortarless units are usually designed to be grouted (see Figure 2.3).

14.3 LENGTH, HEIGHT AND QUANTITIES IN CONCRETE MASONRY WALLS

14.3.1 Length and Height of Walls

Table 14-C shows the number of blocks of various sizes in walls of certain length and height. For Table 14-C to be interpreted properly, the following information should be noted.

- For exact wall length subtract thickness of one mortar joint. This shortfall of one mortar joint can easily be made up in the remainder of the mortar joints for a full nominal module.

- For exact opening dimensions add thickness of one mortar joint to height and width.

- When using combinations of 8 inch (203 mm) high and 4 inch (102 mm) high blocks, a detailed wall section should be made to establish height dimensions.

- The modular chart shown is for 4 inch and 8 inch (102 mm and 203 mm) high units. Six inch (152 mm) high precision and slump block units are typically available throughout the market. Further freedom in dimensioning is now possible using 6 inch (152 mm) high units to start or story out in combination with Table 14-C.

Table 14-C *Number of Blocks in a Wall $^3/_8$" Horizontal and Vertical Mortar Joints.*

(For metric multiply inches by 25.4 mm)

Length	No. 16" Long Blocks	Height	No. 4" High Blocks	No. 8" High Blocks
0'-8"	½	0'-4"	1	
1'-4"	1	0'-8"	2	1
2'-0"	1½	1'-0"	3	
2'-8"	2	1'-4"	4	2
3'-4"	2½	1'-8"	5	
4'-0"	3	2'-0"	6	3
4'-8"	3½	2'-4"	7	
5'-4"	4	2'-4"	8	4
6'-0"	4½	3'-0"	9	
6'-8"	5	3'-4"	10	4
7'-4"	5½	3'-8"	11	
8'-0"	6	4'-0"	12	6
8'-8"	6½	4'-4"	13	
9'-4"	7	4'-8"	14	7
10'-0"	7½	5'-0"	15	
10'-8"	8	5'-4"	16	8
11'-4"	8½	5'-8"	17	
12'-0"	9	6'-0"	18	9
12'-8"	9½	6'-4"	19	
13'-4"	10	6'-8"	20	10
14'-0"	10½	7'-0"	21	
14'-8"	11	7'-4"	22	11
15'-4"	11½	7'-8"	23	
16'-0"	12	8'-0"	24	12
16'-8"	12½	8'-4"	25	
17'-4"	13	8'-8"	26	13
18'-0"	13½	9'-0"	27	
18'-8"	14	9'-4"	28	14
19'-4"	14½	9'-8"	29	

Table 14-C		*Number of Blocks in a Wall $^3/_8$" Horizontal*		
		and Vertical Mortar Joints. (Cont'd)		
Length	No. 16" Long Blocks	Height	No. 4" High Blocks	No. 8" High Blocks
20'-0"	15	10'-0"	30	15
20'-8"	15½	10'-4"	31	
21'-4"	16	10'-8"	32	16
22'-0"	16½	11'-0"	33	
22'-8"	17	11'-4"	34	17
23'-4"	17½	11'-8"	35	
24'-0"	18	12'-0"	36	18
24'-8"	18½	12'-4"	37	
25'-4"	19	12'-8"	38	19
26'-0"	19½	13'-0"	39	
26'-8"	20	13'-4"	40	20
27'-4"	20½	13'-8"	41	
28'-0"	21	14'-0"	42	21
28'-8"	21½	14'-4"	43	
29'-4"	22	14'-8"	44	22
30'-0"	22½	15'-0"	45	
30'-8"	23	15'-4"	46	23
31'-4"	23½	15'-8"	47	
32'-0"	24	16'-0"	48	24
32'-8"	24½	15'-4"	49	
40'-0"	30	16'-8"	50	25
50'-0"	37½	17'-0"	51	
60'-0"	45	17'-4"	52	26
70'-0"	52½	17'-8"	53	
80'-0"	60	18'-0"	54	27
90'-0"	67½	18'-4"	55	
100'-0"	75	18'-8"	56	28
200'-0"	150	19'-0"	57	
300'-0"	225	19'-4"	58	29
400'-0"	300	19'-8"	59	
500'-0"	375	20'-0"	60	30

14.3.2   Quantities of Materials

The following list gives examples of the quantities of different materials required for various jobs:

• When figuring concrete-sand-gravel mixtures, figure one cubic yard (0.76 m³) of material for 80 square feet (7.4 m²) by $3^1/_2$ inches (89 mm) thick.

• Five cubic feet (0.14 m³) of mortar will lay approximately 100, 8" x 8" x 16" (203 mm x 203 mm x 406 mm) concrete blocks.

• One cubic foot (0.03 m³) of mortar will lay approximately 100 bricks.

• One cubic yard (0.76 m³) of stucco will cover approximately 320 square feet (29.7 m²) surface 1 inch (25 mm) thick.

• One ton (907 kg) of wall rock will cover approximately 50 square feet (4.6 m²).

• Six bricks are required per square foot (0.09 m²) in a 4 inch (102 mm) thick wall. In a patio or walk, it takes $4^1/_2$ bricks per square foot (0.09 m²) of surface.

• Slate weighs approximately 5 lbs. per square foot (24.4 kg/m²).

• Flagstone covers about 1 square foot with each 15 lbs. (1 m² with 73.2 kg).

• When mixing mortar, mix 1 part portland cement, $^1/_2$ part hydrated lime to $4^1/_2$ parts sand. (Type S mortar).

Table 14-D	Grout Quantities			
Standard Two Cell Block[1]	Grouted Cells Vert. Steel Spacing	Cu. Yds. of Grout per 100 Sq. Ft. of Wall[2]	Cu. Yds. per 100 Block (8" High) (16" Long)[2]	Block per Cu. Yd. (8" High) (16" Long)
For metric multiply				
by 25.4 for mm		by .7646 for m[2]		
6" THICK WALLS	All Cells Filled	0.93	0.83	120
	16" O.C.	0.55	0.49	205
	24" O.C.	0.42	0.37	270
	32" O.C.	0.35	0.31	320
	40" O.C.	0.31	0.28	360
	48" O.C.	0.28	0.25	396
8" THICK WALLS	All Cells Filled	1.12	1.00	100
	16" O.C.	0.65	0.58	171
	24" O.C.	0.50	0.44	225
	32" O.C.	0.43	0.38	267
	40" O.C.	0.37	0.33	300
	48" O.C.	0.28	0.30	330
10" THICK WALLS	All Cells Filled	1.38	1.23	80
	16" O.C.	0.82	0.73	137
	24" O.C.	0.63	0.56	180
	32" O.C.	0.53	0.47	214
	40" O.C.	0.47	0.42	240
	48" O.C.	0.43	0.38	264
12" THICK WALLS	All Cells Filled	1.73	1.54	65
	16" O.C.	1.01	0.90	111
	24" O.C.	0.76	0.68	146
	32" O.C.	0.64	0.57	174
	40" O.C.	0.57	0.51	195
	48" O.C.	0.53	0.47	215

[1]For open end block add 10% more grout.
 For slumped block deduct 5% grout.
 Horizontal bond beams assumed spaced 4' O.C.
[2]A 3% allowance has been included for loss and job conditions.

Glossary of Terms

ABSORPTION - The amount of water the unit will absorb when immersed in either cold or boiling water for a stated length of time. It is expressed in pounds of water per cubic foot of net volume for concrete blocks.

ACCELERATOR - In masonry, any ingredient added to mortar or grout to impart special properties to the mortar or grout.

ADMIXTURE - Materials added to cement, aggregate and water such as water-repellents, air-entraining or plasticizing aids, pigments or aids to retard or speed up setting.

AGGREGATE - Inert particles such as sand, gravel and rock, which, when bound together with portland cement and water, form mortar, grout or concrete.

AMERICAN SOCIETY FOR TESTING AND MATERIALS (ASTM) - A voluntary organization that sets standards for testing and materials based on a consensus agreement.

ANCHOR TIES - Any type of fastener used to secure masonry to some stable object, such as another wall, usually for tension value.

AREAS:

Bedded Area - The area of the surface of a masonry unit which is in contact with mortar in the plane of the joint.

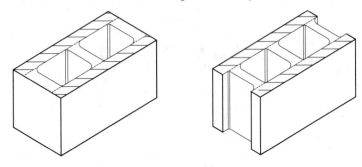

Bedded Area

Effective Area of Reinforcement (A_s) - The cross-sectional area of reinforcement multiplied by the cosine of the angle between the reinforcement and the direction for which effective area is to be determined.

Gross Cross-Sectional Area - The total area of a section perpendicular to the direction of the load, including areas within cells and within re-entrant spaces unless these spaces are to be occupied in the masonry by portions of adjacent masonry. (Note: The gross cross-sectional area of scored units is determined to the outside of the scoring).

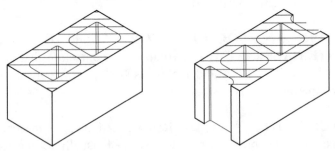

Gross Cross-Sectional Area

Net Cross-Sectional Area - The gross cross-sectional area of a section minus the average area of ungrouted cores or cavities. (Note: The cross-sectional area of grooves in scored units is not usually deducted from the gross cross-sectional area to obtain the net cross-sectional area).

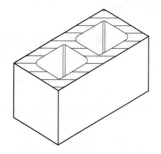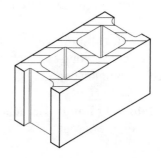

Net Cross-Sectional Area

Transformed Area - The equivalent area of one material to a second based on the ratio of moduli of elasticity of the first material to the second.

BAT - A piece of a masonry unit used in the wall smaller than the length of the field units being used. Generally used to fill out an odd dimension and can be either cut with a saw or brick hammer.

BEARING WALL - Any masonry wall which supports more than 200 pounds per lineal foot (2918 N/m) superimposed load or any such wall supporting its own weight for more than one story.

BED JOINT - See JOINTS

BEVEL - One side of a solid body that is inclined with respect to the other with an angle between the two sides at other than a right angle.

BOND:

Adhesion Bond - The adhesion between masonry units and mortar or grout.

Common Bond - Units laid so that they lap half over each other in successive course. Also called half bond.

Mechanical Bond - Units laid so that they lap over each other in successive courses. Includes quarter bond, third bond, and half or common bond.

Reinforcing Bond - The adhesion between steel reinforcement and mortar or grout.

Running Bond - The placement of masonry units such that the head joints in successive courses are horizontally offset at least one-quarter of the unit length. Placing vertical mortar joints centered over the unit below is called center bond or half bond, while lapping $\frac{1}{3}$ or $\frac{1}{4}$ is called third bond or quarter bond.

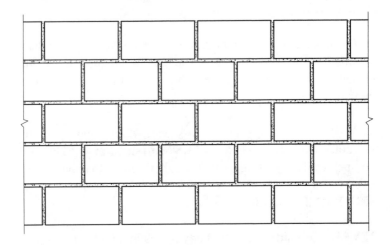

Running Bond

Stack Bond - The placement of masonry units in a bond pattern so that head joints in successive courses are offset less than one quarter of the unit length. Typically, stack bond masonry in laid in a bonding pattern where no unit overlaps either the one above or below and all head joints form a continuous vertical line. Also called plumb joint bond, straight stack, jack bond, jack of jack and checkerboard bond.

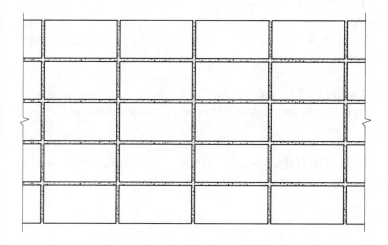

Stack Bond

BOND BEAM - A horizontal grouted element within masonry in which reinforcement is embedded.

BUTTERING - Spreading mortar on masonry units with a trowel.

CAP - Masonry units laid on top of finished masonry wall or pier. Metal caps are units formed of metal, as for flashing.

CAVITY WALL - A wall built of two or more wythes of masonry units arranged to provide a continuous air space within the wall. The facing and backing, outer wythes, are tied together with non-corrosive ties, such as brick or wire.

CELL (CORE) - The molded open space in a concrete masonry unit having a gross cross-sectional area greater than 1½ square inches (967 mm²).

CHASE - A continuous recess built into a wall to enclose service elements such as pipes, ducts or conduits.

CLEANOUT - An opening at the bottom of a grout space of sufficient size to allow for inspection and the removal of debris. The MSJC Code requires that the any minimum dimension of a cleanout be at least 3 inches (76 mm).

CLOSER - The last unit laid in a course. A closer may be a whole unit or one that is shorter and usually appears in the field of the wall.

COLLAR JOINT - The vertical, longitudinal mortared or grouted joint between to wythes of masonry.

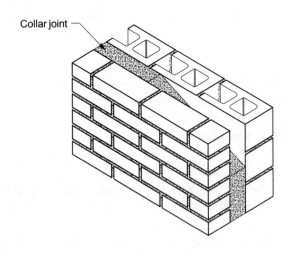

Collar Joint

COLUMN, REINFORCED - A vertical structural member in which both the steel and masonry resist the imposed load.

COLUMN, UNREINFORCED - A vertical structural member whose horizontal dimension measured at right angles to the thickness does not exceed three times the thickness and whose height is at least three times its thickness.

COMPOSITE WALL - Masonry wall in which inner and outer wythes are dissimilar materials, such as block and brick or block and glazed structural units.

COMPRESSIVE STRENGTH - The maximum load required to fracture the masonry unit by applying a compressive force to the upper and lower surface of the unit. Expressed as either gross compressive strength or the net compressive strength.

CONCRETE MASONRY UNIT:

A-Block - A hollow unit with one end closed and the opposite end open, forming two cells when laid in the wall. It is also called a single open-end block.

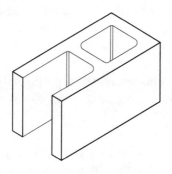

A-Block (Single Open End)

Bond Beam Block - A hollow unit with cross webs depressed sufficiently to permit the forming of a continuous channel for horizontal reinforcing steel and grout.

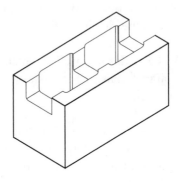

Bond Beam Block

Bullnose Block - A concrete masonry unit that has one or more rounded exterior corners.

Burnished (Ground Face) Block - A precision concrete masonry unit with exposed face shells ground to reveal the aggregate and smooth the texture is a burnished or ground face block.

Channel Block - A hollow unit with portions slightly depressed to permit the forming of a continuous channel for reinforcing steel and grout.

Concrete Block - A hollow concrete masonry unit made from Portland cement and suitable aggregates such as sand, gravely crushed stone, bituminous or anthracite cinders, burned clay or shale, pumice, volcanic scoria, air-cooled or expanded blast furnace slags, with or without the inclusion of other materials.

Concrete Brick - A solid concrete masonry unit made from Portland cement and suitable aggregates, with or without the inclusion of other materials.

Coping Block - A solid concrete masonry unit for use as the top and finished course in wall construction.

Faced Block - Concrete masonry units having a special ceramic, glazed, plastic, polished, ground or similar face or surface.

Flashing Block - In masonry, metal flashing used to block a parapet wall and prevent roof leaks around such a wall.

H-Block - A hollow unit with both ends open commonly called a double open end.

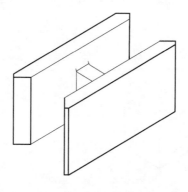

H-Block (Double Open End)

Lintel (or U) Block - A masonry unit consisting of one core or cell with one side open usually placed with the open side up to allow for grouting of the reinforced cells to form a lintel.

Offset Block - A unit which is not rectangular in shape.

Open-End Block - A term applied to both H-blocks and A-blocks in the figure shown, it is commonly called open end unit.

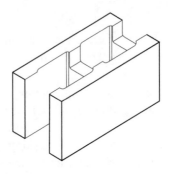

Open-End Bond Beam Block

Pilaster Block - Concrete masonry units designed for use in construction of plain or reinforced concrete masonry pilasters and columns.

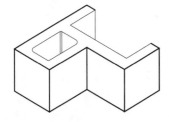

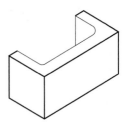

Open center pilaster
or Banjo block

Pilaster alternate
or C block

Pilaster Blocks

Return L Block - Concrete masonry unit designed for use in corner construction for various thickness walls.

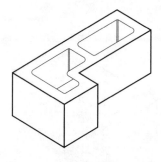

Return (L) Block

Sash Block - A concrete masonry unit which has an end slot for use in openings to receive jambs of doors or windows or premolded expansion joint material.

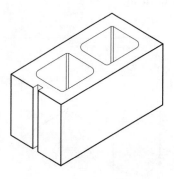

Sash Block

Scored Block - Block with grooves to provide patterns, as for example to simulate raked joints, available in architectural face units.

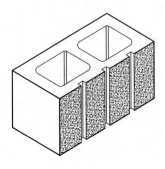

Scored Block

Sculptured Block - Block with specially formed surfaces, in the manner of sculpturing.

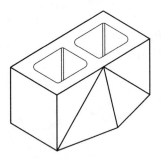

Sculptured Block

Shadow Block - Block with face formed in planes to develop surface patterns.

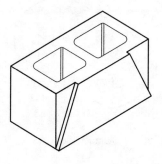

Shadow Block

Sill Block - A solid concrete masonry unit used for sills or openings.

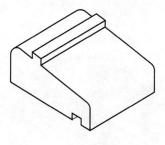

Sill Block

Slumped Block - Concrete masonry units produced so they "slump" or sag in an irregular fashion before they harden to produce an adobe appearance.

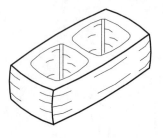

Slumped Block

Solid Unit - Masonry units in which the vertical cores are less than 25% of the cross-sectional area.

Solid Concrete Brick

Split Face Block - Concrete masonry units with one or more faces having a fractured surface for use in masonry wall construction.

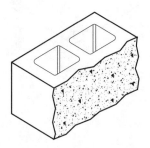

Split Face

CONTROL JOINT – See JOINTS

COPING - The material or units used to form a cap or finish on top of a wall, pier or pilaster.

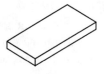

Coping or Cap Block

CORBEL - A shelf or ledge formed by projecting successive courses of masonry out from the face of the wall.

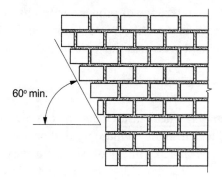

60° min.

Corbel

UBC Section 2107.3.13

2107.3.13   Corbels. The slope of corbelling (angle measured from the horizontal to the face of the corbelled surface) of unreinforced masonry shall not be less than 60 degrees.

The maximum horizontal projection of corbelling from the plane of the wall shall be such that the allowable stresses are not exceeded.

> **MSJC, Section 5.9.4 (Empirical Design)**
> **5.9.4** *Corbelling*
> Solid masonry units shall be used for corbelling. The maximum corbelled projection beyond the face of the wall shall be not more than one-half of the wall thickness or one-half the wythe thickness for hollow walls; the maximum projection of one unit shall neither exceed one-half the height of the unit nor one-third its thickness at right angles to the wall.

CORE - See CELL

COURSE - A continuous horizontal layer of masonry units.

CURING - The maintenance of proper conditions of moisture and temperature during initial set to develop required strength and reduce shrinkage in cementitious products.

DIMENSIONS:

Actual Dimensions - The measured dimensions of a designated item, for example, a designated masonry unit or wall as used in the structure. The actual dimension shall not vary from the specified dimension by more than the amount allowed in the applicable standard.

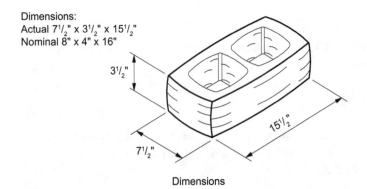

Dimensions:
Actual $7^1/_2$" x $3^1/_2$" x $15^1/_2$"
Nominal 8" x 4" x 16"

$3^1/_2$"

$15^1/_2$"

$7^1/_2$"

Dimensions

Nominal Dimensions - Generally equal to its specified dimension plus the thickness of the joint with which the unit is to be laid.

Specified Dimensions - The dimensions specified for the manufacture or construction of masonry, masonry units, joints or any other component of a structure. Unless otherwise stated, all calculations shall be made using or based on specified dimensions.

DRY PACK - A mixture of Portland cement and fine aggregate, dampened, but not to the extent that it will flow. It is usually rammed or packed in a hole or cell to secure a bar or anchor and it can also be packed under base plates.

EFFLORESCENCE - A whitish powder resulting from the leaching of soluble sulfate salts on the surface of masonry.

EMPIRICAL DESIGN - A design based on the application of physical limitations learned from experience or observations gained through experience, without a structural analysis.

FACE SHELL - The side wall of a hollow concrete masonry unit.

FACED WALL - A wall in which the facing and the backing are so bonded or otherwise tied as to act as a composite element.

FACING - Any material forming a part of a wall and used as a finish surface.

FASCIA - The flat horizontal band in a vertical wall.

FAT MORTAR - See MORTAR

FIRE CLAY - A finely-ground clay highly resistant to heat.

FIRE WALL - Any wall that sub-divides a building to resist the spread of fire.

FIRE-RESISTIVE - In the absence of a specific ruling by the authority having jurisdiction, the term "fire-resistive" is applied to all building materials which are not combustible in temperatures of ordinary fires and will withstand such without serious impairment of their usefulness for at least one hour, two hours, three hours, four hours or more depending on the specified requirement.

FLASHING - A thin impervious material placed in mortar joints and through air spaces in masonry to prevent water penetration and to provide water drainage.

f'_m - The specified compressive strength of masonry at the age of 28 days.

FURRING - A method of finishing the face of a masonry wall to provide space for insulation, prevent moisture transmittance, or to provide a surface for finishing.

GROSS COMPRESSIVE STRENGTH - The compressive strength of the unit based on the total area as defined in "Cross-Sectional Area." Expressed in pounds per square inch (psi) or kilo Pascals (kPa).

GROUT - A mixture of cement, aggregate, water and sometimes an admixture, which is poured into bond beams and vertical cells to encase the steel and to bond units together.

GROUT LIFT - A increment of grout height within the total pour.

GROUT POUR - The total height of a masonry wall to be grouted prior to the erection of additional masonry. A grout pour will consist of one or more grout lifts.

GROUTED MASONRY - Masonry construction made with units that are filled with grout or the cavity between the units is filled with grout.

High Lift Grouting - The technique of grouting masonry in lifts for the full height of the wall, subject to maximum height limitations imposed by the applicable building code.

Low Lift Grouting - The technique of grouting as the wall is constructed.

HEAD JOINT - See JOINTS

HOLLOW MASONRY UNIT - A masonry unit whose net cross-sectional area in any plane parallel to the bearing surface is less than 75% of its cross-sectional area measured in the same plane.

JOINT REINFORCEMENT - Steel wire, bar or prefabricated reinforcement which is placed in mortar bed joint.

JOINTING - The process of finishing mortar joints with a tool.

JOINTS

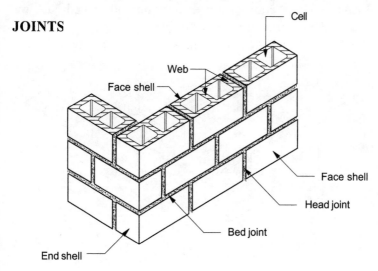

Bed Joint - The mortar joint that is horizontal at the time the masonry units are placed.

Collar Joint - The vertical space separating a wythe of masonry from another wythe or from another continuous material which may be filled with mortar or grout.

Control Joint - A continuous unbonded masonry joint to control the location and amount of separation resulting from the contraction of the masonry wall to avoid the development of excessively high stresses and random cracking in the masonry.

Dry Joint - Head or bed joint without mortar.

Expansion Joint - A vertical joint or space to allow for movement due to volume changes.

Head Joint - The mortar joint between units in the same wythe, usually vertical, sometimes called the cross joint.

Shrinkage Joint - See Control Joint.

LEAD - The section of a wall built up and racked back on successive courses at a corner or end of a wall. The line is attached to the leads and the wall is then built up between them.

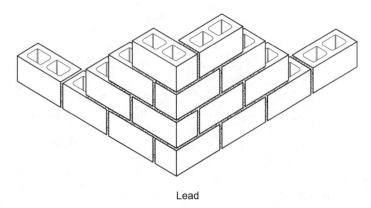

Lead

LEAN MORTAR - see MORTAR.

LIFT - The increment of grout height within the total pour. A pour may consist of one or more grout lifts.

LIME:

Hydrated Lime - Quicklime treated with only enough water to satisfy its chemical demand. Packaged in a powdered form, does not require slaking.

Lime Putty - Slaked quicklime.

Processed Lime - Pulverized quicklime, which must be slaked and cooled prior to use.

Quicklime - A hot or unslaked lime.

LINTEL - A beam placed over an opening in a wall.

LOAD-BEARING WALL - Any wall which in addition to supporting its own weight supports the building and contents above it.

MASONRY UNIT - Natural or manufactured units of burned clay, tile, stone, glass block, concrete block or other similar material.

Hollow Masonry Unit - A masonry unit whose net cross-sectional area in every plane parallel to the bearing surface is less than 75% of the gross cross-section area in the same plane.

Solid Masonry Unit - A masonry unit whose net cross-sectional area in every plane parallel to the bearing surface is 75% or more of the gross cross-sectional area in the same plane.

MEAN DAILY TERMPERATURE - The average daily temperature of temperature extremes predicted by the local weather bureau for the next 24 hours.

MITER - A cut made at an angle for the two individual members to fit together at an angle.

MODULAR DIMENSION - A dimension based on a given module, usually 8 inches (203 mm) in the case of concrete block masonry.

MODULAR MASONRY UNIT - A masonry unit whose actual dimensions are one mortar joint less than the modular dimension, i.e.: 8" x 8" x 16" (203 mm x 203 mm x 407 mm) is actually $7^5/_8$" x $7^5/_8$" x $15^5/_8$" (193 mm x 193 mm x 397 mm) to allow for $^3/_8$" (10 mm) joints.

MORTAR - A plastic mixture of cementitious materials, fine aggregate and water, with or without the inclusion of other specified materials.

Fat Mortar - A mortar that tends to be sticky and adheres to the trowel.

Harsh Mortar - A mortar that, due to insufficient plasticizing material, is difficult to spread.

Lean Mortar - A mortar that, due to a deficiency of cementitious material, is harsh and difficult to spread.

MORTAR BED - A layer of mortar used to seat additional masonry units or structural members.

NET CROSS-SECTIONAL AREA - The gross cross-sectioned area of a section minus the average area of ungrouted spaces. (Note: The cross-sectional area of grooves in scored units is not usually deducted from the gross cross-sectional area to obtain the net cross-sectional area).

NOMINAL DIMENSION - A dimension which may vary from the actual dimension by the thickness of a mortar joint but not more than $\frac{1}{2}$ inch (13 mm). ($\frac{3}{4}$" - $\frac{7}{8}$" (19 mm-22 mm) for some slump units.) The actual dimension is usually $\frac{3}{8}$ inch (10 mm) less than nominal dimension in concrete masonry units.

PARAPET - The part of a wall that extends above the roof level.

PARGING - The process of applying a coat of cement mortar to the back of the facing material or the face of the backing material.

PERMEABILITY - The occurrence of allowing the passage of fluids.

PIER - A vertical member with dimensions defined by the Code which is capable of resisting lateral forces.

PILASTER - An integral portion of the wall which may project on one or both sides and acts as a vertical beam, a column, an architectural feature, or any combination thereof.

POINTING - Filling mortar into a joint after the masonry unit is laid.

PREFABRICATED MASONRY - Masonry constructed in a location other than its final location in the structure. Also commonly known as panelized masonry.

PRISM - Units mortared together in stack bond, forming a wallette or assemblage to simulate "in wall construction," grouted or ungrouted per specification requirements. This is the standard test sample for determination of the compressive strength of the masonry wall.

QUICKLIME - See LIME.

RACKING - A method of building the end of a wall by stepping back each course so that it can be built on to and against without toothing; also used in corner leads.

Racking

REBAR - Reinforcing steel bars of various sizes and shapes used to strengthen masonry.

REINFORCED HOLLOW CONCRETE MASONRY Masonry in which reinforcement is embedded in either mortar or grout.

RETEMPER - To moisten mortar and re-mix to the proper consistency for use.

RODDING - Slang for puddling or consolidating grout in a cavity or core.

RUNNING BOND - See BOND.

SHELL - The outer portion of a hollow masonry unit as placed in masonry.

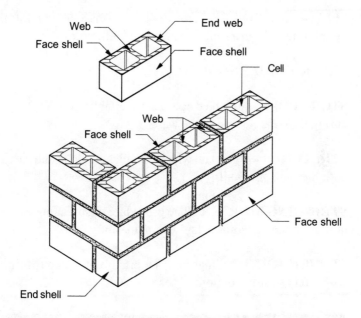

SHOVED JOINT - Head or vertical joints filled by buttering the ends of the units with mortar and shoving them against the units previously laid.

SLAKING - Adding water to quicklime and changing it into lime putty or slaked lime. The addition of water causes the quicklime to heat from hydration and break down into finer pieces.

SLUSHED JOINTS - Head joints filled after units are laid by throwing mortar in with edge of trowel. (Not recommended practice).

SOFFIT - The underside of a beam, lintel or reveal.

SPANDREL - That part of a wall between the head of a window and the sill of the window above it.

SPLIT-FACE FINISH - A rough face on a masonry unit formed by splitting slabs in a split-fate machine (guillotine)

STACK BOND - See BOND.

STORY POLE - A marked pole used to establish vertical heights during the construction of the wall.

STRETCHER - A unit laid with its length horizontal and parallel with the face of a wall.

STRINGING MORTAR - The procedure of spreading enough mortar on the bed joint to lay several masonry units.

STRUCK JOINT - In masonry, a mortar joint which is formed with a recess at the bottom of the joint.

Stringing Mortar

TOOLING - Compressing and shaping the face of a mortar joint with a special tool other than a trowel. Also called jointing.

TOOTHING - The temporary ending of a wall wherein the units in alternate courses project.

TRIG – Masonry units laid in the middle of a wall that act as a guide to eliminate the vertical sag or horizontal bow caused by wind in a masons line

TUCK POINTING - The filling in with fresh mortar of cut-out or defective mortar joints in masonry.

WALLS:

Bonded Wall - A wall in which two or more of its wythes of masonry are adequately bonded together to act as a structural unit.

Cavity Wall - A wall containing continuous air space.

Hollow-Unit Masonry Wall - That type of construction made with hollow masonry units in which the units are laid and set in mortar.

WALL TIE - A mechanical fastener that connects wythes of masonry to each other or to other materials.

WATER RETENTIVITY - The property of mortar which prevents the rapid loss of water.

WEB - The cross member connecting the face shells of a hollow concrete masonry unit.

WYTHE - The portion of a wall which is one masonry unit in thickness; also called *tier*. A collar joint is not considered a wythe.

Uniform Building Code Standards

UNIFORM BUILDING CODE STANDARD 21-3 CONCRETE BUILDING BRICK

Based on Standard Specification C 55-95 of the
American Society for Testing and Materials.
Extracted, with permission, from the
Annual Book of ASTM Standards, copyright
American Society for Testing and Materials
100 Barr Harbor Drive
West Conshohocken, PA 19428

See Section 2102.2, Item 5, *Uniform Building Code*

SECTION 21.301 - SCOPE

This standard covers concrete building brick and similar solid
units made from portland cement, water and suitable mineral
aggregates with or without the inclusion of other materials.

SECTION 21.302 - CLASSIFICATION

21.302.1 Types. Two types of concrete brick in each of two
grades are covered, as follows:

21.302.1.1 Type I, moisture-controlled units. Concrete
brick designated as Type I (Grades N-I and S-I) shall conform to
all requirements of this standard, including the requirements of
Table 21-3-A.

21.302.1.2 Type II, nonmoisture-controlled units. Concrete brick designated as Type II (Grades N-II and S-II) shall conform to all requirements of this standard except the requirements of Table 21-3-A.

21.302.2 Grades. Concrete brick manufactured in accordance with this standard shall conform to two grades as follows:

21.302.2.1 Grade N. For use as architectural veneer and facing units in exterior walls and for use where high strength and resistance to moisture penetration and severe frost action are desired.

21.302.2.2 Grade S. For general use where moderate strength and resistance to frost action and moisture penetration are required.

SECTION 21.303 - MATERIALS

21.303.1 Cementitious Materials. Materials shall conform to the following applicable standards:

1. Portland Cement-ASTM C 150 modified as follows:

    Limitation on insoluble residue-1.5 percent.
    Limitation on air content of mortar,
          Volume percent-22 percent maximum.
    Limitation on loss on ignition-7 percent maximum.
    Limestone with a minimum 85 percent calcium carbonate (CaCO3) content may be added to the cement, provided the requirements of ASTM C 150 as modified above are met.
2. Blended Cements-ASTM C 595.
3. Hydrated Lime, Type S-UBC Standard 21-13.

21.303.2 Other Constituents. Air-entraining agents, coloring pigments, integral water repellents, finely ground silica, etc., shall be previously established as suitable for use in concrete or shall be shown by test or experience not to be detrimental to the durability of the concrete.

SECTION 21.304 - PHYSICAL REQUIREMENTS

At the time of delivery to the work site, the concrete brick shall conform to the physical requirements prescribed in Table 21-3-B.

At the time of delivery to the purchaser, the total linear drying shrinkage of Type II units shall not exceed 0.065 percent when tested in accordance with ASTM C 426.

The moisture content of Type I concrete brick at the time of delivery shall conform to the requirements prescribed in Table 21-3-A.

SECTION 21.305 - DIMENSIONS AND PERMISSIBLE VARIATIONS

Overall dimensions (width, height, or length) shall not differ by more than 1/8 inch (3.2 mm) from the specified standard dimensions.

NOTE: Standard dimensions of concrete brick are the manufacturer's designated dimensions. Nominal dimensions of modular-size concrete brick are equal to the standard dimensions plus 3/8 inch (9.5 mm), the thickness of one standard mortar joint. Nominal dimensions of nonmodular size concrete brick usually exceed the standard dimensions by 1/8 inch to 1/4 inch (3.2 mm to 6.4 mm).

Variations in thickness of architectural units such as split-faced or slumped units will usually vary from the specified tolerances.

SECTION 21.306 - VISUAL INSPECTION

21.306.1 General. All concrete brick shall be sound and free of cracks or other defects that would interfere with the proper placing of the unit or impair the strength or permanence of the construction. Minor cracks incidental to the usual method of manufacture, or minor chipping resulting from customary methods of handling in shipment and delivery, shall not be deemed grounds for rejection.

21.306.2 Brick in Exposed Walls. Where concrete brick is to be used in exposed wall construction, the face or faces that are to be exposed shall be free of chips, cracks or other imperfections when viewed from 20 feet (6100 mm), except that if not more than 5 percent of a shipment contains slight cracks or small chips not larger than 1/2 inch (13 mm), this shall not be deemed grounds for rejection.

SECTION 21.307 - METHODS OF SAMPLING AND TESTING

The purchaser or authorized representative shall be accorded proper facilities to inspect and sample the concrete brick at the place of manufacture from the lots ready for delivery. At least 10 days shall be allowed for completion of the test.

Sample and test concrete brick in accordance with ASTM C 140 and C 426, when applicable.

Total linear drying shrinkage shall be based on tests of concrete brick made with the same materials, concrete mix design, manufacturing process and curing method, conducted in accordance with ASTM C 426 not more than 24 months prior to delivery.

SECTION 21.308 - REJECTION

If the shipment fails to conform to the specific requirements, the manufacturer may sort it, and new specimens shall be selected by the purchaser from the retained lot and tested at the expense of the manufacturer. If the second set of specimens fails to conform to the test requirements, the entire lot shall be rejected.

Table 21-3-A - Moisture Content Requirements for Type I Concrete Brick

Linear Shrinkage, Percent	Moisture Content, Max. Percent of Total Absorption (Average of 3 Concrete Brick)		
	Humidity[1] Conditions at Jobsite or Point of Use		
	Humid	Intermediate	Arid
0.03 or less	45	40	35
From 0.03 to 0.045	40	35	30
0.045 to 0.065, max.	35	30	25

[1] Arid - Average annual relative humidity less than 50 percent.
 Intermediate - Average annual relative humidity 50 to 75 percent.
 Humid - Average annual relative humidity above 75 percent.

Table 21-3-B - Strength and Absorption Requirements

	Compressive Strength, Min., psi (Concrete Brick Tested Flatwise)		Water Absorption, Max., (avg. of 3 Brick) with Oven-Dry Weight of Concrete lb./ft^3		
	x 6.89 kPa		x 16 for kg/m^3		
	Average Gross Area		Weight Classification		
Grade	Avg. of 3 Concrete Brick	Individual Concrete Brick	Light Weight Less than 105	Medium Weight Less Than 125 to 105	Normal Weight 125 or more
N-I	3,500	3,000	15	13	10
N-II	3,500	3,000	15	13	10
S-I	2,500	2,000	18	15	13
S-II	2,500	2,000	18	15	13

UNIFORM BUILDING CODE STANDARD 21-4
HOLLOW AND SOLID LOAD-BEARING
CONCRETE MASONRY UNITS

Based on Standard Specification C 90-95 of the American Society for Testing and Materials. Extracted, with permission, from the *Annual Book of ASTM Standards,* copyright American Society for Testing and Materials 100 Barr Harbor Drive West Conshohocken, PA 19428

SECTION 21.401 - SCOPE

This standard covers solid (units with 75 percent or more net area) and hollow load-bearing concrete masonry units made from portland cement, water and mineral aggregates with or without the inclusion of other materials.

SECTION 21.402 - CLASSIFICATION

21.402.1 Types. Two types of concrete masonry units in each of two grades are covered as follows:

21.402.1.1 Type I, moisture-controlled units. Units designated as Type I shall conform to all requirements of this standard including the moisture content requirements of Table 21-4-A.

21.402.1.2 Type II, nonmoisture-controlled units. Units designated as Type II shall conform to all requirements of this standard except the moisture content requirements of Table 21-4-A.

21.402.2 Grades. Concrete masonry units manufactured in accordance with this standard shall conform to two grades as follows:

21.402.2.1 Grade N. Units having a weight classification of 85 pcf (1360 kg/m3) or greater, for general use such as in exterior walls below and above grade that may or may not be exposed to moisture penetration or the weather and for interior walls and backup.

21.402.2.2 Grade S. Units having a weight classification of less than 85 pcf (1360 kg/m3), for uses limited to above-grade installation in exterior walls with weather-protective coatings and in walls not exposed to the weather.

SECTION 21.403 - MATERIALS

21.403.1 Cementitious Materials. Materials shall conform to the following applicable standards:

1. Portland Cement-ASTM C 150 modified as follows:

   Limitation on insoluble residue-1.5 percent maximum.
   Limitation on air content of mortar,
        Volume percent-22 percent maximum.
   Limitation on loss on ignition-7 percent maximum.
   Limestone with a minimum 85 percent calcium carbonate ($CaCO_3$) content may be added to the cement, provided the requirements of ASTM C 150 as modified above are met.
2. Blended Cements-ASTM C 595.
3. Hydrated Lime, Type S-UBC Standard 21-13.

21.403.2 Other Constituents and Aggregates. Air-entraining agents, coloring pigments, integral water repellents, finely ground silica, aggregates, and other constituents, shall be previously established as suitable for use in concrete or shall be shown by test or experience to not be detrimental to the durability of the concrete.

SECTION 21.404 - PHYSICAL REQUIREMENTS

At the time of delivery to the work site, the units shall conform to the physical requirements prescribed in Table 21-4-B. The moisture content of Type I concrete masonry units at time of delivery shall conform to the requirements prescribed in Table 21-4-A.

At the time of delivery to the purchaser, the linear shrinkage of Type II units shall not exceed 0.065 percent.

SECTION 21.405 - MINIMUM FACE-SHELL AND WEB THICKNESSES

Face-shell (FST) and web (WT) thicknesses shall conform to the requirements listed in Table 21-4-C.

SECTION 21.406 - PERMISSIBLE VARIATIONS IN DIMENSIONS

21.406.1 Precision Units. For precision units, no overall dimension (width, height and length) shall differ by more than 1/8 inch (3.2 mm) from the specified standard dimensions.

21.406.2 Particular Feature Units. For particular feature units, dimensions shall be in accordance with the following:

1. For molded face units, no overall dimension (width, height and length) shall differ by more than 1/8 inch (3.2 mm) from the specified standard dimension. Dimensions of molded features (ribs, scores, hex-shapes, patterns, etc.) shall be within 1/16 inch (1.6 mm) of the specified standard dimensions and shall be within 1/16 inch (1.6 mm) of the specified placement of the unit.

2. For split-faced units, all non-split overall dimensions (width, height and length) shall differ by no more than 1/8 inch (3.2 mm) from the specified standard dimensions. On faces that are split, overall dimensions will vary. Local suppliers should be consulted to determine dimensional tolerances achievable.

3. For slumped units, no overall height dimension shall differ by more than 1/8 inch (3.2 mm) from the specified standard dimension. On faces that are slumped, overall dimensions will vary. Local suppliers should be consulted to determine dimension tolerances achievable.

NOTE: Standard dimensions of units are the manufacturer's designated dimensions. Nominal dimensions of modular size units, except slumped units, are equal to the standard dimensions plus 3/8 inch (9.5 mm), the thickness of one standard mortar joint. Slumped units are equal to the standard dimensions plus 1/2 inch (13 mm), the thickness of one standard mortar joint. Nominal dimensions of nonmodular size units usually exceed the standard dimensions by 1/8 inch to 1/4 inch (3.2 mm to 6.4 mm).

SECTION 21.407 - VISUAL INSPECTION

All units shall be sound and free of cracks or other defects that would interfere with the proper placing of the unit or impair the strength or permanence of the construction. Units may have minor cracks incidental to the usual method of manufacture, or minor chipping resulting from customary methods of handling in shipment and delivery.

Units that are intended to serve as a base for plaster or stucco shall have a sufficiently rough surface to afford a good bond.

Where units are to be used in exposed wall construction, the face or faces that are to be exposed shall be free of chips, cracks or other imperfections when viewed from 20 feet (6100 mm), except that not more than 5 percent of a shipment may have slight cracks or small chips not larger than 1 inch (25.4 mm).

SECTION 21.408 - METHODS OF SAMPLING AND TESTING

The purchaser or authorized representative shall be accorded proper facilities to inspect and sample the units at the place of manufacture from the lots ready for delivery.

Sample and test units in accordance with ASTM C 140.

Total linear drying shrinkage shall be based on tests of concrete masonry units made with the same materials, concrete mix design, manufacturing process and curing method, conducted in accordance with ASTM C 426 and not more than 24 months prior to delivery.

SECTION 21.409 - REJECTION

If the samples tested from a shipment fail to conform to the specified requirements, the manufacturer may sort it, and new specimens shall be selected by the purchaser from the retained lot and tested at the expense of the manufacturer. If the second set of specimens fails to conform to the specified requirements, the entire lot shall be rejected.

Table 21-4-A - Moisture Content requirements for Type I Units

	Moisture Content, Max. Percent of Total Absorption (Average of 3 Concrete Units)		
	Humidity Conditions at Jobsite or Point of Use		
Linear Shrinkage, Percent	Humid[1]	Intermediate[2]	Arid[3]
0.03 or less	45	40	35
From 0.03 to 0.045	40	35	30
0.045 to 0.065, max.	35	30	25

[1] Arid - Average annual relative humidity less than 50 percent.
[2] Intermediate - Average annual relative humidity 50 to 75 percent.
[3] Humid - Average annual relative humidity above 75 percent.

Table 21-4-B - Strength and Absorption Requirements

Compressive Strength, Min., psi (MPa)		Water Absorption, Max., lb./ft. (kg/m) (Average of 3 Units)		
Average Net Area		Weight Classification - Oven-dry Weight of Concrete, lb./ft. (kg/m)		
Average of 3 Units	Individual Unit	Lightweight, Less than 105 (1680)	Medium Weight, 105 to less than 125 (1680-2000)	Normal Weight, 125 (2000) or more
1900 (13.1)	1700 (11.7)	18(288)	15 (240)	13 (208)

Table 21-4-C - Minimum Thickness of Face-Shells and Webs

Nominal Width (W) of Unit (inches)	Face-Shell Thickness (FST) Min., (inches)[1,4]	Web Thickness (WT)	
		Webs[1] Min., (inches)	Equivalent Web Thickness, Min., In./Lin. Ft[2]
x 25.4 for mm			x 83 for mm/lin. m
3 and 4	$3/4$	$3/4$	$1^5/_8$
6	1	1	$2^1/_4$
8	$1^1/_4$	1	$2^1/_4$
10	$1^3/_8$ $1^1/_4$	$1^1/_8$	$2^1/_2$
12	$1^1/_2$ $1^1/_4$	$1^1/_8$	$2^1/_8$

[1] Average of measurements on three units taken at the thinnest point

[2] Sum of the measured thickness of all webs in the unit, multiplied by 12 (305 when using metric), and divided by the length of the unit. In the case of open-ended units where the open-ended portion is solid grouted, the length of that open-ended portion shall be deducted from the overall length of the unit.

[3] This face-shell thickness (FST) is applicable where allowable design load is reduced in proportion to the reduction in thicknesses shown, except that allowable design load on solid-grouted units shall not be reduced.

[4] For split-faced units, a minimum of 10 percent of a shipment may have face-shell thickness less than those shown, but in no case less than $3/_4$ inch (19 mm).

UNIFORM BUILDING CODE STANDARD 21-5 NONLOAD-BEARING CONCRETE MASONRY UNITS

Based on Standard Specification C 129-95 (1980) of the American Society for Testing and Materials. Extracted, with permission, from the *Annual Book of ASTM Standards,* copyright American Society for Testing and Materials 100 Barr Harbor Drive West Conshohocken, PA 19428

See Section 2102.2, Item 5, *Uniform Building Code*

SECTION 21.501 - SCOPE

This standard covers hollow and solid nonload-bearing concrete masonry units made from portland cement, water, and mineral aggregates with or without the inclusion of other materials. Such units are intended for use in nonload-bearing partitions but under certain conditions may be suitable for use in nonload-bearing exterior walls above grade, where effectively protected from the weather.

SECTION 21.502 - CLASSIFICATION

21.502.1 Weight Classifications. Nonload-bearing concrete masonry units manufactured in accordance with this standard shall conform to one of three weight classifications and two types as follows:

Weight Classification	Oven-Dry Weight of Concrete lb./cu.ft.
Lightweight	105 (1680 kg/m³) max.
Medium weight	105-125 (1680-2000 kg/m³)
Normal weight	125 (2000 kg/m³) min.

21.502.2 Types. Nonload-bearing concrete masonry units shall be of two types as follows:

439

21.502.2.1 Type I, moisture-controlled units. Type I units shall conform to all requirements of this standard, including the requirements of Table 21-5-A.

21.502.2.2 Type II, nonmoisture-controlled units. Type II units shall conform to all requirements of this standard, except the requirements listed in Table 21-5-A.

SECTION 21.503 - MATERIALS

21.503.1 Cementitious Materials. Cementitious materials shall conform to the following applicable standards:

1. Portland Cement-ASTM C 150 modified as follows:

Limitation on insoluble residue-1.5 percent.
Limitation on air content of mortar,
    Volume percent-22 percent maximum.
Limitation on loss on ignition-7 percent maximum.
Limestone with a minimum 85 percent calcium carbonate
    ($CaCO_3$) content may be added to the cement, provided
    the requirements of ASTM C 150 as modified above are
    met.
2. Blended Cements-ASTM C 595.
3. Hydrated Lime, Type S-UBC Standard 21-13.

21.503.2 Other Constituents. Air-entraining agents, coloring pigments, integral water repellents, finely ground silica, etc., shall be previously established as suitable for use in concrete or shall be shown by test or experience not to be detrimental to the durability of the concrete.

SECTION 21.504 - PHYSICAL REQUIREMENTS

At the time of delivery to the work site, the units shall conform to the strength requirements prescribed in Table 21-5-B.

The moisture content of Type I concrete masonry units at the time of delivery shall conform to the requirements prescribed in Table 21-5-A.

At the time of delivery to the purchaser, the total linear drying of Type II units shall not exceed 0.065 percent.

SECTION 21.505 - DIMENSIONS AND PERMISSIBLE VARIATIONS

Minimum face-shell thickness shall not be less than 1/2 inch (13 mm).

No overall dimension (width, height or length) shall differ by more than 1/8 inch (3.2 mm) from the specified standard dimensions.

NOTE: Standard dimensions of units are the manufacturer's designated dimensions. Nominal dimensions of modular-size units are equal to the standard dimensions plus 3/8 inch (9.5 mm), the thickness of one standard mortar joint. Nominal dimensions of nonmodular size units usually exceed the standard dimensions by 1/8 inch to 1/4 inch (3.2 mm to 6.4 mm).

Variations in thickness of architectural units such as split-faced or slumped units will usually exceed the specified tolerances.

SECTION 21.506 - VISUAL INSPECTION

21.506.1 General. All units shall be sound and free of cracks or other defects that would interfere with the proper placing of the units or impair the strength or permanence of the construction. Units may have minor cracks incidental to the usual method of manufacture, or minor chipping resulting from customary methods of handling in shipment and delivery.

21.506.2 Exposed Units. Where units are to be used in exposed wall construction, the face or faces that are to be exposed shall be free of chips, cracks or other imperfections when viewed from 20 feet (6100 mm), except that not more than 5 percent of a shipment may have slight cracks or small chips not larger than 1 inch (25 mm).

21.506.3 Identification. Nonloading concrete masonry units shall be clearly marked in a manner to preclude their use as load-bearing units.

SECTION 21.507 - METHODS OF SAMPLING AND TESTING

The purchaser or authorized representative shall be accorded proper facilities to inspect and sample the units at the place of manufacture from the lots ready for delivery. At least 10 days shall be allowed for the completion of the tests.

Sample and test units in accordance with ASTM C 140 and ASTM C 426 when applicable.

Total linear drying shrinkage shall be based on tests of concrete masonry units made with the same materials, concrete mix design, manufacturing process and curing method, conducted in accordance with ASTM C 426 and not more than 24 months prior to delivery.

SECTION 21.508 - REJECTION

If the shipment fails to conform to the specified requirements, the manufacturer may sort it, and new specimens shall be selected by the purchaser from the retained lot and tested at the expense of the manufacturer. If the second set of specimens fails to conform to the specified requirements, the entire lot shall be rejected.

Table 21-5-A - Moisture Content Requirements for Type I Units

	Moisture Content, Max. Percent of Total Absorption (Average of 3 Concrete Brick)		
	Humidity[1] Conditions at Jobsite or Point of Use		
Linear Shrinkage, Percent	Humid	Intermediate	Arid
0.03 or less	45	40	35
From 0.03 to 0.045	40	35	30
0.045 to 0.065, max.	35	30	25

[1] Arid - Average annual relative humidity less than 50 percent.
Intermediate - Average annual relative humidity 50 to 75 percent.
Humid - Average annual relative humidity above 75 percent.

Table 21-5-B - Strength Requirements

	Compressive Strength (Average Net Area) Min., psi
	x 6.89 for kPa
Average of 3 units	600
Individual units	500

UNIFORM BUILDING CODE STANDARD 21-10
JOINT REINFORCEMENT FOR MASONRY

Specification Standard of the International Conference of Building Officials

See Sections 2102.2; 2104 and 2106.1.12.4, Item 2, *Uniform Building Code*

Part I-Joint Reinforcement for Masonry

SECTION 21.1001 - SCOPE

This standard covers joint reinforcement fabricated from cold-drawn steel wire for reinforcing masonry.

SECTION 21.1002 - DESCRIPTION

Joint reinforcement consists of deformed longitudinal wires welded to cross wires (Figure 21-10-1) in sizes suitable for placing in mortar joints between masonry courses.

SECTION 21.1003 - CONFIGURATION AND SIZE OF LONGITUDINAL AND CROSS WIRES

21.1003.1 General. The distance between longitudinal wires and the configuration of cross wires connecting the longitudinal wires shall conform to the design and the requirements of Figure 21-10-1.

21.1003.2 Longitudinal Wires. The diameter of longitudinal wires shall not be less than 0.148 inch (3.76 mm) or more than one half the mortar joint thickness.

21.1003.3 Cross Wires. The diameter of cross wires shall not be less than (No. 9 gage) 0.148-inch (3.76 mm) diameter nor more than the diameter of the longitudinal wires. Cross wires shall not project beyond the outside longitudinal wires by more than 1/8 inch (3.2 mm).

21.1003.4 Width. The width of joint reinforcement shall be the out-to-out distance between outside longitudinal wires. Variation in the width shall not exceed 1/8 inch (3.2 mm).

21.1003.5 Length. The length of pieces of joint reinforcement shall not vary more than 1/2 inch (13 mm) or 1.0 percent of the specified length, whichever is less.

SECTION 21.1004 - MATERIAL REQUIREMENTS

21.1004.1 Tensile Properties. Wire of the finished product shall meet the following requirements:

Tensile strength, minimum	75,000 psi (517 MPa)
Yield strength, minimum	60,000 psi (414 MPa)
Reduction of area, minimum	30 percent

For wire testing over 100,000 psi (689 MPa), the reduction of area shall not be less than 25 percent.

21.1004.2 Bend Properties. Wire shall not break or crack along the outside diameter of the bend when tested in accordance with Section 21.1008.

21.1004.3 Weld Shear Properties. The least weld shear strength in pounds shall not be less than 25,000 (11.3 Mg) multiplied by the specified area of the smaller wire in square inches.

SECTION 21.1005 - FABRICATION

Wire shall be fabricated and finished in a workmanlike manner, shall be free from injurious imperfections and shall conform to this standard.

The wires shall be assembled by automatic machines or by other suitable mechanical means which will assure accurate spacing and alignment of all members of the finished product.

Longitudinal and cross wires shall be securely connected at every intersection by a process of electric-resistance welding.

Longitudinal wires shall be deformed. One set of four deformations shall occur around the perimeter of the wire at a maximum spacing of 0.7 times the diameter of the wire but not less than eight sets per inch (25.4 mm) of length. The overall length of each deformation within the set shall be such that the summation of gaps between the ends of the deformations shall not exceed 25 percent of the perimeter of the wire. The height or depth of the deformations shall be 0.012 inch (0.305 mm) for 3/16 inch (4.76 mm) diameter or larger wire, 0.011 (0.28 mm) for 0.162-inch (4.11 mm) diameter wire and 0.009 inch (0.23 mm) for 0.148-inch (3.76 mm) diameter wire.

SECTION 21.1006 - TENSION TESTS

Tension tests shall be made on individual wires cut from the finished product across the welds.

Tension tests across a weld shall have the welded joint located approximately at the center of the wire being tested.

Tensile strength shall be the average of four test values determined by dividing the maximum test load by the specified cross-sectional area of the wire.

Reduction of area shall be determined by measuring the ruptured section of a specimen which has been tested.

SECTION 21.1007 - WELD SHEAR STRENGTH TESTS

Test specimens shall be obtained from the finished product by cutting a section of wire which includes one weld.

Weld shear strength tests shall be conducted using a fixture of such design as to prevent rotation of the cross wire. The cross wire shall be placed in the anvil of the testing device which is secured in the tensile machine and the load then applied to the longitudinal wire.

Weld shear strength shall be the average test load in pounds of four tests.

SECTION 21.1008 - BEND TESTS

Test specimens shall be obtained from the finished product by cutting a section of wire without welds.

The test specimens shall be bent cold through 180 degrees around a pin, the diameter of which is equal to the diameter of the specimen.

The specimen shall not break nor shall there be visual cracks on the outside diameter of the bend.

SECTION 21.1009 - FREQUENCY OF TESTS

One set of tension tests, weld strength shear tests and bend tests shall be performed for each 2,000,000 lineal feet (610 000 m) of joint reinforcement, but not less than monthly.

SECTION 21.1010 - CORROSION PROTECTION

When corrosion protection of joint reinforcement is provided, it shall be in accordance with one of the following:

21.1010.1 Brite Basic. No coating.

21.1010.2 Mill Galvanized. Zinc coated, by the hot-dipped method, with no minimum thickness of zinc coating. The coating may be applied before fabrication.

21.1010.3 Class I Mill Galvanized. Zinc coated, by the hot-dipped method, with a minimum of 0.40 ounce of zinc per square foot (0.12 kg/m2) of surface area. The coating may be applied before fabrication.

21.1010.4 Class III Mill Galvanized. Zinc coated, by the hot-dipped method, with a minimum of 0.80 ounce of zinc per square foot (0.24 kg/m2) of surface area. The coating may be applied before fabrication.

21.1010.5 Hot-dipped Galvanized. Zinc coated, by the hot-dipped method, with a minimum of 1.50 ounces of zinc per square foot (0.45 kg/m2) of surface area. The coating shall be applied after fabrication.

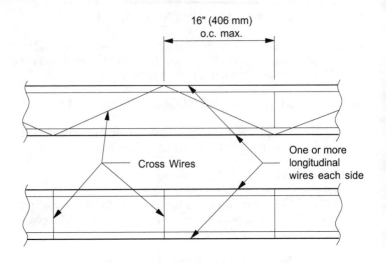

Figure 21-10-1 - Joint Reinforcement

Part II-Cold-drawn Steel Wire for Concrete Reinforcement

Based on Standard Specification A 82-90a of the American Society for Testing and Materials. Extracted, with permission, from the *Annual Book of ASTM Standards,* copyright American Society for Testing and Materials 100 Barr Harbor Drive West Conshohocken, PA 19428

See Sections 2101.3; 2104 and 2106.1.12.4, Item 2, *Uniform Building Code*

SECTION 21.1011 - SCOPE

This standard covers cold-drawn steel wire to be used as such or in fabricated form, for the reinforcement as follows:

SIZE NUMBER	NOMINAL DIAMETER (inch) (x 25.4 for mm)	NOMINAL AREA (square inch) (x 645 for mm²)
W 31	0.628	0.310
W 30	0.618	0.300
W 28	0.597	0.280
W 26	0.575	0.260
W 24	0.553	0.240
W 22	0.529	0.220
W 20	0.505	0.200
W 18	0.479	0.180
W 16	0.451	0.160
W 14	0.422	0.140
W 12	0.391	0.120
W 10	0.357	0.100
W 8	0.319	0.080
W 6	0.276	0.060
W 5.5	0.265	0.055
W 5	0.252	0.050
W 4.5	0.239	0.045
W 4	0.226	0.040
W 3.5	0.211	0.035
W 2.9	0.192	0.029
W 2.5	0.178	0.025
W 2	0.160	0.020
W 1.4	0.134	0.014
W 1.2	0.124	0.012
W 0.5	0.080	0.005

SECTION 21.1012 - PROCESS

The steel shall be made by one or more of the following processes: open hearth, electric furnace or basic oxygen.

The wire shall be cold drawn from rods that have been hot rolled from billets.

Unless otherwise specified, the wire shall be "as cold drawn," except wire smaller than size number W 1.2 for welded fabric, which shall be galvanized at finish size.

SECTION 21.1013 - TENSILE PROPERTIES

The material, except as specified in this section, shall conform to the following tensile property requirements based on nominal area of wire:

Tensile strength, minimum, psi	80,000 (552 MPa)
Yield strength, minimum, psi	70,000 (483 MPa)
Reduction of area, minimum, percent	30

For material testing over 100,000 pounds per square inch (689 MPa) tensile strength, the reduction of area shall not be less than 25 percent.

For material to be used in the fabrication of welded fabric, the following tensile and yield strength properties based on nominal area of wire shall apply:

	Size W. 1.2 Larger	Smaller than Size W 1.2
Tensile strength, minimum, psi	75,000 (517 MPa)	70,000 (483 MPa)
Yield strength, minimum, psi	65,000 (448 MPa)	56,000 (386 MPa)

The yield strength shall be determined at an extension of 0.005 inch per inch (0.005 mm per mm) of gage length.

The material shall not exhibit a definite yield point as evidenced by a distinct drop of the beam or halt in the gage of the testing machine prior to reaching ultimate tensile load.

SECTION 21.1014 - BENDING PROPERTIES

The bend test specimen shall stand being bent cold through 180 degrees without cracking on the outside of the bent portion, as follows:

Size Number of Wire	Bend Test
W 7 and smaller	Bend around a pin, the diameter of which is equal to the diameter of the specimen.
Larger than W 7	Bend around a pin, the diameter of which is equal to twice the diameter of the specimen.

SECTION 21.1015 - TEST SPECIMENS

Tension and bend test specimens shall be of the full section of the wire and shall be obtained from ends of wire coils.

SECTION 21.1016 - NUMBER OF TESTS

One tension test and one bend test shall be made from each 10 tons (89 kN) or less of each size of wire or fraction thereof in a lot, or a total of seven samples, whichever is less. A lot shall consist of all the coils of a single size offered for delivery at the same time.

If any test specimen shows imperfections or develops flaws, it may be discarded and another specimen substituted.

SECTION 21.1017 - PERMISSIBLE VARIATIONS IN WIRE DIAMETER

The permissible variation in the diameter of the wire shall conform to the following:

Size Number	Permissible Variation Plus and Minus (inch) (x 25.4 for mm)
Smaller than W 5	0.003
W 5 to W 12, inclusive	0.004
Over W 12 to W 20, inclusive	0.006
Over W 20	0.008

451

The difference between the maximum and minimum diameter, as measured on any given cross section of the wire, shall be more than the tolerances shown above for the given wire size.

SECTION 21.1018 - FINISH
The wire shall be free from injurious imperfections and shall have a workmanlike finish with smooth surface.

Galvanized wire shall be completely covered in a workmanlike manner with a zinc coating.

UNIFORM BUILDING CODE STANDARD 21-11
CEMENT, MASONRY

Based on Standard Specification C 91-93 of the
American Society for Testing and Materials.
Extracted, with permission, from the
Annual Book of ASTM Standards, copyright
American Society for Testing and Materials
100 Barr Harbor Drive
West Conshohocken, PA 19428

See Section 2102.2, Item 2 and Table 21-A,
Uniform Building Code

SECTION 21.1101 - SCOPE

This standard covers three types of masonry cement for use in masonry mortars.

SECTION 21.1102 - CLASSIFICATIONS

21.1102.1 General. Masonry cement complying with this standard shall be classified as one of the types set forth in this section.

21.1102.2 Type N. Type N cement is for use as the cementitious material in the preparation of UBC Standard 21-15 Type N and Type O mortars. It is for use in combination with portland or blended hydraulic cements in the preparation of Type S or Type M mortars.

21.1102.3 Type S. Type S cement is for use as the cementitious material in the preparation of UBC Standard 21-15 Type S mortar.

21.1102.4 Type M. Type M cement is for use as the cementitious material in the preparation of UBC Standard 21-15 Type M mortar.

SECTION 21.1103 - PHYSICAL REQUIREMENTS

Masonry cement shall conform to the requirements set forth in Table 21-11-A for its classifications.

SECTION 21.1104 - PACKAGE LABELING
Masonry cement packages shall carry a statement indicating that the product conforms to requirements of this standard and shall include the brand, name of manufacturer, type of masonry cement and net weight of the package in pounds.

SECTION 21.1105 - CERTIFICATION

Certification shall be submitted upon request of the building official and shall certify compliance with the requirements of this standard.

SECTION 21.1106 - SAMPLING AND TESTING

Every 90 days, each masonry cement producer shall retain an approved agency to obtain a random sample from a local point of supply in the market area served by the producer.

The agency shall test the masonry cement for compliance with the physical requirements of Table 21-11-A.

Upon request of the building official, the producer shall furnish (at no cost) test results to the building official, architect, structural engineer, general contractor and masonry contractor.

SECTION 21.1107 - TEMPERATURE AND HUMIDITY

The temperature of the air in the vicinity of the mixing slab and dry materials, molds, base plates and mixing bowl shall be maintained between 68°F and 81.5°F (20°C and 27.5°C). The temperature of the mixing water, moist cabinet or moist room, and water in the storage tank shall not vary from 73.4°F (23°C) by more than 3°F (1.7°C).

The relative humidity of the laboratory air shall not be less than 50 percent. The moist cabinet or moist room atmosphere shall have a relative humidity of not less than 90 percent.

The moist cabinet or moist room shall conform to applicable standards.

SECTION 21.1108 - FINENESS

The fineness of the cement shall be determined from the residue on the No. 325 (45 mm) sieve.

SECTION 21.1109 - NORMAL CONSISTENCY

Determine normal consistency by the Vicat apparatus.

SECTION 21.1110 - AUTOCLAVE EXPANSION

The autoclave expansion shall be determined. After molding, store the bars in the moist cabinet or room for 48 hours ± 30 minutes before removal from the molds for measurement and test in the autoclave. Calculate the difference in the lengths of the test specimen before and after autoclaving to the nearest 0.01 percent of the effective gage length and report as the autoclave expansion of the masonry cement.

SECTION 21.1111 - TIME OF SETTING

The time of setting shall be determined by the Gillmore needle method.

SECTION 21.1112 - DENSITY

The density of the masonry cement shall be determined by using kerosene as the liquid. Use the density so determined in the calculation of the air content of the mortars.

SECTION 21.1113 - APPARATUS FOR MORTAR TESTS

The apparatus for mortar tests shall be in accordance with applicable standards.

SECTION 21.1114 - BLENDED SAND

The sand shall be a blend of equal parts by weight of graded standard sand and Standard 20-30 sand.

SECTION 21.1115 - PREPARATION OF MORTAR

21.1115.1 Proportions for Mortar. Mortar for air entrainment, compressive strength and water-retention tests shall be proportioned to contain the weight of cement, in grams, equal to six times the printed bag weight in pounds (13.228 times the printed bag weight in kilograms) and 1,440 grams of sand. The sand shall consist of 720 grams of graded Ottawa sand and 720 grams of Standard 20-30 sand. The quantity of water, measured in milliliters, shall be such as to produce a flow of 110 ± 5 as determined by the flow table.

21.1115.2 Mixing of Mortars. The mortar shall be mixed in accordance with the applicable standards.

21.1115.3 Determination of Flow. The flow shall be determined in accordance with applicable standards.

SECTION 21.1116 - AIR ENTRAINMENT

21.1116.1 Procedure. If the mortar has the correct flow, use a separate portion of the mortar for the determination of entrained air. Determine the mass of 400 ml of the mortar.

21.1116.2 Calculation. Calculate the air content of the mortar and report it to the nearest 0.1 percent as follows:

$$D = (W_1 + W_2 + V_w) \; [(W_1/S_1) + (W_2/S_2) + V_w]$$
$$A = 100 - (w_m/4D)$$

WHERE:

A = volume percent of entrained air.
D = density of air-free mortar, g/ml.
S_1 = density of cement, g/ml.
S_2 = density of standard sand, 2.65 g/ml.
V_w = milliliters-grams of water used.
W_m = mass of 400 ml.
W_1 = mass of cement, g.
W_2 = mass of sand, g.

SECTION 21.1117 - COMPRESSIVE STRENGTH

21.1117.1 Test Specimens.

21.1117.1.1 Molding. Immediately after determining the flow and the mass of 400 ml of mortar, return all the mortar to the mixing bowl and remix for 15 seconds at the medium speed. Then mold test specimens in accordance with applicable standards, except that elapsed time for mixing mortar, determining flow, determining air entrainment and starting the molding of cubes shall be within eight minutes.

21.1117.1.2 Storage. Store all test specimens immediately after molding in the molds on plane plates in a moist cabinet or moist room for 48 to 52 hours, in such a manner that the upper surfaces shall be exposed to the moist air. Then remove the cubes from the molds and place in the moist cabinet or moist room for five days in such a manner as to allow free circulation of air around at least five faces of the specimens. At the age of seven days, immerse the cubes for the 28-day tests in saturated lime water in storage tanks of noncorrodible materials.

21.1117.2 Procedure. Test the cube specimens immediately after their removal from the moist cabinet or moist room for seven-day specimens, and immediately after their removal from storage water for all other specimens. If more than one specimen at a time is removed from the moist cabinet or moist room for seven-day tests, cover these cubes with a damp cloth until time of testing. If more than one specimen at a time is removed from the storage water for testing, place these cubes in a pan of water at a temperature of 73.4°F ± 3°F (23°C ± 1.7°C), and of sufficient depth to completely immerse each cube until time of testing.

The remainder of the testing procedure shall conform to applicable standards.

SECTION 21.1118 - WATER RETENTION

21.1118.1 Apparatus. The water-retention test shall conform to applicable standards.

21.1118.2 Procedure. Adjust the mercury relief column to maintain a vacuum of 51 ± 3 mm as indicated by the manometer. Seat the perforated dish on the greased gasket or greased rim of the funnel.

Place a wetted filter paper in the bottom of the dish. Turn the stopcock to apply the vacuum to the funnel and check the apparatus for leaks and to determine that the required vacuum is obtained. Then turn the stopcock to shut off the vacuum from the funnel.

Mix the mortar to a flow of 110 ± 5 percent in accordance with applicable standards. Immediately after making the flow test, return the mortar on the flow table to the mixing bowl and remix the entire batch for 15 seconds at medium speed. Immediately after remixing the mortar, fill the perforated dish with the mortar to slightly above the rim. Tamp the mortar 15 times with the tamper. Apply 10 of the tamping strokes at approximately uniform spacing adjacent to the rim of the dish and with the long axis of the tamping face held at right angles to the radius of the dish. Apply the remaining five tamping strokes at random points distributed over the central area of the dish. The tamping pressure shall be just sufficient to ensure filling of the dish. On completion of the tamping, the top of the mortar will extend slightly above the rim of the dish. Smooth off the mortar by drawing the flat side of the straightedge (with the leading edge slightly raised) across the top of the dish. Then cut off the mortar to a plane surface flush with the rim of the dish by drawing the straightedge with a sawing motion across the top of the dish in two cutting strokes, starting each cut from near the center of the dish. If the mortar is pulled away from the side of the dish during the process of drawing the straightedge across the dish, gently press the mortar back into contact with the side of the dish using the tamper.

Turn the stopcock to apply the vacuum to the funnel. The time elapsed from the start of mixing the cement and water to the time of applying the vacuum shall not exceed eight minutes. After suction for 60 seconds, quickly turn the stopcock to expose the funnel to atmospheric pressure. Immediately slide the perforated dish off from the funnel, touch it momentarily on a damp cloth to remove droplets of water, and set the dish on the table. Then, using the bowl scraper, plow and mix the mortar in the dish for 15 seconds. Upon completion of mixing, place the mortar in the flow mold and determine the flow. The entire operation shall be carried out without interruption and as quickly as possible, and shall be completed within an elapsed time of 11 minutes after the start of mixing the cement and water for the first flow determination. Both flow determinations shall be made in accordance with applicable standards.

21.1118.3 Calculation. Calculate the water-retention value for the mortar as follows:

Water-retention value = (A/B) x 100

WHERE:

A = flow after suction.
B = flow immediately after mixing.

Table 21-11-A - Physical Requirements

Masonry Cement Type	N	S	M
Fineness, residue on a No. 325 (45 µm) sieve, maximum percent	24	24	24
Soundness: Autoclave expansion, maximum, percent	1.0	1.0	1.0

Time of setting, Gilmore method:
    Initial set, minimum, hour................
    Final set, maximum, hour................
	2
	24
		$1^1/_2$
		24
			$1^1/_2$
			24

Compressive Strength
    (average of 3 cubes):
    Initial compressive strength of mortar cubes, composed of 1 part cement and 3 parts blended sand (half Graded Ottawa sand, and half Standard 20-30 Ottawa sand) by volume, prepared and tested in accordance with this specification shall be equal to or higher than the values specified for the ages indicated below:
    7 days, psi...................................
 	
    28 days, psi..............................
	500
	(3445 kPa)
	
	900
	(6201 kPa)
		1,300
		(8957 kPa)
		
		2,100
		(14, 469 kPa)
			1,800
			(12,402 kPa)
			
			2,900
			(19,981 kPa)

Air content of mortar:
    Minimum percent by volume............
    Maximum percent by volume..........
	8
	21
		8
		19
			8
			19

Water retention, flow after suction, minimum, percent of original flow	70	70	70

UNIFORM BUILDING CODE STANDARD 21-12
QUICKLIME FOR STRUCTURAL PURPOSES

Based on Standard Specification C 5-79 (Reapproved 1992) of the American Society for Testing and Materials. Extracted, with permission, from the *Annual Book of ASTM Standards,* copyright American Society for Testing and Materials 100 Barr Harbor Drive West Conshohocken, PA 19428

See Section 2102.2, Item 3, *Uniform Building Code*

SECTION 21.1201 - SCOPE

This standard covers all classes of quicklime, such as crushed lime, granular lime, ground lime, lump lime, pebble lime and pulverized lime, used for structural purposes.

SECTION 21.1202 - GENERAL REQUIREMENTS

Quicklime shall be slaked and aged in accordance with the printed directions of the manufacturer. The resulting lime putty shall be stored until cool.

SECTION 21.1203 - CHEMICAL COMPOSITION

The quicklime shall conform to the following requirements as to chemical composition, calculated to the nonvolatile basis:

	Calcium Lime	Magnesium Lime
Calcium oxide, minimum, percent	75	-
Magnesium oxide, minimum, percent	-	20
Calcium and magnesium oxides, minimum, percent	95	95
Silica, alumina, and oxide of iron, maximum, percent	5	5
Carbon dioxide, maximum, percent:		
If sample is taken at the place of manufacture	3	3
If sample is taken at any other place	10	10

SECTION 21.1204 - RESIDUE

The quicklime shall not contain more than 15 percent by weight of residue.

SECTION 21.1205 - QUALITY CONTROL

Every 90 days, each lime producer shall retain an approved agency to obtain a random sample from a local point of supply in the market area served by the producer.

The agency shall test the lime for compliance with the physical requirements of Section 21.1204.

Upon request of the building official, the producer shall furnish (at no cost) test results to the building official, architect, structural engineer, general contractor and masonry contractor.

UNIFORM BUILDING CODE STANDARD 21-13
HYDRATED LIME FOR MASONRY PURPOSES

**Based on Standard Specification C 207-91
(Reapproved 1992) of the American Society for Testing
and Materials. Extracted, with permission, from the
Annual Book of ASTM Standards, copyright
American Society for Testing and Materials
100 Barr Harbor Drive
West Conshohocken, PA 19428**

See Section 2102.2, Item 3, *Uniform Building Code*

SECTION 21.1301 - SCOPE

This standard covers four types of hydrated lime. Types N and S are suitable for use in mortar, in the scratch and brown coats of cement plaster, for stucco, and for addition to portland-cement concrete. Types NA and SA are air-entrained hydrated limes that are suitable for use in any of the above uses where the inherent properties of lime and air entrainment are desired. The four types of lime sold under this specification shall be designated as follows:

Type N-Normal hydrated lime for masonry purposes.
Type S-Special hydrated lime for masonry purposes.
Type NA-Normal air-entraining hydrated lime for masonry purposes.
Type SA-Special air-entraining hydrated lime for masonry purposes.

NOTE: Type S, special hydrated lime, and Type SA, special air-entraining hydrated lime, are differentiated from Type N, normal hydrated lime, and Type NA, normal air-entraining hydrated lime, principally by their ability to develop high, early plasticity and higher water retentivity and by a limitation on their unhydrated oxide content.

SECTION 21.1302 - DEFINITION

HYDRATED LIME. The hydrated lime covered by Type N or S in this standard shall contain no additives for the purpose of entraining air. The air content of cement-lime mortars made with Type N or S shall not exceed 7 percent. Types NA and SA shall contain an air-entraining additive as specified by Section 21.1305. The air content of cement-lime mortars made with Type NA or SA shall have a minimum of 7 percent and a maximum of 14 percent.

SECTION 21.1303 - ADDITIONS

Types NA and SA hydrated lime covered by this standard shall contain additives for the purpose of entraining air.

SECTION 21.1304 - MANUFACTURER'S STATEMENT

Where required, the nature, amount and identity of the air-entraining agent used and of any processing addition that may have been used shall be provided, as well as test data showing compliance of such air-entraining addition.

SECTION 21.1305 - CHEMICAL REQUIREMENTS COMPOSITION

Hydrated lime for masonry purposes shall conform to the requirements as to chemical composition set forth in Table 21-13-A.

SECTION 21.1306 - RESIDUE, POPPING AND PITTING

The four types of hydrated lime for masonry purposes shall conform to one of the following requirements:

1. The residue retained on a No. 30 (600 mm) sieve shall not be more than 0.5 percent, or

2. If the residue retained on a No. 30 (600 mm) sieve is over 0.5 percent, the lime shall show no pops and pits when tested.

SECTION 21.1307 - PLASTICITY

The putty made from Type S, special hydrate, or Type SA, special air-entraining hydrate, shall have a plasticity figure of not less than 200 within 30 minutes after mixing with water, when tested.

SECTION 21.1308 - WATER RETENTION

Hydrated lime mortar made with Type N, normal hydrated lime, or Type NA, normal air-entraining hydrated lime, after suction for 60 seconds, shall have a water-retention value of not less than 75 percent when tested in a standard mortar made from the dry hydrate or from putty made from the hydrate which has been soaked for a period of 16 to 24 hours.

Hydrated lime mortar made with Type S, special hydrated lime, or Type SA, special air-entraining hydrated lime, after suction for 60 seconds, shall have a water-retention value of not less than 85 percent when tested in a standard mortar made from the dry hydrate.

SECTION 21.1309 - SPECIAL MARKING

When Type NA or SA air-entraining hydrated lime is delivered in packages, the type under this standard and the words "air-entraining" shall be plainly indicated thereon or, in case of bulk shipments, so indicated on shipping notices.

SECTION 21.1310 - QUALITY CONTROL

Every 90 days, each lime producer shall retain an approved agency to obtain a random sample from a local point of supply in the market area served by the producer.

The agency shall test the lime for compliance with the physical requirements of Sections 21.1306, 21.1307 and 21.1308.

Upon request of the building official, the producer shall furnish (at no cost) test results to the building official, architect, structural engineer, general contractor and masonry contractor.

Table 21-13-A - Chemical Requirements

	Hydrates Types			
	N	NA	S	SA
Calcium and magnesium oxides (nonvolatile basis), min. percent	95	95	95	95
Carbon dioxide (as-received basis), max. percent				
If sample is taken at place of manufacture	5	5	5	5
If sample is taken at any other place	7	7	7	7
Unhydrated oxides (as-received basis), max. percent	-	-	8	8

UNIFORM BUILDING CODE STANDARD 21-14
MORTAR CEMENT

Test Standard of the International Conference of Building Officials

See Section 2102.2, Item 2, *Uniform Building Code*

SECTION 21.1401 - SCOPE

This standard covers mortar cement for use in masonry mortars.

SECTION 21.1402 - CLASSIFICATIONS

There are three types of mortar cement:

1. **Type N.** For use as the cementitious material in the preparation of UBC Standard 21-15 Type N and Type O mortars. For use in combination with portland or blended hydraulic cements in the preparation of Type S or Type M mortars.

2. **Type S.** For use as the cementitious material in the preparation of UBC Standard 21-15 Type S mortar.

3. **Type M.** For use as the cementitious material in the preparation of UBC Standard 21-15 Type M mortar.

SECTION 21.1403 - PHYSICAL REQUIREMENTS

Mortar cement shall conform to the requirements set forth in Table 21-14-A for its classifications.

SECTION 21.1404 - CONSTITUENT MATERIALS

Upon request of the building official, the constituent materials shall be provided to the building official and engineer of record.

SECTION 21.1405 - RESTRICTED MATERIALS

Materials used in mortar cement shall conform to the requirements set forth in Table 21-14-B.

SECTION 21.1406 - DELETERIOUS MATERIAL

Materials listed in Table 21-14-C shall not be used in mortar cement.

SECTION 21.1407 - PACKAGE LABELING

Mortar cement packages shall carry a statement indicating that the product conforms to requirements of this standard and shall include the brand, name of manufacturer, type of mortar cement and net weight of the package in pounds.

SECTION 21.1408 - CERTIFICATION

Certification shall be submitted upon request of the building official and shall certify compliance with the requirements of this standard.

SECTION 21.1409 - SAMPLING AND TESTING

Every 90 days, each mortar cement producer shall retain an approved agency to obtain a random sample from a local point of supply in the market area served by the producer.

The agency shall test the mortar cement for compliance with the physical requirements of Table 21-14-A.

Upon request of the building official, the producer shall furnish (at no cost) test results to the building official, architect, structural engineer, general contractor and masonry contractor.

SECTION 21.1410 - TEMPERATURE AND HUMIDITY

The temperature of the air in the vicinity of the mixing slab and dry materials, molds, base plates and mixing bowl shall be maintained between 68°F and 81.5°F (20°C and 27.5°C). The temperature of the mixing water, moist cabinet or moist room, and water in the storage tank shall not vary from 73.4°F (23°C) by more than 3°F (1.7°C).

The relative humidity of the laboratory air shall not be less than 50 percent. The moist cabinet or moist room atmosphere shall have a relative humidity of not less than 90 percent.

The moist cabinet or moist room shall conform to applicable standards.

SECTION 21.1411 - FINENESS

Determine the residue on the No. 325 (45 mm) sieve.

SECTION 21.1412 - NORMAL CONSISTENCY

Determine normal consistency by the Vicat apparatus.

SECTION 21.1413 - AUTOCLAVE EXPANSION

Determine autoclave expansion. After molding, store bars in the moist cabinet or room for 48 hours, plus or minus 30 minutes, before removal from the molds for measurement and test in the autoclave.

Calculate the difference in length of the test specimen before and after autoclaving to the nearest 0.01 percent of the effective gauge length and report as the autoclave expansion of the mortar cement.

SECTION 21.1414 - TIME OF SETTING

Determine the time of setting by the Gillmore needle method.

SECTION 21.1415 - DENSITY

Determine the density of the mortar cement using kerosene as the liquid. Use the density so determined in the calculation of the air content of the mortars.

SECTION 21.1416 - APPARATUS FOR MORTAR TESTS

Apparatus shall be in accordance with applicable standards.

SECTION 21.1417 - BLENDED SAND

The sand shall be a blend of equal parts by weight of graded Ottawa sand and Standard 20-30 Ottawa sand.

SECTION 21.1418 - PREPARATION OF MORTAR

21.1418.1 Proportions for Mortar. Mortar for air entrainment, compressive strength and water-retention tests shall be proportioned to contain the weight of cement, in grams, equal to six times the printed bag weight in pounds (13.228 times the printed bag weight in kilograms) and 1,440 grams of sand. The sand shall consist of 720 grams of graded Ottawa sand and 720 grams of Standard 20-30 sand. The quantity of water, measured in milliliters, shall be such as to produce a flow of 110 ± 5 as determined by the flow table.

21.1418.2 Mixing of Mortars. Mix the mortar in accordance with applicable standards.

21.1418.3 Determination of Flow. Determine the flow in accordance with applicable standards.

SECTION 21.1419 - AIR ENTRAINMENT

21.1419.1 Procedure. If the mortar has the correct flow, use a separate portion of the mortar for the determination of entrained air. Determine the weight of 400 cm³ of mortar.

21.1419.2 Calculation. Calculate the air content of the mortar and report it to the nearest 0.1 percent as follows:

$$D = (W_1 + W_2 + V_w) / [(W_1/S_1) + (W_2/S_2) + V_w]$$
$$A = 100 - (W_m/4D)$$

WHERE:
A = volume percent of entrained air.
D = density of air-free mortar, g/cm³.
S_1 = density of cement, g/cm³.
S_2 = density of standard sand, 2.65 g/cm³.
V_w = milliliters-grams of water used.
W_m = mass of 400 ml of mortar, g.
W_1 = weight of cement, g.
W_2 = weight of sand, g.

SECTION 21.1420 - COMPRESSIVE STRENGTH OF TEST SPECIMENS

21.1420.1 Molding. Immediately after determining the flow and the weight of 400 cm³ or mortar, return all the mortar to the mixing bowl and remix for 15 seconds at the medium speed. Then mold test specimens in accordance with applicable standards, except that the elapsed time for mixing mortar, determining flow, determining air entrainment and starting the molding of cubes shall be within eight minutes.

21.1420.2 Storage. Store all test specimens immediately after molding in the molds on plane plates in a moist cabinet maintained at a relative humidity of 90 percent or more for 48 to 52 hours in such a manner that the upper surfaces shall be exposed to the moist air. Then remove the cubes from the molds and place in the moist cabinet for five days in such a manner as to allow free circulation of air around at least five faces of the specimens. At the age of seven days, immerse the cubes for the 28-day tests in saturated lime water in storage tanks of noncorrodible materials.

SECTION 21.1421 - PROCEDURE

Test the cube specimens immediately after their removal from the moist cabinet for seven-day specimens, and immediately after their removal from storage water for all other specimens. If more than one specimen at a time is removed from the moist closet for seven- day tests, cover these cubes with a damp cloth until time of testing.

If more than one specimen at a time is removed from the storage water for testing, place these cubes in a pan of water at a temperature of 73.4°F ± 3°F (23°C ± 1.7°C), and of sufficient depth to completely immerse each cube until time of testing.

The remainder of the testing procedure shall conform to applicable standards.

SECTION 21.1422 - WATER RETENTION

21.1422.1 Water-retention Apparatus. For the water-retention test, and apparatus essentially the same as that shown in Figure 21-14-1 shall be used. This apparatus consists of a water aspirator or other source of vacuum controlled by a mercury-relief column and connected by way of a three-way stopcock to a funnel upon which rests a perforated dish. The perforated dish shall be made of metal not attacked by masonry mortar. The metal in the base of the dish shall have a thickness of 1.7 to 1.9 mm and shall conform to the requirements given in Figure 21-14-1. The bore of the stopcock shall have a 4 mm plus or minus 0.5 mm diameter, and the connecting glass tubing shall have a minimum inside diameter of 4 mm. A mercury manometer, connected as shown in Figure 21-14-1, indicates the vacuum. The contact surface of the funnel and perforated dish shall be plane and shall be lapped to ensure intimate contact. An airtight seal shall be maintained between the funnel and the dish during a test. This shall be accomplished by either of the following procedures: (1) a synthetic (grease-resistant) rubber gasket may be permanently sealed to the top of the funnel, using petrolatum or light grease to ensure a seal between the funnel and dish, or (2) the top of the funnel may be lightly coated with petrolatum or light grease to ensure a seal between the funnel and dish. Care should be taken to ensure that none of the holes in the perforated dish are clogged from the grease. Hardened, very smooth, not rapid filter paper shall be used. It shall be of such diameter that it will lie flat and completely cover the bottom of the dish.

A steel straightedge not less than 8 inches (203 mm) long and not less than 1/16 inch (1.6 mm) nor more than 1/8-inch (3.2 mm) thickness shall be used.

Other apparatus required for the water-retention tests shall conform to the applicable requirements of Section 21.1416.

21.1422.2 Procedure. Adjust the mercury-relief column to maintain a vacuum of 50.8 mm as measured on the manometer. Seat the perforated dish on the greased gasket of the funnel. Place a wetted filter paper in the bottom of the dish. Turn the stopcock to apply the vacuum to the funnel and check the apparatus for leaks and to determine that the required vacuum is obtained. Then turn the stopcock to shut off the vacuum from the funnel.

Mix the mortar to a flow of 110 plus or minus 5 percent in accordance with applicable standards. Immediately after making the flow test, return the mortar on the flow table to the mixing bowl and remix the entire batch for 15 seconds at medium speed.

Immediately after remixing the mortar, fill the perforated dish with the mortar to slightly above the rim. Tamp the mortar 15 times with the tamper. Apply 10 of the tamping strokes at approximately uniform spacing adjacent to the rim of the dish and with the long axis of the tamping face held at right angles to the radius of the dish. Apply the remaining five tamping strokes at random points distributed over the central area of the dish. The tamping pressure shall be just sufficient to ensure filling of the dish. On completion of the tamping, the top of the mortar should extend slightly above the rim of the dish. Smooth off the mortar by drawing the flat side of the straightedge (with the leading edge slightly raised) across the top of the dish. Then cut off the mortar to a plane surface flush with the rim of the dish by drawing the straightedge with a sawing motion across the top of the dish in two cutting strokes, starting each cut from near the center of the dish. If the mortar is pulled away from the side of the dish during the process of drawing the straightedge across the dish, gently press the mortar back into contact with the side of the dish using the tamper.

Turn the stopcock to apply the vacuum to the funnel. The time elapsed from the start of mixing the cement and water to the time of applying the vacuum shall not exceed eight minutes. After suction for 60 seconds, quickly turn the stopcock to expose the funnel to atmospheric pressure. Immediately slide the perforated dish off from the funnel, touch it momentarily on a damp cloth to remove droplets of water, and set the dish on the table. Then, using the bowl scraper, in accordance with applicable standards, plow and mix the mortar in the dish for 15 seconds. Upon completion of mixing, place the mortar in the flow mold and determine the flow. The entire operation shall be carried out without interruption and as quickly as possible, and shall be completed within an elapsed time of 11 minutes after the start of mixing the cement and water for the first flow determination. Both flow determinations shall be made in accordance with applicable standards.

21.1422.3 Calculation. Calculate the water-retention value for the mortar as follows:

Water-retention value = (a/b) x 100

WHERE:

a = flow after suction.
b = flow immediately after mixing.

Mortar Cement Type	N	S	M
Fineness, residue on a No. 325 (45 µm) sieve Maximum percent	24	24	24
Autoclave expansion Maximum, percent	1.0	1.0	1.0
Time of setting, Gillmore method: Initial set, minimum, hour Final set, maximum, hour	2 24	$1\frac{1}{2}$ 24	$1\frac{1}{2}$ 24
Compressive strength[1] 7 days, minimum psi 28 days, minimum psi	500 (3445 kPa) 900 (6201 kPa)	1300 (8957 kPa) 2100 (14 469 kPa)	1800 (12 402 kPa) 2900 (19 981 kPa)
Flexural bond strength[2] 28 days, minimum psi	71 (489 kPa)	104 (717 kPa)	116 (799 kPa)
Air content of mortar Minimum percent by volume Maximum percent by volume	8 16	8 14	8 14
Water Retention Minimum, percent	70	70	70

[1] Compressive strength shall be based on the average of three mortar cubes composed of one part mortar cement and three parts blended sand (one half graded Ottawa sand, and one half Standard 20-30 Ottawa sand) by volume and tested in accordance with this standard.
[2] Flexural bond strength shall be determined in accordance with UBC Standard 21-20

Table 21-14-B - Restricted Materials

Material	Maximum Limit (percentage)
Chrloride salts	0.06
Carboxylic acids	0.25
Sugars	1.00
Glycols	1.00
Lignin and derivatives	0.50
Stearates	0.50
Fly ash	No Limit
Clay (except fireclay)	5.00

Table 21-14-C - Deleterious Materials not Permitted in Mortar Cement

Epoxy resins and derivatives
Phenols
Asbestos fiber
Fireclays

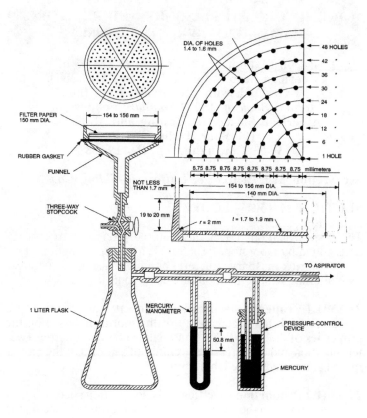

Figure 21-14-1 - Apparatus Assembly for the Water Retention Test

UNIFORM BUILDING CODE STANDARD 21-15 MORTAR FOR UNIT MASONRY AND REINFORCED MASONRY OTHER THAN GYPSUM

Based on Standard Specification C 270-95 of the American Society for Testing and Materials. Extracted, with permission, from the *Annual Book of ASTM Standards,* copyright American Society for Testing and Materials 100 Barr Harbor Drive West Conshohocken, PA 19428

See Section 2102.2, Item 8, *Uniform Building Code*

SECTION 21.1501 - SCOPE

These specifications cover the required properties of mortars determined by laboratory tests for use in the construction of reinforced brick masonry structures and unit masonry structures. Two alternative specifications are covered as follows:

21.1501.1 Property specifications. Property specifications are those in which the acceptability of the mortar is based on the properties of the ingredients (materials) and the properties (water retention and compressive strength) of samples of the mortar mixed and tested in the laboratory.

21.1501.2 Proportion specifications. Proportion specifications are those in which the acceptability of the mortar is based on the properties of the ingredients (materials) and a definite composition of the mortar consisting of fixed proportions of these ingredients.

Unless data are presented to show that the mortar meets the requirements of the physical property specifications, the proportion specifications shall govern. For field tests of grout and mortars see UBC Standard 21-16

Property Specifications

SECTION 21.1502 - MATERIALS

21.1502.1 General. Materials used as ingredients in the mortar shall conform to the requirements specified in the pertinent UBC Standards.

21.1502.2 Cementitious Materials. Cementitious materials shall conform to the following specifications:

1. **Portland cement.** Type I, IA, II, IIA, III or IIIA of ASTM C 150.
2. **Blended hydraulic cement.** Type IS, IS-A, S, S-A, IP, IP-A, I(PM) or I(PM)-A of ASTM C 1157.
3. **Plastic cement.** Plastic cement conforming to the requirements of UBC Standard 25-1 and UBC Standard 21-11, when used in lieu of masonry cement.
4. **Mortar cement.** UBC Standard 21-14.
5. **Masonry cements.** UBC Standard 21-11.
6. **Quicklime.** UBC Standard 21-12.
7. **Hydrated lime.** UBC Standard 21-13.

21.1502.3 Water. Water shall be clean and free of deleterious amounts of acids, alkalies or organic materials.

21.1502.4 Admixtures or Mortar Colors. Admixtures or mortar colors shall not be added to the mortar at the time of mixing unless provided for in the contract specifications and, after the material is so added, the mortar shall conform to the requirements of the property specifications.

Only pure mineral mortar colors shall be used.

21.1502.5 Antifreeze Compounds. No antifreeze liquid, salts or other substances shall be used in the mortar to lower the freezing point.

21.1502.6 Storage of Materials. Cementitious materials and aggregates shall be stored in such a manner as to prevent deterioration or intrusion of foreign material. Any material that has become unsuitable for good construction shall not be used.

SECTION 21.1503 - MIXING MORTAR

Mortar blended on the jobsite shall be mixed for a minimum period of three minutes, with the amount of water required to produce the desired workability, in a drum-type batch mixer. Factory-dry blended mortar shall be mixed with water in a mechanical mixer until workable but not to exceed 10 minutes.

SECTION 21.1504 - MORTAR

21.1504.1 Mortar for Unit Masonry. Mortar conforming to the proportion specifications shall consist of a mixture of cementitious material and aggregate conforming to the requirements of Section 21.1502, and the measurement and mixing requirements of Section 21.1503, and shall be proportioned within the limits given in Table 21-15-B for each mortar type specified.

21.1504.2 Mortar for Reinforced Masonry. In mortar used for reinforced masonry the following special requirements shall be met: Sufficient water has been added to bring the mixture to a plastic state. The volume of aggregate in mortar shall be at least two and one-fourth times but not more than three times the volume of cementitious materials.

21.1504.3 Aggregate Ratio. The volume of damp, loose aggregate in mortar used in brick masonry shall be not less than two and one-fourth times or more than three times the total separate volumes of cementitious materials used.

21.1504.4 Water Retention. Mortar shall conform to the water retention requirements of Table 21-15-A.

21.1504.5 Air Content. Mortar shall conform to the air content requirements of Table 21-15-A.

SECTION 21.1505 - COMPRESSIVE STRENGTH

The average compressive strength of three 2-inch (51 mm) cubes of mortar (before thinning) shall not be less than the strength given in Table 21-15-A for the mortar type specified.

Proportion Specifications

SECTION 21.1506 - MATERIALS

21.1506.1 General. Materials used as ingredients in the mortar shall conform to the requirements of Section 21.1502 and to the requirements of this section.

21.1506.2 Portland Cement. Portland cement shall conform to the requirements of ASTM C 150.

21.1506.3 Blended Hydraulic Cements. Blended hydraulic cements of Type IS, IS-A, IP, IP-A, I(PM) or I(PM)-A shall conform to the requirements of ASTM C 595, when used in lieu of masonry cement.

21.1506.4 Plastic Cement. Plastic cement conforming to the requirements of UBC Standard 25-1 and UBC Standard 21-11.

21.1506.5 Mortar Cement. Mortar cement shall conform to the requirements of UBC Standard 21-14.

21.1506.6 Masonry Cement. Masonry cement shall conform to the requirements of UBC Standard 21-11.

21.1506.7 Hydrated Lime. Hydrated lime shall conform to either of the two following requirements:

1. The total free (unhydrated) calcium oxide (CaO) and magnesium oxide (MgO) shall not be more than 8 percent by weight (calculated on the as-received basis for hydrates).

2. When the hydrated lime is mixed with portland cement in the proportion set forth in Table 21-15-B, the mixture shall give an autoclave expansion of not more than 0.50 percent.

Hydrated lime intended for use when mixed dry with other mortar ingredients shall have a plasticity figure of not less than 200 when tested 15 minutes after adding water.

21.1506.8 Lime Putty. Lime putty made from either quicklime or hydrated lime shall be soaked for a period sufficient to produce a plasticity figure of not less than 200 and shall conform to

either the requirements for limitation on total free oxides of calcium and magnesium or the autoclave test specified for hydrated
lime in Section 21.1506.5.

SECTION 21.1507 - MORTAR

Mortar shall consist of a mixture of cementitious materials and
aggregate conforming to the requirements specified in Section
21.1504, mixed in one of the proportions shown in Table 21-15-
B, to which sufficient water has been added to reduce the mixture to a plastic state.

Table 21-15-A - Property Specifications for Mortar[1]

Mortar	Type	Average Compressive Strength of 2-inch (51 mm) cubes at 28 days (Min., psi) x 6.89 for kPa	Water Retention (Min., percent)	Air Content (Max. percent)[2]	Aggregate Measured in a Damp, Loose Condition
Cement-lime or mortar cement	M	2,500	75	12	Not less than 2¼ and not more than 3½ times the sum of the separate volumes of cementitious materials
	S	1,800	75	12	
	N	750	75	14[3]	
	O	350	75	14[3]	
Masonry Cement	M	2,500	75	18	
	S	1,800	75	18	
	N	750	75	18	
	O	350	75	18	

[1] Laboratory-prepared mortar only.
[2] Determined in accordance with applicable standards.
[3] When structural reinforcement is incorporated in cement-lime or mortar, the
maximum air content shall be 12 percent.

Table 21-15-B - Mortar Proportions for Unit Masonry

Mortar	Type	Portland Cement or Blended Cement[1]	Masonry Cement[2] M	S	N	Mortar Cement[3] M	S	N	Hydrated lime or lime putty[1]	Aggregate Measured in a damp, loose condition
Cement-lime	M	1	-	-	-	-	-	-	1/4	Not less than 2 1/4 and not more than 3 times the sum of the separate volumes of cementitious materials.
	S	1	-	-	-	-	-	-	over 1/4 to 1/2	
	N	1	-	-	-	-	-	-	over 1/2 to 1 1/4	
	O	1	-	-	-	-	-	-	over 1 1/4 to 2 1/2	
Mortar cement	M	1	-	-	-	-	-	1	-	
	M	-	-	-	-	1	-	-	-	
	S	1/2	-	-	-	-	-	1	-	
	S	-	-	-	-	-	1	-	-	
	N	-	-	-	-	-	-	1	-	
Masonry cement	M	1	-	-	1	-	-	-	-	
	M	1	-	-	-	-	-	-	-	
	S	-	1	-	-	-	-	-	-	
	S	-	-	1	-	-	-	-	-	
	N	-	-	1	-	-	-	-	-	
	O	-	-	1	-	-	-	-	-	

[1] When plastic cement is used in lieu of portland cement, hydrated lime or putty may be added, but not in excess of one tenth of the volume of cement.

[2] Masonry cement conforming to the requirements of UBC Standard 21-11.

[3] Mortar cement conforming to the requirements of UBC Standard 21-14.

UNIFORM BUILDING CODE STANDARD 21-16 FIELD TESTS SPECIMENS FOR MORTAR

Test Standard of the International Conference of Building Officials

See Section 2102.2, Item 8, *Uniform Building Code*

SECTION 21.1601 - FIELD COMPRESSIVE TEST SPECIMEN FOR MORTAR

Spread mortar on the masonry units 1/2 inch to 5/8 inch (13 mm to 16 mm) thick, and allow to stand for one minute, then remove mortar and place in a 2-inch by 4-inch (51 mm by 102 mm) cylinder in two layers, compressing the mortar into the cylinder using a flat-end stick or fingers. Lightly tap mold on opposite sides, level off and immediately cover molds and keep them damp until taken to the laboratory. After 48 hours' set, have the laboratory remove molds and place them in the fog room until tested in damp condition.

SECTION 21.1602 - REQUIREMENTS

Each such mortar test specimen shall exhibit a minimum ultimate compressive strength of 1,500 pounds per square inch (10 304 kPa).

UNIFORM BUILDING CODE STANDARD 21-17 TEST METHOD FOR COMPRESSIVE STRENGTH OF MASONRY PRISMS

Based on Standard Test Method E 447-92 of the
American Society for Testing and Materials.
Extracted, with permission, from the
Annual Book of ASTM Standards, copyright
American Society for Testing and Materials
100 Barr Harbor Drive
West Conshohocken, PA 19428

See Sections 2102.2, Item 6.4; 2105.3.2; and 2105.3.3,
Uniform Building Code

SECTION 21.1701 - SCOPE

This standard covers procedures for masonry prism construction, testing and procedures for determining the compressive strength of masonry.

SECTION 21.1702 - CONSTRUCTION OF PRISMS

Prisms shall be constructed on a flat, level base. Masonry units used in the prism shall be representative of the units used in the corresponding construction. Each prism shall be built in an opened moisture-tight bag which is large enough to enclose and seal the completed prism. The orientation of units, where top and bottom cross sections vary due to taper of the cells, or where the architectural surface of either side of the unit varies, shall be the same orientation as used in the corresponding construction. Prisms shall be a single wythe in thickness and laid up in stack bond (see Figure 21-17-1).

The length of masonry prisms may be reduced by saw cutting; however, prisms composed of regular shaped hollow units shall have at least one complete cell with one full-width cross web on either end. Prisms composed of irregular-shaped units shall be cut to obtain as symmetrical a cross section as possible. The minimum length of saw-cut prisms shall be 4 inches (102 mm).

Masonry prisms shall be laid in a full mortar bed (mortar bed both webs and face shells). Mortar shall be representative of that used in the corresponding construction. Mortar joint thickness, the tooling of joints and the method of positioning and aligning units shall be representative of the corresponding construction.

Prisms shall be a minimum of two units in height, but the total height shall not be less than 1.3 times the least actual thickness or more than 5.0 times the least actual thickness. Immediately following the construction of the prism, the moisture-tight bag shall be drawn around the prism and sealed.

Where the corresponding construction is to be solid grouted, prisms shall be solid grouted. Grout shall be representative of that used in the corresponding construction. Grout shall be placed not less than one day nor more than two days following the construction of the prism. Grout consolidation shall be representative of that used in the construction. Additional grout shall be placed in the prism after reconsolidation and settlement due to water loss, but prior to the grout setting. Excess grout shall be screeded off level with the top of the prism. Where open-end units are used, additional masonry units shall be used as forms to confine the grout during placement. Masonry unit forms shall be sufficiently braced to prevent displacement during grouting. Immediately following the grouting operation, the moisture-tight bag shall be drawn around the prism and resealed.

Where the corresponding construction is to be partially grouted, two sets of prisms shall be constructed; one set shall be grouted solid and the other set shall not be grouted.

Where the corresponding construction is of multiwythe composite masonry, masonry prisms representative of each wythe shall be built and tested separately.

Prisms shall be left undisturbed for at least two days after construction.

SECTION 21.1703 - TRANSPORTING MASONRY PRISMS

Prior to transporting each prism, strap or clamp the prism together to prevent damage during handling and transportation. Secure prism to prevent jarring, bouncing or falling over during transporting.

SECTION 21.1704 - CURING

Prisms shall remain sealed in the moisture-tight bag until two days prior to testing; the moisture-tight bag shall then be removed and curing continued in laboratory air maintained at a temperature of 75°F ± 15°F (24°C ± 8°C). Prisms shall be tested at 28 days after constructing the prism or at test age designated.

SECTION 21.1705 - PREPARATION FOR TESTING

21.1705.1 Capping the Prism. Cap top and bottom of the prism prior to testing with sulfur-filled capping or with high-strength gypsum plaster capping (such as "Hydrostone" or "Hyprocal White"). Sulfur-filled capping material shall be 40 to 60 percent by weight sulfur, the remainder being ground fireclay or other suitable inert material passing a No. 100 (150 mm) sieve, with or without a plasticizer. Spread the capping material over a level surface which is plane within 0.003 inch (0.076 mm) in 16 inches (406 mm). Bring the surface to be capped into contact with the capping paste; firmly press down the specimen, holding it so that its axis is at right angles to the capping surfaces. The average thickness of the cap shall not exceed 1/8 inch (3.2 mm). Allow caps to age at least two hours before testing.

21.1705.2 Measurement of the Prism. Measure the length and thickness of the prism to the nearest 0.01 inch (0.25 mm) by averaging three measurements taken at the center and quarter points of the height of the specimen. Measure the height of the prism, including caps, to the nearest 0.1 inch (2.54 mm).

SECTION 21.1706 - TEST PROCEDURE

21.1706.1 Test Apparatus. The test machine shall have an accuracy of plus or minus 1.0 percent over the load range. The upper bearing shall be spherically seated, hardened metal block firmly attached at the center of the upper head of the machine. The center of the sphere shall lie at the center of the surface held in its spherical seat, but shall be free to turn in any direction, and its perimeter shall have at least 1/4-inch (6.4 mm) clearance from the head to allow for specimens whose bearing surfaces are not exactly parallel. The diameter of the bearing surface shall be at least 5 inches (127 mm). A hardened metal bearing block may be used beneath the specimen to minimize wear of the lower platen of the machine. The bearing block surfaces intended for contact with the specimen shall have a hardness not less than 60 HRC (620 HB). These surfaces shall not depart from plane surfaces by more than 0.001 inch (0.0254 mm) in any 6-inch (153 mm) dimension. When the bearing area of the spherical bearing block is not sufficient to cover the area of the specimen, a steel plate with surfaces machined to true planes within plus or minus 0.001 inch (0.0254 mm) in any 6-inch (153 mm) dimension, and with a thickness equal to at least the distance from the edge of the spherical bearings to the most distant corner, shall be placed between the spherical bearing block and the capped specimen.

21.1706.2 Installing the Prism in the Test Machine. Wipe clean the bearing faces of the upper and lower platens or bearing blocks and of the test specimen and place the test specimen on the lower platen or bearing block. Align both centroidal axes of the specimen with the center of thrust of the test machine. As the spherically seated block is brought to bear on the specimen, rotate its movable portion gently by hand so that uniform seating is obtained.

21.1706.3 Loading. Apply the load, up one half of the expected minimum load, at any convenient rate, after which adjust the controls of the machine so that the remaining load is applied at a uniform rate in not less than one or more than two minutes.

21.1706.4 Observations. Describe the mode of failure as fully as possible or illustrate crack patterns, spalling, etc., on a sketch, or both. Note whether failure occurred on one side or one end of the prism prior to failure of the opposing side or end of the prism.

SECTION 21.1707 - CALCULATIONS

Calculations of test results shall be as follows:

21.1707.1 Net cross-sectional area. Determine the net cross-sectional area [square inches (mm^2)] of solid grouted prisms by multiplying the average measured width dimension [inches (mm)] by the average measured length dimension [inches (mm)]. The net cross-sectional area of ungrouted prisms shall be taken as the net cross-sectional area of masonry units determined from a representative sample of units.

21.1707.2 Masonry prism strength. Determine the compressive strength of each prism [psi (kPa)] by dividing the maximum compressive load sustained [pounds (N)] by the net cross-sectional area of the prism [square inches (mm^2 x 1,000,000)].

21.1707.3 Compressive strength of masonry. The compressive strength of masonry [psi (kPa)] for each set of prisms shall be the lesser of the average strength of the prisms in the set, or 1.25 times the least prism strength multiplied by the prism height-to-thickness correction factor from Table 21-17-A. Where a set of grouted and nongrouted prisms are tested, the compressive strength of masonry shall be determined for the grouted set and for the nongrouted set separately. Where a set of prisms is tested for each wythe of a multiwythe wall, the compressive strength of masonry shall be determined for each wythe separately.

SECTION 21.1708 - MASONRY PRISM TEST REPORT

The test report shall include the following:

1. Name of testing laboratory and name of professional engineer responsible for the tests.

2. Designation of each prism tested and description of prism, including width, height and length dimensions, mortar type, grout and masonry unit used in the construction.

3. Age of prism at time of test.

4. Maximum compressive load sustained by each prism, net cross-sectional area of each prism and net area compressive strength of each prism.

5. Test observations for each prism in accordance with Section 21.1706.

6. Compressive strength of masonry for each set of prisms.

Table 21-17-A

Prisms h/t_p[1]	1.30	1.50	2.00	2.50	3.00	4.00	5.00
Correction factor	0.75	0.86	1.00	1.04	1.07	1.15	1.22

[1] h/t_p - ratio of prism height to least actual lateral dimension of prism.

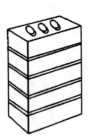
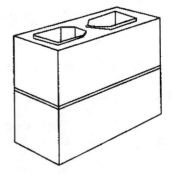

Figure 21-17-1

UNIFORM BUILDING CODE STANDARD 21-18
METHOD OF SAMPLING
AND TESTING GROUT

**Based on Standard Method C 1019-89a (93) of the
American Society for Testing and Materials.
Extracted, with permission, from the
Annual Book of ASTM Standards, copyright
American Society for Testing and Materials
100 Barr Harbor Drive
West Conshohocken, PA 19428**

**See Section 2102.2, Item 9; and Table 21-B,
*Uniform Building Code***

SECTION 21.1801 - SCOPE

This method covers procedures for both field and laboratory
sampling and compression testing of grout used in masonry
construction.

SECTION 21.1802 - APPARATUS

21.1802.1 Maximum-Minimum Thermometer.

21.1802.2 Straightedge. A steel straightedge not less than 6
inches (152.4 mm) long and not less than 1/16 inch (1.6 mm) in
thickness.

21.1802.3 Tamping Rod. A nonabsorbent smooth rod, either
round or square in cross section nominally 5/8 inch (15.9 mm) in
dimension with ends rounded to hemispherical tips of the same
diameter. The rod shall be a minimum length of 12 inches (304.8
mm).

21.1802.4 Wooden Blocks. Wooden squares with side dimensions equal to one-half the desired grout specimen height, within
a tolerance of 5 percent, and of sufficient quantity or thickness
to yield the desired grout specimen height, as shown in Figures
21-18-1 and 21-18-2.

Wooden blocks shall be soaked in limewater for 24 hours, sealed with varnish or wax, or covered with an impermeable material prior to use.

SECTION 21.1803 - SAMPLING

21.1803.1 Size of Sample. Grout samples to be used for slump and compressive strength tests shall be a minimum of 1/2 ft.^{3} (0.014 m^3).

21.1803.2 Field Sample. Take grout samples as the grout is being placed into the wall. Field samples may be taken at any time except for the first and last 10 percent of the batch volume.

SECTION 21.1804 - TEST SPECIMEN AND SAMPLE

21.1804.1 Each grout specimen shall be a square prism, nominally 3 inches (76.2 mm) or larger on the sides and twice as high as its width. Dimensional tolerances shall be within 5 percent of the nominal width selected.

21.1804.2 Three specimens constitute one sample.

SECTION 21.1805 - PROCEDURE

21.1805.1 Select a level location where the molds can remain undisturbed for 48 hours.

21.1805.2 Mold Construction.

21.1805.2.1 The mold space should simulate the grout location in the wall. If the grout is placed between two different types of masonry units, both types should be used to construct the mold.

21.1805.2.2 Form a square prism space, nominally 3 inches (76.2 mm) or larger on each side and twice as high as its width, by stacking masonry units of the same type and moisture condition as those being used in the construction. Place wooden blocks, cut to proper size and of the proper thickness or quantity, at the bottom of the space to achieve the necessary height of specimen. Tolerance on space and specimen dimensions shall be within 5 percent of the specimen width. See Figures 21-18-1 and 21-18-2.

21.1805.2.3 Line the masonry surfaces that will be in contact with the grout specimen with a permeable material, such as paper towel, to prevent bond to the masonry units.

21.1805.3 Measure and record the slump of the grout.

21.1805.4 Fill the mold with grout in two layers. Rod each layer 15 times with the tamping rod penetrating 1/2 inch (12.7 mm) into the lower layer. Distribute the strokes uniformly over the cross section of the mold.

21.1805.5 Level the top surface of the specimen with a straightedge and cover immediately with a damp absorbent material such as cloth or paper towel. Keep the top surface of the sample damp by wetting the absorbent material and do not disturb the specimen for 48 hours.

21.1805.6 Protect the sample from freezing and variations in temperature. Store an indicating maximum-minimum thermometer with the sample and record the maximum and minimum temperatures experienced prior to the time the specimens are placed in the moist room.

21.1805.7 Remove the masonry units after 48 hours. Transport field specimens to the laboratory, keeping the specimens damp and in a protective container.

21.1805.8 Store in a moist room conforming to nationally recognized standards.

21.1805.9 Cap the specimens in accordance with the applicable requirements of UBC Standard 21-17.

21.1805.10 Measure and record the width of each face at midheight. Measure and record the height of each face at midwidth. Measure and record the amount out of plumb at midwidth of each face.

21.1805.11 Test the specimens in a damp condition in accordance with applicable requirements of UBC Standard 21-17.

SECTION 21.1806 - CALCULATIONS

The report shall include the following:

1. Mix design.
2. Slump of the grout.
3. Type and number of units used to form mold for specimens.
4. Description of the specimens-dimensions, amount out of plumb-in percent.
5. Curing history, including maximum and minimum temperatures and age of specimen, when transported to laboratory and when tested.
6. Maximum load and compressive strength of the sample.
7. Description of failure.

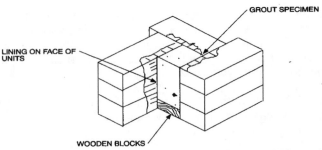

Figure 21-18-1 - Grout Mold [Units 6 inches (152 mm) or Less in Height, 2$^1/_2$ inch-high (63.5 mm) Brick Shown]

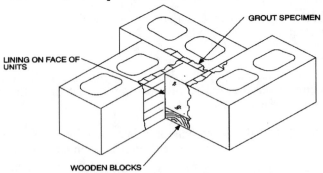

Figure 21-18-2 - Grout Mold [Units greater than 6 inches (152 mm) in Height, 8-inches-high (203 mm) Concrete Masonry unit Shown]

UNIFORM BUILDING CODE STANDARD 21-19
GROUT FOR MASONRY

**Based on Standard Specification C 476-91 of the
American Society for Testing and Materials.
Extracted, with permission, from the
Annual Book of ASTM Standards, copyright
American Society for Testing and Materials
100 Barr Harbor Drive
West Conshohocken, PA 19428**

See Section 2102.2, Item 9, *Uniform Building Code*

SECTION 21.1901 - SCOPE

This standard covers grout for use in the construction of reinforced and nonreinforced masonry structures.

SECTION 21.1902 - MATERIALS Materials used as ingredients in grout shall conform to the following:

21.1902.1 Cementitious Materials. Cementitious materials shall conform to one of the following standards:

   A. Portland Cement-Types I, II and III of ASTM C 150.
   B. Blended Cement-Type IS, IS(MS) or IP of ASTM C 595.
   C. Quicklime-UBC Standard 21-12.
   D. Hydrated lime-Type S of UBC Standard 21-13.

21.1902.2 Water. Water shall be clean and potable.

21.1902.3 Admixtures. Additives and admixtures to grout shall not be used unless approved by the building official.

21.1902.4 Antifreeze Compounds. No antifreeze liquids, chloride salts or other substances shall be used in grout.

21.1902.5 Storage of Materials. Cementitious materials and aggregates shall be stored in such a manner as to prevent deterioration or intrusion of foreign material or moisture. Any material that has become unsuitable for good construction shall not be used.

SECTION 21.1903 - MEASUREMENT OF MATERIALS

The method of measuring materials for the grout used in construction shall be such that the specified proportions of the grout materials can be controlled and accurately maintained.

SECTION 21.1904 - GROUT

Grout shall consist of cementitious material and aggregate that have been mixed thoroughly for a minimum of five minutes in a mechanical mixer with sufficient water to bring the mixture to the desired consistency. The grout proportions and any additives shall be based on laboratory or field experience considering the grout ingredients and the masonry units to be used, or the grout shall be proportioned within the limits given in Table 21-B of this code, or the grout shall have a minimum compressive strength when tested in accordance with UBC Standard 21-18 equal to its specified strength, but not less than 2,000 psi (13 800 kPa).

> **EXCEPTION:** Dry mixes for grout which are blended in the factory and mixed at the jobsite shall be mixed in mechanical mixers until workable, but not to exceed 10 minutes.

UNIFORM BUILDING CODE STANDARD 21-20 STANDARD TEST METHOD FOR FLEXURAL BOND STRENGTH OF MORTAR CEMENT

Test Standard of the International Conference of Building Officials

See Section 2102.2, Item 8, *Uniform Building Code*, and UBC Standard 21-14, Table 21-14-A

SECTION 21.2001 - SCOPE

This method covers the laboratory evaluation of the flexural bond strength of a standardized mortar and a standardized masonry unit.

SECTION 21.2002 - APPARATUS

The test apparatus consists of a metal frame designed to support a prism as shown in Figures 21-20-1 and 21-20-2. The prism support system shall be adjustable to support prisms ranging in height from two to seven masonry units. The upper clamping bracket that is clamped to the top masonry unit of the prism shall not come into contact with the lower clamping bracket during the test. An alignment jig, mortar template, and drop hammer as shown in Figures 21-20-3, 21-20-4 and 21-20-5 are used in the fabrication of prism specimens for testing.

SECTION 21.2003 - MATERIALS

21.2003.1 Masonry units used shall be standard masonry units selected for the purpose of determining the flexural bond strength properties of mortar cement mortars. The standard unit shall be in accordance with the following requirements:

1. Dimensions of units shall be 3 5/8 inches (92 mm) wide by 2 1/4 inches (57 mm) high by 7 5/8 inches (194 mm) long within a tolerance of plus or minus 1/8 inch (3.2 mm) and shall be 100 percent solid.

2. The unit material shall be concrete masonry manufactured with the following material proportions by volume:

One part portland cement to eight parts aggregate

3. Aggregate used in the manufacture of the unit shall be as follows:

Bulk Specific Gravity Gradation	2.6 to 2.7 Percent Retained by Weight
3/8-inch (9.5 µm) sieve	0
No. 4 (4.75 µm) sieve	0 to 5
No. 8 (2.36 µm) sieve	20 to 30
No. 16 (1.18 µm) sieve	20 to 30
No. 30 (600 µm) sieve	15 to 25
No. 50 (300 µm) sieve	5 to 15
No. 100 (150 µm) sieve	5 to 10
Pan	5 to 10

4. Density of the unit shall be 125 to 135 pounds per cubic foot (2000 to 2160 kg/m3).

5. Unit shall be cured in a 100 percent relative humidity environment at 140°F ± 10°F (60°C ± 5.6°C) at atmospheric pressure for 10 to 20 hours. Additional curing, under covered atmospheric conditions, shall continue for at least 28 days. Unit shall be loose stacked in the cube (separated by a 1/4-inch (6.4 mm) gap) to allow air to circulate during drying.

6. At the time of fabricating the prisms, units shall have a moisture content in the range of 25 percent to 35 percent.

7. Upon delivery units shall be stored in the laboratory at normal temperature and humidity. Units shall not be wetted or surface treated prior to or during prism fabrication.

21.2003.2 Mortar. Mortar shall be prepared in accordance with the following:

1. Mortar proportions shall be in accordance with Table 21-20-A. The aggregate shall consist of a blend of one-half graded Ottawa sand and one-half Standard 20-30 Ottawa sand.

2. Mortar materials shall be mixed in a drum-type batch mixer for five minutes.

3. Determine mortar flow in accordance with applicable standards and adjust water until a flow of 125 ± 5 is achieved.

4. Determine mortar density, air content and initial cone penetration immediately after mixing the mortar in accordance with applicable standards. Mortar shall not be used when cone penetration is less than 80 percent of the initial cone penetration value.

SECTION 21.2004 - TEST SPECIMENS

21.2004.1 Number. Test specimens shall consist of one set of six prisms constructed with the mortar cement mortar. Each prism shall be six units in height.

21.2004.2 Prism Construction. (1) Each prism shall be built in an opened moisture-tight bag which is large enough to enclose and seal the completed prism. Set the first unit on a 1/2-inch (13 mm) plywood pallet in an alignment jig as shown in Figure 21-20-3. (2) Place the mortar template shown in Figure 21-20-4 on the unit such that the mortar bed depth prior to compaction is 1/2 inch (13 mm). Place mortar in template and strike off excess mortar with straight edge. (3) Remove template and immediately place the next unit on the mortar bed in contact with the three alignment bolts for that course using a bulls-eye level to assure uniform initial contact of the unit surface and bed mortar. Carefully position drop hammer apparatus shown in Figure 21-20-5 on top of unit and drop its 4-pound (1.81 kg) weight, round end down, once from a height of 1.5 inches (38 mm). (4) Repeat (2) and (3) until the prisms are complete. (5) Joints shall be cut flush after the prism is completely built. Joints shall not be tooled. (6) One hour, ± 15 minutes after completion of construction, place two masonry units of the type used to construct the prism upon the top course. (7) Identify all prisms using a water-resistant marker. (8) Draw and seal the moisture-tight bag around the prism. (9) All prisms should be cured for 28 days. Two days prior to testing remove the moisture-tight bag and continue curing in the laboratory air, maintained at a temperature of 75°F ± 15°F (23.9°C ± 8.3°C), with a relative humidity between 30 to 70 percent.

SECTION 21.2005 - TEST PROCEDURE

Place the prism vertically in the support frame as shown in Figure 21-20-1 and clamp firmly into a locked position using the lower clamping bracket. Orient the prism so that the face of the joint intended to be subjected to flexural tension is on the same side of the specimen as the clamping screws. The prism shall be positioned at the required elevation that results in a single unit projecting above the lower clamping bracket. A soft bearing material (for example, polystyrene) at least 1/2-inch (13 mm) thick shall be placed between the bottom of the prism and the adjustable prism base support.

Attach the upper clamping bracket to the top unit as shown in Figure 21-20-1. Tighten each clamping bolt using a torque not greater than 20 inch-pounds (2.26 N-m).

Apply the load at a uniform rate so that the total load is applied in not less than one minute or more than three minutes. Measure load to an accuracy of ± 2 percent with maximum error of five pounds (22.2 N).

SECTION 21.2006 - CALCULATIONS

Calculate the modulus of rupture of each mortar joint as follows:

$$f_r = \frac{6\left(PL + P_1 L_1\right)}{bd^2} - \frac{\left(P + P_1\right)}{bd}$$

For **SI:** $$f_r = \frac{6\left(PL + P_1 L_1\right)}{1000\,bd^2} - \frac{\left(P + P_1\right)}{1000\,bd}$$

WHERE:

b = average width of cross section of failure surface, inches (mm).

d = average thickness of cross section of failure surface, inches (mm).

f_r = modulus of rupture, psi (kPa).

L = distance from center of prism to loading point, inches (mm).

L_1 = distance from center of prism to centroid of loading arm, inches (mm).

P = maximum applied load, pounds (N).

P_1 = weight of loading arm, pounds (N).

The flexural bond strength of mortar shall be determined as the average modulus of rupture of 30 joints minus 1.28 times the standard deviation of the sample which yields a value that a mortar joint's modulus of rupture will equal or exceed nine out of 10 times.

SECTION 21.2007 - REPORT

The report shall include the manufacturer of the mortar cement being evaluated, the source of manufacture, type of mortar cement, date of testing, laboratory name and laboratory personnel.

Report mortar density, air content, flow and cone penetration test data. Report the following data for the mortar cement mortar being evaluated:

Prism No.	Prism Weight (lbs.) (kg)	Joint No.	Test Load (lbs.) (N)	Moment (in.-lbs.) (N•m)	MODULUS OF RUPTURE			
					f_r psi (kPa)	Mean psi (kPa)	Std. Dev. psi[1] (kPa)	COV %
1	-	1	-	-	-	-	-	-
		2	-	-	-			
		3	-	-	-			
		4	-	-	-			
		5	-	-	-			

Also, report the standard deviation for all six prisms (30 joints)

499

Table 21-20-A - Mortar Proportions by Volume for Evaluating Flexural Bond

Mortar	Mortar Cement Type	PROPORTIONS	
		Mortar Cement	Aggregate
Type N	N	1	3
Type S	S	1	3
Type M	M	2	3

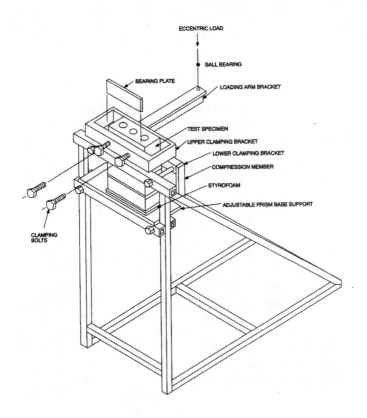

Figure 21-20-1 - Bond Wrench Test Apparatus

References

1997 Uniform Building Code published by International Conference of Building Officials, Whittier, California.

1997 Uniform Building Code Standards published by International Conference of Building Officials, Whittier, California.

2000 International Building Code published by the International Code Council.

Advance Masonry Skills by Richard T. Kreh, Sr., 1978 Van Nostrand-Reinhold Co., New York City, NY.

American Society for Testing and Materials (ASTM):
As listed in Chapter 2.

Building Code Requirements for Masonry Structures (ACI 530-99/ASCE 5-99/TMS 402-99) Masonry Standards Joint Committee, 1999 (Referred to as *MSJC Code*)

California Youth Authority, Masonry, General Requirements Sections 04001, 04050, 04220 and 04221.

Cement Colors and Colored Concrete Products, Williams, 1972 Technical Report, Pfizer Co., New York City, NY.

Cement-Lime Mortars by T. Ritchie and J.I. Davison - BRI Building Research, Mar/Apr 1964.

Commentary to Chapter 21, Masonry of the 1997 Uniform Building Code published by The Masonry Society, 2000.

Hot & Cold Weather Masonry Construction, published by the Masonry Industry Council, 1999.

Concrete Masonry Design Manual published by Concrete Masonry Association of California and Nevada, CA 1981.

Effect of Mortar Properties on the Flexural Bond Strength of Masonry by G.C. Robinson; *Bonding of Brick to Mortar; Influence of the Type of Mortar and Air Content on Bond Strength,* Clemson University, Clemson, S. Carolina, 1986.

Masonry Design and Detailing, 4th Edition, by Christine Beall, AIA, McGraw Hill, Inc., New York, NY, 1997.

Masonry Design Manual by J.E. Amrhein and J.J. Kesler et al, 1979 published by Masonry Industry Advancement Committee.

Masonry: Materials, Design, Construction by R.C. Smith, T.L. Honkala and C.K. Andres, 1979, Prentice-Hall, Inc., Englewood Cliffs, NJ.

Reinforced Concrete Masonry Inspector's Manual by Concrete Masonry Association of California and Nevada, 1983.

Reinforced Masonry Engineering Handbook, 5th Edition, Updated by J.E. Amrhein, published by Masonry Institute of America, 1995.

Specification for Masonry Structures (ACI 530.1-99/ASCE 6-99/TMS 602-99), Masonry Standards Joint Committee, 1999 (Referred to as *MSJC Specification*).

Standard Practice for Bracing Masonry Walls Under Construction, published by the Mason Contractors Association of America, et al, 2001.

Sub-Committee Testing Guidelines for Construction Materials by Nezih Gunal, P.E., Chairman, Report No. 2 Masonry and Masonry Materials, 1986, Structural Engineers Association of Southern California, 1986.

TEK Manual for Concrete Masonry Design and Construction, published by the National Concrete Masonry Association, Herndon, Virginia (Various Dates).

Why Masonry Walls Leak by Walter C. Voss, Ph. D., published by National Lime Association, 1938.

Index

A

B

C

D

E

F

G

H

I

M

N

Q

R

S

T

U

V

W

Y

2000 MASONRY Codes and Specifications

MIA — Masonry Institute of America

Available from:
 Masonry Institute of America
 International Code Council
 The Masonry Society

Available from:
  Masonry Institute of America
  International Code Council
  The Masonry Society

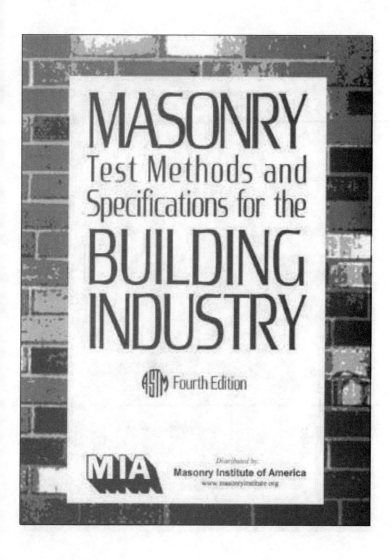

MASONRY
Test Methods and Specifications for the
BUILDING
INDUSTRY

ASTM Fourth Edition

MIA
Distributed by:
Masonry Institute of America
www.masonryinstitute.org

<u>Available from:</u>
Masonry Institute of America
International Code Council
The Masonry Society

529

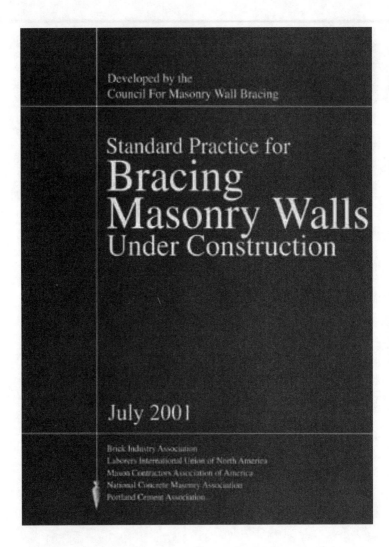

Developed by the
Council For Masonry Wall Bracing

Standard Practice for
Bracing
Masonry Walls
Under Construction

July 2001

Brick Industry Association
Laborers International Union of North America
Mason Contractors Association of America
National Concrete Masonry Association
Portland Cement Association

Available from:
Masonry Institute of America

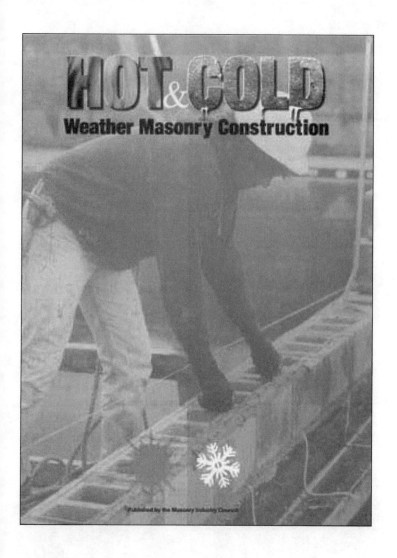

HOT & COLD
Weather Masonry Construction

Published by the Masonry Industry Council

Available from:
   Masonry Institute of America

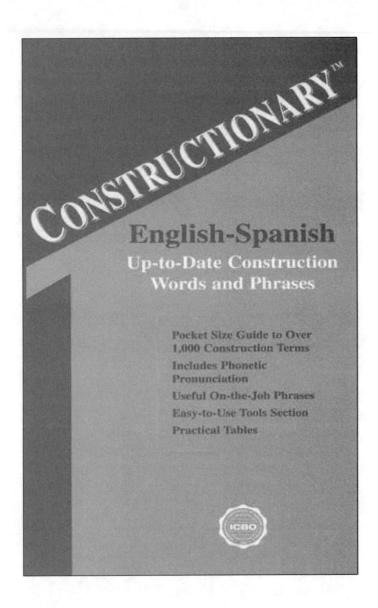

CONSTRUCTIONARY™

English-Spanish
Up-to-Date Construction
Words and Phrases

Pocket Size Guide to Over
1,000 Construction Terms

Includes Phonetic
Pronunciation

Useful On-the-Job Phrases

Easy-to-Use Tools Section

Practical Tables

ICBO

Available from:
   Masonry Institute of America
   International Code Council

532

Related Products

2000 Masonry Codes and Specifications
This manual, published by the Masonry Institute of America and ICBO, is intended for use as a ready reference which furnishes the various code requirements for masonry from the 2000 International Building Code, 2000 International Residential Code and the 1998 California Building Code. These are the codes to be used in conjunction with the Building Code Requirements for Masonry Structures (ACI 530-95/ASCE 5-95/TMS 402-95) and Specification for Masonry Structures (ACI 530.1-95/ASCE 6-95/TMS 602-95).
Product #: 354H2K   Price: $30.00 (Member Price: $27.00)

ACI 530-99/ASCE 5-99/TMS 402
This standard covers the design and construction of masonry structures. It is written in such form that it may be adopted by reference in a general building code. Among the subjects covered are: definitions, contract documents; quality assurance; materials; placement of embedded items; analysis and design; strength and serviceability; flexural and axial loads; shear; details and development of reinforcement; walls; columns; pilasters; beams and lintels; seismic design; glass unit masonry; and veneers.
Product #: 355S99   Price: $85.00 (Member Price: $69.95)

Masonry Structures: Behavior and Design
The most widely used masonry textbook, Masonry Structures, from The Masonry Society, is now available. The textbook has been completely updated to reference the 1997 UBC. Includes coverage of strength design, seismic design requirements, prestressed masonry, and new topics such as glass unit masonry, deep beams, mortarless interlocking masonry, and wall-frame construction.
Product #: 143H99   Price: $98.95 (Member Price: $89.50)

Constructionary - Construccionario

The Constructionary is a unique pocket-size dictionary of up-to-date construction words and phrases in English-Spanish and Spanish-English. The Constructionary is the construction professional's on-the-job communication assistant — bridging the communication gap between English and Spanish speakers to keep them working together successfully. A handy tool of more than 210 pages with over 1,000 construction terms and over 70 phrases including: phonetic pronunciation, helpful construction terms, useful on-the-job phrases, a tools section, and practical tables.

Product #: 100Z02   Price: $16.95 (Member Price: $14.95)

Bolt It Down! (Video)

This video and reference guide demonstrate how to strengthen a one-story, raised-floor, wood-framed home against the potential damaging effects of an earthquake. You will learn how to inspect the crawl space underneath your house, identify the type of foundation, draw a floor plan, select the best method to attach your house to the foundation, brace walls, and choose the appropriate tools and materials. (25 minutes)

Product #: 288X93   Price: $14.00 (Member Price: $14.00)

2000 International Building Code 3-Volume Set (Soft cover)

This 3-volume set provides a complete regulatory package covering nonstructural and structural building requirements for all occupancy types. Also includes 240 ASTM standards adopted by reference in the 2000 IBC in addition to more than 110 ASTM standards adopted by reference in the 2000 IRC.

The International Building Code Set includes:
- 2000 *International Building Code*
- 2000 *International Residential Code*
- 2000 *IBC: ASTM Referenced Standards*

Product #: 096S2K
Price: $199.00 (Member Price: $179.00)

2000 International Building Code 3-Volume Set (Loose-leaf)

This 3-volume set provides a complete regulatory package covering nonstructural and structural building requirements for all occupancy types. Also includes 240 ASTM standards adopted by reference in the 2000 IBC in addition to more than 110 ASTM standards adopted by reference in the 2000 IRC.

The International Building Code Set includes:
- 2000 *International Building Code*
- 2000 *International Residential Code*
- 2000 *IBC: ASTM Referenced Standards*

Product #: 096L2K
Price: $245.00 (Member Price: $220.00)

Call (800) 284-4406 to order or visit www.icbo.org

Useful Resources

Structural Masonry Special Inspector Exam

The examination for Structural Masonry Special Inspector consists of two parts. One part is based on code references and is open book. The other part is based on plan reading questions referenced to a set of plans. You will be provided with a set of plans at the beginning of the exam. While you are taking the exam, both parts will be administered together as a single exam without a break. You will be given a total of three and one-half hours to complete the exam. Visit www.icbo.org to receive more information.

ICC Code Campus

The International Code Council's on-line training initiative, is a professional development opportunity for code enforcement and fire officials, architects, engineers, builders and others in the construction industry.

ICC's virtual campus allows anyone in the construction industry to take training courses anytime, anywhere there is access to the Internet. The campus offers over 70 courses over a diverse range of topics including technology, codes, enforcement, management issues, office operations, accounting and finance, computer operations and personal development. People who successfully complete any of the courses earn continuing education units either through the model code organizations, AIA programs or several state licensing programs.

Visit www.icccampus.org for course listings or more information.

Do you understand masonry design, construction, and evaluation?

Are you looking for practical information on masonry to help you with your masonry projects?

If so, The Masonry Society (TMS) has the resources you need. Whether you need continuing education through seminars and workshops, or whether you need a deskside reference to help you with your design or construction projects, TMS has it, or knows where you can get the information.

The Masonry Society is a not-for-profit professional society dedicated to the advancement of knowledge on masonry. Our members come from all areas of the masonry design, construction, evaluation, repair and rehabilitation communities and have the knowledge and expertise to help you and your company succeed with your masonry projects.

Learn more about The Masonry Society, and the benefits of membership, by contacting:

The Masonry Society
3970 Broadway, Suite 201-D
Boulder, CO 80304-1135
Phone: 303-939-9700
Website: www.masonrysociety.org

Benefits of Membership

As a TMS member you will receive numerous benefits, while having the opportunity to make a difference. TMS Members receive *TMS News* (our bimonthly newsletter), *TMS Responds*, and *TMS Journal*, plus they have access to the members' area of our website. Members also receive substantial discounts on TMS publications, seminars, workshops, and conferences.

But possibly even more valuable will be the opportunities you will have to network with experts on every aspect of masonry. Through your interactions with other TMS members, you will be able to learn about masonry design, construction and evaluation, and in turn, you will be able to teach others about masonry as you become an expert on masonry systems. TMS needs dedicated people that are knowledgeable about masonry. Join today!